SIDE EFFECTS

In the last hours of his hectic life, Simon Apple faces up to the hard truth that his very survival represents a prescription for disaster, not only for the pharmaceutical industry but for the nation itself!

How Simon is transformed from an innocent, loving child in a small midwestern city into *Public Enemy Number One* by a series of dizzying Side Effects makes for an unforgettable medical misadventure in an age when a new miracle drug, promising paradise, comes along every day—just in time for the Evening News.

Side Effects is a rollicking read, the story of a hapless hero caught in an existential whirl where there's a pill for every problem, give or take some unexpected consequences.

REVIEWS OF THE AUTHOR'S
PREVIOUS BOOKS

Bells clanging, lights aflash, the plot's ball bangs and rebounds. . . . A wonderful and wonderfully funny book.

JAMES SALLIS
LA TIMES

His characters are haunting. . . . I have rarely enjoyed finding a writer as much as I have enjoyed my own discovery of Jacobs.

ROBERT CROMIE
CHICAGO TRIBUNE

He manages to satirize our all-too-human foibles and failures without becoming too blackly unforgiving.

THOMAS M. DISCH
WASHINGTON POST

Quietly amused, wry approach that gives distinction to Mr. Jacobs' work . . . his dry humor would be hard to improve on.

ELIZABETH EASTON
THE SATURDAY REVIEW

A wonderfully engrossing read. . . . I recommend it to everyone who has given up of ever again being entertained at such a high level of aspiration.

MICHAEL MOORCOCK

A bawdy, joyous romp . . . it's a wonderful book.

JACK DANN

Look upon the amazing world of Harvey Jacobs! Come one, come all, for an experience never to be forgotten!

FRED CHAPPELL

Like Doctorow's *Ragtime* and George R. R. Martin's *Fevre Dream,* it's totally realized.

HOWARD WALDROP

A great book should aspire (and succeed) in making you laugh, making you cry and just maybe, making you think. . . . Harvey's novels will do all that.

JOHN PELAN

Harvey Jacobs is an award-winning writer who, in addition to the novels and short story collections listed below, has written widely for television, the Earplay Project for radio drama, and helped create and name the Obie Awards for the *Village Voice*. He was publisher of the counterculture newspaper, *East*. His short fiction has appeared in a wide spectrum of magazines in the USA and abroad including *Esquire, The Paris Review, Playboy, Fantasy & Science Fiction, New Worlds,* and many anthologies. He received a fellowship from the National Endowment for the Arts, a New York Arts Council CAPS award for drama, a Playboy Fiction Award, and a Writers Guild of America script award.

He lives and works in Sag Harbor, New York.

Other Books by Harvey Jacobs

Novels

Summer on a Mountain of Spices

The Juror

Beautiful Soup

American Goliath

Short Story Collections

The Egg of the Glak and Other Stories

My Rose and My Glove

FOR INFORMATION ABOUT THESE TITLES
PLEASE CONTACT:
CELADON PRESS
P.O. Box 2724, Sag Harbor, NY 11963
or
www.SideEffectsNovel.com

SIDE EFFECTS

A NOVEL

BY

HARVEY JACOBS

Celadon Press

new york

Cover & title page illustrations: Gahan Wilson
Design & composition: Chet Gottfried

ISBN 9780963418517
Library of Congress Control Number 2008936838

For permission, please address:

CELADON PRESS
P.O. Box 2724
Sag Harbor, New York 11963
or
www.SideEffectsNovel.com

*To Estelle, Adam,
Ross, Charlotte and Mel*

When did it happen that Side Effects replaced fate?
—Simon Apple

Shake well before using!
—Author Unknown

1

On the day of his execution, Simon Apple did push-ups and knee bends. Being of reasonably sound mind, he recognized that any such activity was futile, even comical. But the exertion was strangely comforting.

As Simon strained against reluctant muscles and tendons, he wondered why the subject of his innocence or guilt bothered others more than it bothered him. He felt it would be better if his persecutors at least had the courage of indifference.

They all knew that, aside from the usual deadly sins, he was crime free, the victim of an understandable conspiracy. Simon, who fully understood that it was necessary for him to die at midnight, was resigned. Except for moments of sudden outrage.

It was ordained that the Supreme Court would reject any half-assed arguments for clemency advanced by Marvin Klipstein, Esq. That final appeal was another charade, more for them than for him. *Pro bono, pro forma,* a striving after wind. There would be no last minute calls from the president or the governor.

After predictable outcries from the anti-death penalty crowd and sparse coverage of Simon's demise by the media, the whole incident would fade to quick oblivion. Simon couldn't blame the journalists for looking in safer directions. How many reporters and commentators and their plump little children and juicy wives had been thug-threatened: "This is a matter of national security. You have the right to remain vertical if you accept your obligation as a patriot to remain silent."

Simon knew his only epitaph would be a footnote in a book of blank pages hidden on a shelf in the Library of Congress; maybe a line of coding on a CD in the Justice Department archives. Or was that too optimistic an expectation?

He stood and wiped the sweat off his face with his sleeve. Simon noticed he wasn't even breathing hard; he felt better than he had in years. All those months of pushing, bending and jumping, his regular prison regimen, renewed his energy. The irony pleased him. The prison doctor told Simon his arteries were pristine, his heart a showcase, the heart of a young ape.

While he did aerobics, facing the stark fact that in a few hours he'd be strapped to a gurney and shipped, collect, to eternity, Simon wondered if he had courage enough to die with grace. Or would he plead and slobber in front of the assembled witnesses?

Would he qualify for an afterlife?

What might that be like?

Some believed liberated souls were laundered by cherubs, sanitized by angels, purged of identity then recycled as newborns.

Others made claims for the persistence of genetic memory. Seemingly sane adults had clear visions of past lives in ancient places, of ancestors praying to lightning bolts.

Simon read there were pregnant woman who played classical music near their navels to give their fetus spiritual and financial advantages; there seemed to be some statistical proof favoring Mozart. If Simon was slated for rebirth, he hoped his bulging new mother would choose that prodigy's concertos for oboe, clarinet, horn, flute and harp to serenade him in the seminal sac.

He wondered if his new incarnation would have any memory of the current Simon Apple popping up in its nightmares.

Suppose his replacement was a dumb, complacent infant slurping and gooing over action figures inspired by Saturday morning television shows?

Could it be that reincarnation was repetitious?

Did he want conditional immortality?

The day before, in a misguided effort to comfort him, the warden gave Simon a best-selling book fashioned from conversations between a dying professor and a former student. The doomed man suffered from a progressive disease that robbed him of everything but slurred speech and loose bowels. Yet his essential message was an affirmation of life and the human spirit so, in essence, the story had a happy ending; the stricken professor transformed not only to a best seller but a television movie-of-the-week.

Simon Apple wondered what his Boswell could write if he had a Boswell:

They chose to execute Mr. Apple by lethal injection. That phrase affected him in a most peculiar way. It brought on tumescence, that is to say it gave him a hard-on, a real boner, as if it were he who prepared to do the injecting. One reason for his strange reaction was that Apple was a relatively young man, hardly forty. Arrows of possibility flew out of him; he was a man of thrust and vigor. Outer directed. It was unnatural for him to feel victimized, the penetratee rather than the penetrator. To official observers peering into the death chamber, his erection was regarded as arrogant as asparagus. With his last breath, Apple made a vain effort to apologize for what he claimed was only a reflex, but the infusion of toxins disallowed oration. He died at the stroke of . . .

Simon snapped out of his daydreams. He heard a moan from one of his neighbors. "Hey, Billy, what's happening?"

"Same shit."

Billy, in the cell to Simon Apple's left, was a minor rap star who'd murdered his manager. The man in the cage to his right, Big Bobo, had bludgeoned his wife's lover.

"Yo, Bo, what's happening?"

"Not a lot."

Simon envied his neighbors their eruptions. They'd earned capital punishment. A thieving manager and a compulsive seducer were respectable targets. Simon Apple wished he could fashion a rod from the satisfaction of justified revenge to shore up his jellied spine when they came for him.

Even thinking about the trumped-up charges against him made him wince: *Monk murder in the first degree. Arguably responsible for the death of an entire cult of devoted followers.* The worst kind of rap sheet for a man like Simon Apple who thought of himself as a pacifist.

2

Regis Van Clay, CEO of Regis Pharmaceuticals, followed certain rituals. He ate sparingly. He visited a gym three times weekly for a workout supervised by his personal trainer who he called Kong. On the first of each month he went to the studio of a woman named Belladonna who subjected him to sensible, agonizing humiliation.

At Belladonna's loft, bare of frills, dark and dismal as a bank vault, Regis stripped naked, neatly folded his clothes, prepared himself for insult by emptying his mind of all memory of honors and triumphs. Then, feeling a flush of anticipation, he padded on bare feet to the room where his tormentor paced back and forth on a purple carpet.

Belladonna was a large woman, full-breasted, muscular, with a small head crowned by a massive black wig in the shape of a beehive. Her thigh was tattooed with the image of a scorpion. She wore a silver corset, red net stockings held up by spiked garters, shiny purple boots with high dagger heels, and a thick alligator belt that dangled handcuffs, pliers, a miniature stun gun, and the kind of whip jockeys use on horses charging down the stretch.

Belladonna ordered Regis to stand before a full-length mirror framed by a carved snake with emerald eyes. "Look at yourself, spindly old man. Pathetic fossil. Oh, how Satan smacks his crusted lips waiting for your soul. Send him to me. Send him now! There's a special place in my house for you, Regis Van Clay, an eternal regimen of unspeakable horrors; you are marked for delicious punishment, scalp to genitals, nostrils to pores. How you will beg for succor. How you will sweat salt and dribble snot asking mercy. But you are beyond redemption, barred from salvation. There will be only pain, no respite. Now, crawl on your belly and suck the muck between my toes, you lecherous, greedy bug of a man. Larval slug, murderous scum, you stain on God's hairy ass."

After the mandatory toe sucking, which Regis found only moderately demeaning, he was cuffed, thrown over a stool, and spanked until his buttocks burned. Then he was turned onto his back while Belladonna lit a thick votive candle and let hot wax drip onto his privates. Subject to her mood, Regis could expect to be wrapped in packs of dry ice or jolted by blue electric sparks, sometimes both, depending on Belladonna's generosity.

She was a creative and sincere professional who devised special methods for inflicting torment on her most distinguished client. She used a shoehorn to shove an eggplant into his mouth. His cheeks stretched into a grimace like a Halloween pumpkin. Belladonna squeezed them together with a custom-made clothespin.

The woman was a wonder.

When their session was done, Regis took a brisk shower, dressed, thanked Belladonna, handed her five hundred-dollar bills, scheduled his next visit, then went back to his office refreshed and reinvigorated.

On the fifteenth of each month, Regis entered a terraced building on Park Avenue, rode the elevator to the penthouse floor where Trilby Morning waited for him in her posh pink and gold nest. He pressed her door chime, which played the first bars of "Amazing Grace," and felt his heart thump when he heard her click open the dead-bolt lock.

Trilby greeted him in silence with a hug and a long, moist kiss. She was always neatly dressed in a simple outfit—a blouse, skirt, silver hoop earrings and Mary Jane slippers—looking adorable in her motorized chrome wheelchair. The chair was a gift from Regis, one of the multitudes of home care products manufactured by Rovabout Industries, a wholly owned subsidiary of Regis Pharmaceuticals. The girl, hardly twenty, was in perfect health, an outstanding athlete and former ice-skating champion, but the conceit of Trilby as a disabled beauty, a broken flower, excited him to instant desire.

Before a word was spoken, he would follow her humming chair into a bedroom welcoming as a swan's feathered belly. There was a huge bed with a soft embracing mattress, satin sheets, a lush quilt with great downy pillows, an enormous stuffed chair, a bureau in the French Provincial style holding an army of art glass perfume bottles that reminded Regis of young girls spilling out of school, a Persian rug, a glowing chandelier that sprinkled rosy light through crystal icicles, a large bay window shrouded with chiffon drapery, posters by Mucha and Cheri hanging on walls papered with a bucolic scene of grazing sheep and flute-playing shepherds. Baroque music played from speakers hidden somewhere in the ceiling.

Regis would undress Trilby in her wheelchair while she whispered, "No, please, no," while she clicked switches that spun the chair in a tight circle. Regis pretended to dance with her while he kicked off his shoes, dropped his pants and boxer shorts, then lifted Trilby onto the incredible bed and took her while he gently stroked her hair with one hand and rubbed her chest with the other. Trilby's protests changed to moans of the deepest pleasure.

As Regis mounted to climax, Trilby whispered in her splendid singsong voice, "You are my beautiful boy, my love and my salvation. To think of what you've done for the sick and troubled, to imagine what you will do to work future miracles of healing, to extend the gifts of life and hope, oh darling, my darling, my ageless angel, my own, fuck me, fuck me, fuck me." Her monologue once was longer but, at 75, Regis's staying power edited her praise to one simple paragraph.

When he finished with Trilby Morning, Regis took a long, hot shower, dressed, thanked her, handed her a thousand dollars, presented her with some silly token, a teddy bear, a music box, some toy for her amusement, scheduled his next appointment, then went home to his wife and family in Greenwich, Connecticut, calm, content, satisfied and secure.

On this special day near the end of October, Simon Apple's last day alive, Regis felt a huge power surge; he made two discreet calls on his private line. He saw Belladonna after lunch then went directly to Trilby Morning. Both women received Patek Philippe watches circled with diamonds in appreciation for accommodating him on such short notice.

Regis told them that, by midnight, his worst nightmare would end, that he could enjoy the rest of his years in relative peace. When they saw the watches, Belladonna kneed him in the groin, Trilby blew warm air in his ear. That sometimes you actually get what you pay for justified Regis's resolve to live forever and a day. He thought about taking his wife on a cruise to some exotic place for Christmas. He had another watch in his coat pocket inscribed with the name of her poodle, Earthling.

3

Being a mix of Catholic (dad) and Jewish (mom) heritage, Simon Apple was regularly visited in the Death House by Rabbi Shmul Bakla and Father Tim Mahoney. On this last and final day, both clerics were uncomfortable in the presence of the condemned man. They did their best to feign tranquility, bracketing Simon on his narrow cot.

The prisoner wondered about their nervous fidgeting since the whole idea of capital punishment was a basic metaphor for mankind's transient existence, a mainstay of their motivating philosophies. And they had to know or suspect that God was the ultimate serial killer.

Simon saw that the rabbi was particularly agitated. "You know, Simon, there's already a small crowd demonstrating outside the prison," Rabbi Bakla said.

"To be expected. Those people show up at every execution," Simon said.

"Not *those* people. Nobody is protesting your execution. I'm talking about the animal rights crowd and a few ultra-orthodox Jews. It's the lobster thing."

When they came to ask Simon about his last meal he'd chosen broiled Maine lobster, twice-baked potatoes, Brussels sprouts and a mixed green salad with blue cheese dressing. A local reporter did a feature on favorite last meals. "Aside from the animal rights fanatics," the rabbi said, "after I made such a fuss about the ingredients in the lethal injection being in accordance with kosher laws, you order a shellfish?"

"I'm sorry if I upset anybody," Simon said. "It's hard to explain in any rational way, but since I was sentenced to death I keep thinking about some mindless crustacean splashing around in deliciously cold, salty water off the New England coast marked for the same fate as mine. I'm not proud of such infantile musings, Rabbi Bakla, but those thoughts give me a lift. Believe me, I have nothing against that lobster. I recognize how ridiculous it is to focus a desire for revenge against some blameless creature. I want my lobster hot, red, flame-curled, split, cracked, upside-down on my plate. Horrific, but there it is."

"To strike out at a lobster is pathetic," Father Mahoney said. "I wouldn't expect you to go the vegetarian route but couldn't you indulge those same feelings with, say, a rack of lamb?"

"Or a steak?" Rabbi Bakla said. "A roast chicken? Simon, you must realize that what you do reflects on the Hebrew community. It will be hard for me to say *Kaddish* for a man whose last meal was *traif.*"

"On the other hand, if I was in your shoes I think I'd choose a lobster," Father Mahoney said. "With lemon and garlic butter. Boiled, not broiled. A side of coleslaw instead of salad and maybe honeyed acorn squash."

"Between us," Simon said, "I don't expect to be very hungry tonight. I never understood the fuss over charnel house banquets. Do I care what they feed me? I might not swallow a bite but I want that lobster dead."

"Bitter lad. The basic problem, Simon, is that you still insist on your innocence despite reams of proof beyond any reasonable doubt," Father Mahoney said.

"I don't feel guilty," Simon said. "Did you bring me cigarettes?"

"You know you're not allowed to smoke in here," Rabbi Bakla said. "Smoking is bad for you, the other inmates and the guards. Secondhand smoke kills. You want us to break the law?"

"Why am I not sorry to depart this world?" Simon said.

"Do I detect self-pity?" Father Mahoney said.

"There's still the Supreme Court. Always a vestige of hope," Rabbi Bakla said.

Simon looked into the rabbi's sincere, clean-shaven face. Beardless, he looked more corporate than Old Testament, a middle management guide to the grave. Father Mahoney was abstracted, possibly thinking about good and evil or lunch.

"I did bring you a nicotine patch," the priest said, snapping out of his trance. "It was between the patch and the gum. I thought the patch would be neater. Instructions are on the box."

"Thanks," Simon said, "but a patch is not a smoke. I need the taste of smoke. A patch is like giving Sitting Bull a heating pad to send signals."

"We'll be back tonight," Rabbi Bakla said.

"I really appreciate your concern," Simon said. "But it isn't productive for you and Father Mahoney to waste time on a lost cause. Simon Apple is doomed and damned."

"You needn't sound proud of it," Father Mahoney said.

"Put away childish thoughts," Rabbi Bakla said.

"Put them where? Where should I put them? I often wondered about that," Simon said.

When Father Mahoney and Rabbi Bakla stood to leave, Simon felt a rush of cold. He missed their body heat. The powers-that-be kept the cell cold. His guard said it was the warden's attempt to save on the cost of heating oil. Simon supposed it was to preserve his fragile meat.

4

Simon Apple played a game with himself. He dangled his arms until his hands scraped the cement floor, then pranced around grunting like an ape. He tried a handstand, then a somersault, then climbed the bars of the cell door. He knew he was on suicide watch, that his antics were broadcast to some video monitor, but no guard rushed to investigate; they were used to his simian routine.

Simon kept moving until he exhausted himself, the point of all that nonsense, then lay on his cot, closed his eyes and let his mind wander through its own jungle. If today was the time for his life to pass before his eyes, the parade was proving to be a shadowy procession of wisps and fragments. He struggled to piece together memories of his early years from specks of dust, the detritus of overheard telephone calls, nursery conversations, family gossip and his father's famous sleep talking, those garbled monologues babbled on a dark stage for an invisible audience. Was his father trying to tell him something there in the dark, carefully coding the messages among coughs, snores and snorts?

Simon was born a month premature, four pounds, six ounces, a lusty baby "impatient to get his tail slapped" his father, Robert J. Apple liked to say. His first weeks were spent in an incubator warmed by light bulbs. All he recalled about that claustrophobic pod was blazing yellow light without the balm of darkness. That light stayed with him even after he was plucked from his cocoon.

Simon couldn't swear to exact details—filtered through time's distorting prism—but he seemed to remember being baptized and circumcised on the same day. He was yanked from sleep, wrapped in swaddling and hustled out of the hospital to a chapel in Blessed Queen of Angels Church where he was dunked and certified as a Roman Catholic.

From there, a rented Lincoln Continental carried him to Sons of Israel Synagogue. His father, a semi-lapsed Catholic, insisted on twin ceremonies. Simon's baptism was a fillip to his father's family and made Robert J. Apple feel better about himself. His mother, Francine, born Jewish, also had left a trail of wounded relatives when she married outside her tribe. She wanted her son to be circumcised if only for the record.

So Robert J. hired the resident *mohel* at the synagogue, a famous specialist in removing foreskins, to perform the *bris*. A naked Simon, still damp from holy water, waited while the *mohel* dipped a wad of Johnson & Johnson cotton into a silver cup of Manichewitz Concord Grape wine and painted it across Simon's flailing tongue. The baby licked at the fuzzy pink cloud of anesthesia. Then came the slice, worse than the freezing baptismal bath. Simon went from sprinkled to snipped, from icy chill to hot pain, screaming protest with a passion that frightened everybody in the *shul*. Simon's startled eyeballs blinked like traffic lights. He wouldn't stop howling.

When Simon's parents got him home he began to run a sweaty fever. Robert J. called Dr. Henry Fikel who still made house calls back in the nineteen-sixties.

Dr. Fikel couldn't tell if the infant's problem was caused by baptismal bacteria or trauma from the *mohel's* blunt blade. Whatever the cause, the doctor recognized that Simon was burning up because of a serious infection that could cancel him out in a matter of hours.

"Listen, the battle is not lost," Dr. Fikel said. "I've been involved with testing a new drug called *Cripthalizine* developed by Regis Pharmaceuticals. It's about to be approved by the FDA. The test results have been tremendously positive. The drug is hugely expensive but lucky for you I've got samples. If you agree, I'll administer a dose now. It should be repeated every eight hours until his fever breaks."

Cripthalizine
Trade name: *Cribangel*
Another miracle from Regis Pharmaceuticals

"Do it," Robert J. said. Dr. Fikel produced a small bottle of greenish liquid from his bag along with a medicine dropper, sucked an inch of *Cripthalizine* into the glass tube, squeezed open Simon's mouth and squirted the emulsion down his throat. Before Simon could react to its oily taste, a rubber nipple was stuck between his bare gums. He sucked at formula, warm and sweet.

Simon Apple knew he'd been bottle fed from overheard conversations that became family lore. Despite heavy pressure, Francine Apple had opted for symmetrical tits over the arguable joys of in-flight fueling. There were extenuating circumstances; Simon's first baby teeth were like little razor-sharp tusks. Not even the most devoted of mothers could have endured the assaults of his appetite. Simon's first nickname was The Little Ripper. (Years later that was mentioned at his trial.)

Cripthalizine worked quickly and well. Within 24 hours his fever was gone, the infection subdued.

There would be certain catastrophic side effects but they took time to manifest.

5

Agent Brian Beem, a tall, lanky man, a crane with a rugged human face, wore his traditional black suit, navy shirt, gray tie, ribbed black socks and black shoes. The outfit set off his tidal wave of white hair, a beach of pale skin and wide, wet eyes with pupils that seemed to float on blue-green lakes. Beem pulled out a pack of Marlboros, lit one with a wooden match, snapped the match as if it were a wishbone, inhaled deeply and blew a tunnel of smoke rings toward Simon Apple who lay splayed on his cot staring at the ceiling.

Simon sat up, greedily accepted a cigarette, touched it to the glowing orange tip of Beem's and took a long drag. He watched Beem flip open the lid of a small, round portable ashtray decorated with the Swiss Army insignia of a white cross on a red circle and drop his broken match into the container. Beem cleaned up his messes. Simon flicked his own worm of ashes onto the concrete floor.

"You look depressed," Beem said.

"Really?" Simon said. "What have I got to be depressed about?"

"There are worse ways to die."

"Ah. Thanks. I feel much more cheerful now."

"Simon, I've been authorized to answer some of your questions," Beem said.

"I don't know if I care anymore. But I suppose it will make you feel better to get some of that pus off your manly chest. Everybody seems eager to make their peace before they kill me. As if it matters who I love or hate."

"First the disclaimer," Beem said. "Nothing I tell you won't be denied under oath."

Beem's voice lowered to a barely audible whisper designed to confound any hidden microphones in the cell. "Apple, can you get it through your thick head that we *want* you to know the truth? Bottom line, we're all in your debt. This morning the President of the United States of America got down on his knees and prayed for your immortal soul. We're not without gratitude."

"Do I seem ungrateful for your gratitude? Don't I know what must be must be? What I resent is that you boys took the decision away from me. If you'd just presented the facts I would have gladly stuck my head in the oven."

"We couldn't be certain of your reaction, Apple."

"What's done is done. But I would like to know the details. They say the Devil is in the details, right? And since I might meet the Devil in a few hours I wouldn't mind being one up on the bastard. Why was it all so complicated and how did you pull it off?"

"You already know you were framed. And the very good reason why. Are you sure that isn't enough baggage to carry down the glory trail?"

"How much baggage am I allowed to carry? Is there a weight restriction? Listen, Brian, I need to know the hows and whos."

"Even I don't know the whos," Beem said.

"Then the hows? I'd settle for the hows."

"Before getting to hows, which are arguably irrelevant, I've got to feel certain that you fully understand that what was done was done only after much deliberation at the highest levels. There was never gloating, no smug guffaws at those meetings. We care. We take you as seriously as we take the flag."

"As seriously as you take an unborn fetus? A stem cell?"

"Cheap shot, Apple," Beem said.

"You're right. Forget I said that."

"There is no reasonable alternative. You can't be left alive."

"Please stop apologizing," Simon said. "Some things are past apology. Look, I feel like I walked into the theater when the movie was half over. I'll be out of popcorn before the loop comes around again. I'll never catch up with the plot and I won't be here for closing credits. So please fill in the missing pieces. That would make these last hours much easier to endure."

"I'll do my best. First, you must see that if we simply blew you away, even if it was made to look like an accident, there might have been questions. It had to seem like you deserved your demise. Which, in a way, you do."

"One murder was enough to convict me. Then why so excessive? Why magnify the body count?"

"Flawed planning. Human error. Collateral damage. Lousy luck," Beem said. "Hey, Apple, we all know shit happens." Simon watched Beem take a long tug on his cigarette and let the smoke leak from his nose and mouth as if his guts were simmering.

"You know why I want to know how you guys pulled it off?" Simon said. "Even if it makes no difference? Because I hate loose ends."

"I can relate to that," Agent Beem said.

6

Francine Apple announced to Robert J. that she did not take gracefully to the traditional role of housewife and mother. She told her husband her time would be better spent following a career where her full potential could be realized.

Utterly in love with his trim, pretty, perky, strong-minded, capable wife, Robert J. feared that Francine might interpret any opposition to her voyage of self-discovery as oppressive. Too many seemingly established couples the Apples knew were recently divorced citing conflicts of interest as the reason for separation. Winds of change were uprooting even rock solid marriages. The idea of subtracting Francine from his life and his bed was unthinkable. Inwardly conflicted, Robert J. agreed that Francine should test her ambition. He agreed to be a supportive spouse.

It was decided that a nanny should be employed to watch over baby Simon. His mother would then be free to spend her days working beside his father at Quikpix, a store that processed film and offered glossy prints in one hour. Quikpix had recently expanded to offer a full range of necessities to amateur photographers. Two new machines were installed for photocopying documents of letter and legal size. Francine argued that the salary Robert J. paid to his clerk would be better kept in the family, albeit in Francine's personal checking account.

Losing the clerk in question, Rowena Trask, was not an easy thing for Robert J. Apple. The peppy cheerleader from Glenda High was a pleasure to have around. After school on weekdays and for half a day on Saturday, Rowena came exploding into Quikpix spewing huge energy and eager efficiency. Plump, blonde, well endowed, a natural extrovert, Rowena was a definite asset to the business. She made customers happy. She made her boss. happy. She radiated happiness. Like Robert J., Rowena Trask was fascinated with the whole idea of photography.

When Quikpix was empty of customers, and after hours, Robert J. instructed her in the use of her 35mm Nikon, a gift from her grandfather. He taught her about light meters, shutter speeds, film sensitivity, the importance of composition. He impressed upon her that "a camera is the equivalent of an artist's brush, a marvelous tool in the eternal search for truth and beauty." Rowena brought out a poetry of expression Robert J. never suspected drowsed inside him.

Rowena allowed Robert J. to take spicy Polaroids of her fresh-from-the-garden body in the tiny studio he'd set up in back of the store, but only from the waist up. Her boss had a file exclusively dedicated to pictures of her fledgling breasts, their rosy spigots pointed bravely toward his GE floodlight. Robert J.'s plan was to translate Rowena into a private calendar. He was hopeful that soon Rowena would slough off what remained of her girlish modesty and slide out of her jeans and panties.

To hasten that lovely moment of revelation, Robert J. swore Rowena to secrecy and showed her his private collection of stills culled from thousands of Kodak rolls shot by their neighbors in Glenda.

Every so often, in the midst of familiar images of locals at work and at play—friends, aunts, uncles, grandpas, grandmas, kids, cousins, dogs, cats, birds, turtles, gerbils, whatever—Robert J. would confront some astonishing vision among the drying celluloid strips. There was Mrs. Cornby's naked bottom displayed on a cushion, Professor Haliday's battle-worn genitals gripped by an unknown hand, one of Rowena's coy classmates, blurred but recognizable, servicing a football jock in the back of a pickup. This pantheon of astonishing intimacies made what had seemed to be the expected and familiar suddenly decidedly unfamiliar. Rowena felt as if she'd been given X-ray vision, the kind usually saved for comic books superheroes.

Those strangely sad and innocent erotic studies were both illegal and immoral by accepted standards. Quikpix and similar establishments were required to confiscate anything resembling pornography and report it to the proper authorities. Robert J. was a law-abiding man but he felt that being entrusted to develop the community's photographs gave him a certain immunity from mandatory disclosure, an almost priestly exemption as privileged communicator.

That feeling of specialty was enforced by the fact that several of his "naughty" pictures involved local politicians, police, volunteer firemen and members of the clergy. So he delivered uncensored product to his clients without comment but not before making an extra copy of the best prints for himself. Sometimes he enlarged the photos so he could study them at leisure without using his reading glasses.

Rowena Trask responded to the amazing collection with giggles and gasps but without any evidence of shock or horror. As Robert J. suspected—gambled on—Rowena was not only tolerant of those photographs, she was touchingly reverent toward both their subjects and the unknown photographers. Instead of breathing hard while she browsed his kinky album, Rowena actually wept. As he'd suspected, the girl was blessed with a generous heart.

The evening he fired Rowena Trask, using economics as his excuse, Robert J. gave her a modest bonus, a glowing letter of reference, a gift certificate from Schneir's Department Store and a kiss on the cheek. He broke the news that it would be best to destroy the semi-nudes she'd posed for, all things considered.

They were both silent as he tore those Polaroids into scraps. There was a shared sense of loss. Rowena had responded quickly when Robert J. explained "photography is the poor man's triumph over time and change." That was when she'd first agreed to unbutton her blouse.

Before the last of the Rowenas was fragmented, she begged her boss for just one souvenir of herself, a single reminder from the portfolio he'd described as "transient moments of ripening beauty already imprisoned in the past," but Robert J. was a careful man and refused her that modest request. Francine Apple was a bloodhound; if she ever got wind of those pictures he would be forced to eat boiled cow flop for eternity.

His former clerk watched him gather up the shards of her ripening beauty and toss them into a wastebasket. When that carnage was complete, without so much as a word, Rowena locked the Quikpix door, turned off the sign in the window, doused the store's lights, led Robert J. to the back room studio, flicked on a red lamp and stripped to her bare skin. Her shadow swallowed him in one gulp.

Robert J., who considered himself faithful to his wife, realized it could do the tender girl terrible harm if he refused her nice parting gift. The two of them cuddled on cold linoleum and whispered last goodbyes. She moistened his sex with her mouth and helped him slide into her slowly, slowly, slowly. Rowena said she felt as if they were posing for Jesus' camera, that the picture they made together, naked and tangled, was already preserved in Heaven's stained glass.

Later, after more kisses and tears, Rowena Trask gathered up her modest severance pay (two weeks, minimum wage), a very positive reference letter, the twenty-five dollar gift certificate redeemable at Schneir's, her school books and knapsack, then went on her way.

Robert J. felt her vanish into the future, a journey no camera could capture. He thought about his Rowena calendar, still missing vital fall and winter months. Left with a torrent of regret, he fell to his knees and said a prayer for Rowena Trask. Help like that was hard to find.

During all this, Simon Apple lay in his crib listening to his mother's flat voice read him the story of a rabbit transformed from a plush toy into the real thing. Simon wondered if that ending was happy or miserable—Francine's tone left room for ambiguity—but he was too comfortable to care.

7

With his mother beginning her new career, someone had to look after baby Simon. Francine Apple interviewed a host of candidates for the position of resident nanny, among them a Polish woman, Victoria Wyzowik. After browsing letters of recommendation, including a paean from Dr. Henry Fikel, Francine invited Victoria to the house and listened while the lady recited a list of impressive credentials. But it was Victoria's awful history that got Francine's attention.

Having lived a protected American life, Francine was hypnotized as Victoria struggled with the English language, nearly gasping between sentences. Francine had the feeling that the woman was badly dubbed, like actors in the foreign films that occasionally played at the Glenda Triplex; her lips and words seemed out of sync. But Victoria's story was better then most of those dark dramas.

She was just five when the Nazis invaded Poland in 1939. Her gentle father was drafted into the Polish army. A month later, she was told he died of typhoid in a prison camp outside Warsaw. Her mother, a sweet soul from Danzig, was turned into a whore for SS officers. Victoria went to live with her ancient grandmother in a Krakow slum. She spent her days foraging for food, coal, anything that might be used to sustain life. She ransacked garbage cans and begged German soldiers for coins and candy. She wandered like a rat through dismal streets fighting other rats for discards turned to treasures. At night she dipped rancid bread into sewer soup, then crawled into bed beside her father's mother who gave off less heat than a candle stub.

By 1944, when the Russian liberators came, Victoria's grandmother was too feeble to care for anyone; the girl was shipped to a state orphanage. At the orphanage she was taught to read, write and sing inspirational songs in praise of the Communist regime. Because the child had a talented voice, strong and pure, she was chosen to be part of a choir that traveled through ruined cities mouthing uplifting ballads for captive audiences of school children and battered workers.

The day Victoria turned fifteen she met a violinist twenty years her senior and gave him her love and trust. With the help of small miracles they escaped Poland, walked across Europe and somehow found their way to Paris. While his young mistress worked ten hours a day in a hospital laundry, her lover met a woman who owned a successful cabaret in the Marais. Victoria was discarded like an unwanted pet. She quit her job, switching allegiance from laundry soap to a religious vision of terminal filth; she made a living by renting her only real estate, her shapely body, to be used as a mattress by battalions of local predators.

Luckily, the hapless bit of flotsam was rescued from oblivion by an organization of Quakers who managed to find her a position caring for the children of an American diplomat and his wife. Victoria loved her new job, the family loved Victoria. When they returned to the United States, they arranged for her to accompany them to Washington, D.C.

Victoria was twenty-three, chubby and hopeful, when she took her second lover, a salesman named Hobart Burl who transported her to Minneapolis. They had a good life together until Hobart was "downsized" by the company he'd thought of as his second father. When he was "downsized" with no notice or excuse, the man cracked like an egg, spilling wrath and rage, striking out in all directions.

Police called by a neighbor saved Victoria from being strangled by the electric cord that dangled from one of the appliances Hobart once sold in the Midwest territory. That same night she packed her small suitcase and caught the first Greyhound bus out of town. It took her to Glenda.

She found a room downtown, bought a copy of the Glenda Express, and circled the Help Wanted ads. By the end of the week Victoria was hired as live-in companion to Dr. Henry Fikel's mother-in-law, Lorna Erp, stricken by what was diagnosed as senile dementia brought on by hardening of the arteries.

Lorna Erp, all ninety pounds of her, was in the process of forgetting everything and everyone she'd ever loved or hated. She spent whole days and nights watching people on her Zenith TV screen, accusing them of spying on her. Those two-dimensional invaders were accompanied by sounds of witless laughter and terrible music. They ate, drank, fornicated, fired guns, raced cars through her living room, rode horses, herded cattle, flew planes that dropped bombs, sailed submarines that spit missiles, used bad language, hissed snippy barbs between porcelain teeth guarding wet, angry mouths hidden under perfect pink noses and large, empty eyes. They insisted Lorna do this, buy that, go there, take laxatives, chew gum, soak her dentures, gargle blue water, fly to strange places, eat flame-broiled hamburgers, drive bloated cars at murderous speeds.

Puzzled, Lorna asked Victoria how those strangers got inside her defended house and what it was they wanted of her. When Lorna got too agitated and tried to shoo the television phantoms out the door or through her curtained window, Victoria gave her some Phenobarbital, massaged her neck and hummed a lullaby imported from a country she hardly remembered.

One evening, during *Nightly News and Weather*, one of the flat people detached from the video screen, beckoned to Lorna, skipped over to where she sat, took her hand and lifted her from her reclining chair. She went lightly, walking with a grace and dignity, then vanished into a commercial for Phillips' Milk of Magnesia.

It was soon after Lorna Erp died that Dr. Fikel sent Victoria Wyzowik to meet Francine Apple who felt dazzled, guilty, a bit intimidated by, and oddly envious of a woman who'd survived such horrors.

Victoria wore her past like a bride followed by a train woven by bloodthirsty spiders.

She told her tale with quiet pride. If Victoria Wyzowik made Francine Apple a little nervous, still, Simon's mother relished the prospect of having her son cared for by someone worldly wise who exuded confidence, capability and compassion. In balance, Victoria struck Francine as more a find than a threat. It helped that the woman was no raving beauty; she had the quality of everyday dishes, bland wallpaper, a self-contained presence that fit nicely into the Apple landscape. In a major motion picture Victoria would be played by Ingrid Bergman. In real life she was familiar as a cantaloupe with her open, scrubbed face, peasant body, pleasant features and optimistic outlook.

Victoria simmered with matronly warmth. She radiated happiness. This was no wild thing. This was a woman who lusted for order in a respectable home. Francine hired her on the spot even before her husband had his say.

Robert J. agreed with his wife's choice. Other candidates he'd met smelled like sour milk and baby oil. This new nanny smelled more like Aunt Jemima pancakes. Having Victoria in the house didn't compensate for losing Rowena Trask in the Quikpix but she was a benevolent presence. Little Simon sparkled whenever Victoria aimed her peaceful Slavic breasts in his direction. Robert J. thought about photographing Victoria's busy bumblebee body someday, possibly doing a motion study of her daily domestic athletics. There was beauty in the way she moved through her chores, even in clothes, the fractured frame-by-frame beauty of the Muybridge study of a racehorse at full gallop, the landmark study that proved all four hoofs simultaneously left the ground. Victoria Wyzowik seemed Zephyrous while she cooked, washed dishes, mopped, vacuumed, ironed shirts, rocked Simon to sleep; she had the same mystical St. Thomas Aquinas–style elevation Robert J. saw in waitresses who floated through the late shift in all-night diners.

The Naked Nanny, Photographs by Robert J. Apple, was the kind of coffee table book that could make his reputation. He squashed that fantasy. There were still lines of no crossing, at least in Glenda.

8

Simon Apple adored his keeper. On crisp, sunny days Victoria bundled him like a holiday package and whisked him around the neighborhood. He rode inside a regal carriage imported from France equipped with a canopy to protect him from brutal sun and errant winds. As they went along, she sang strange, sad songs in a rich, deep voice that made his skin vibrate in sympathy.

Often they crossed paths with another pram, a straightforward American model from Sears, inhabited by a swaddled puff called Polly Moon. That carriage was powered by a thick German lady named Fritzel Vonderbraun. Soon Victoria and Fritzel became cautious friends, carrying on an endless conversation about weather, their quirky bosses, the dinner menu, the latest scandal on the front page of supermarket tabloids like *The National Enquirer* (for those with inquiring minds) and *The Star* for readers with brains that fit easily into thimbles.

Simon Apple and Polly Moon developed a more complicated relationship. For Simon, riding beside Polly was like being bathed in tepid water, lathered with Castile soap, then pat-dried and powdered with ZBT. He squirmed and gurgled when he saw her, waving his arms and kicking at his blanket. Polly reacted by screaming and gagging, drawing herself into a fetal knot.

Fritzel shoved a bottle into Polly's valentine face to calm those tantrums. Simon didn't need comforting; he was perfectly happy in Polly's sphere. He never regarded her fits as signs of displeasure or rejection. When she bubbled in his direction he accepted the glob as a gift, as part of her charm. "Look how he loves my little bitch," Fritzel would say. "He wants to get in her pants."

Her friend's risqué remarks made Victoria erupt with laughter, somehow proud to hear her Simon assessed as a nascent bundle of lust. That laughter, those sudden joyful geysers, showered over Simon like spring rain. He was utterly content with his world.

It was Fritzel who first questioned the spiny growths that began to sprout on Simon's face and neck.

When Fritzel said, "Your boy looks like a cactus," Victoria was forced to acknowledge the ugly needles. She knew they also covered his back and behind but had kept that information to herself hoping they would disappear as suddenly as they'd emerged. Victoria didn't want to take blame for causing any trouble or sounding unnecessary alarms.

But once Fritzel made that comment, and went on to accuse Simon of being contagious, since a tiny tuft of what felt like Brillo had appeared on Polly's bottom, Simon's parents had to be let in on the aberration.

If Victoria had kept quiet, the Apples might never have noticed their son's peculiar affliction. Robert J. worked long days expanding Quikpix with Francine beside him. In the evenings, when they saw Simon, he was already asleep in a room wrapped in shadows. The night Victoria mentioned Simon's "rash," they scanned him with a flashlight. After a quick conference, they called the doctor.

Dr. Fikel first prescribed heavy applications of zinc ointment. The pasty cream did nothing to ameliorate Simon's symptoms. Next he suggested oatmeal poultices. Simon was put in a bathtub with gauzy bags of cereal dangling in the water. Instead of helping, the oatmeal seemed to nourish whatever it was that plagued the infant. Within a week Simon's skin turned rough and green as a Hass avocado.

"Soon the little man will sprout roots," Fritzel said, upsetting Victoria greatly, "and they'll put him in a pot. Watch, you'll have to water him twice a day. I've heard of such cases in Dusseldorf."

Victoria made such a fuss Francine was forced to take a day off and wheel Simon to Dr. Fikel's office. Fikel and his nurse turned pale when they examined him. What Dr. Fikel thought was prickly heat or some fungus, easily treatable, was now diagnosed as much more serious, an unknown malady, possibly life-threatening. Tests were taken of Simon's bodily fluids and one of the nasty needles was plucked from a chubby thigh. A few days later, the Apples were summoned to Dr. Fikel's consultation room.

"I sent the tissue sample to the Centers for Disease Control," the doctor said. "And it's a good thing I did. This is only the third case on record. They think it might be an allergic reaction to *Cripthalizine*. That drug is derived from the twigs of a Bolivian bush used by the natives to manufacture deadly darts.

"You'll be happy to know that because of Simon's condition the Food and Drug Administration ordered Regis Pharmaceuticals to include a warning on every *Cripthalizine* label. That's drastic action considering the drug was approved for human use with no restrictions or evidence of adverse reactions. Millions of prescriptions have been written under the trade name *Cribangel*. But from this day, *Priklopathy Spontanatus* will be cited as a rare side effect. I have a note from the Surgeon General thanking me and commending you for coming forward. So at least we have a name and possible cause for Simon's ailment."

"Well that's good news," Robert J. said. "At least we know what we're dealing with. But is there a cure? What happened to those other two cases?"

"They died," Dr. Fikel said, lowering his eyes. "Otherwise robust children. But fortunately, the Regis people believed they have an antidote. *Nonacripthae*. It works on laboratory rodents and chances are it will work for Simon. But you must understand the risk. There've been no human trials."

"And if we don't agree to allow our only child to be a guinea pig?" Francine said.

"The prognosis is not positive. He should hang on into autumn, then things will fall off him," Dr. Fikel snapped. "You must accept that Simon's situation is an anomaly. Every scientific breakthrough has a price tag, sometimes tragic. But *Cripthalizine* has saved many lives. There are always a few subjects who compromise otherwise pristine results."

"You sound angry," Robert J. said. "This isn't Simon's fault."

"I'm certainly not angry," Dr. Fikel said. "But it's always disappointing when the promise of a miracle drug is diluted by some genetically defective—what I'm trying to get across to you is that every doctor, research chemist and health professional shares your sorrow. Not to mention stockholders in a company like Regis Pharmaceuticals. Do you have an inkling of what's involved in nurturing a product like *Cripthalizine?* Countless hours, endless frustrations of trial and error, a million tests, fortunes of money, an unimaginable tangle of red tape to navigate before government bureaucracy . . ."

"We own some Regis stock ourselves," Francine said. "It's done well for us. It split twice in the last five years."

"Blue Chip," Dr. Fikel said. "A compassionate company. Do you know they're willing to offer *Nonacripthae* to your boy at no cost? Not even for shipping and handling. That's a gift worth thousands of dollars, and an option to buy 5000 shares of Regis stock at a hundred dollars a share. All in exchange for your agreement to abstain from any legal action stemming from Simon's use of either drug."

"You mean if, God forbid, Simon should pass away right now we'd have a case?" said Francine.

"You might conceivably win a settlement after years of litigation. By that time you and your husband might be dust and bones."

"Stop that kind of talk," said Robert J. "Of course we'll agree. Get the medicine."

Nonacripthae
Trade name: *Hercumite*
Another breakthrough from Regis Pharmaceuticals

Simon Apple was given a daily dose of twenty *Nonacripthae* tablets for six months. The family was sworn to secrecy since the drug's official approval was mired in a bureaucratic maze. Victoria kept the timetable of his regimen to the minute and made things easier for the patient by soothing his burning throat with colorful combinations of Jell-O and gobs of vanilla ice cream.

Nonacripthae, along with the prospect of resuming his rides alongside Polly Moon, helped Simon recover. His spines wilted and shriveled like the bristles of an old toothbrush; his greenish hue faded away. Dr. Fikel reported that his blood tests were normal. Simon was Simon again, responsive and playful.

Polly Moon had been brought to Dr. Fikel's office soon after he examined Simon Apple. Fritzel convinced her parents that she suffered from the same disease. Dr. Fikel knew the children had come into frequent contact. The girl showed unmistakable signs of having contracted Simon's malady and he had once prescribed a dose of *Cripthalizine* to get her through the flu. Still, Dr. Fikel told the Moon family that her skin condition was merely a common reaction to the synthetic diapers she wore. Fritzel didn't buy his diagnosis but thought better of questioning a respected medical professional.

Dr. Fikel compromised his ethics in the name of science. He took it upon himself to administer a placebo to Polly Moon in place of *Nonacripthae*, nothing more potent than double virgin olive oil. He'd always wanted the chance to participate in some vital research project, and while he was only a pawn in a Regis Pharmaceuticals study, he took the opportunity presented by Polly Moon's behind to push the envelope.

Amazingly, the small cluster of infection on Polly's rump vanished in three weeks. The doctor vowed to keep that news to himself, at least for the moment. He reasoned that he could open himself to litigation by the child's family since he had risked her life and, more important, it might upset the folks at Regis. His little experiment was entirely unauthorized, and Dr. Fikel saw how the Regis people rejoiced at news of Simon Apple's recovery. They'd written him off before he swallowed his first *Nonacripthae* tablet.

Complicating their rapture with news of a positive placebo effect seemed counterproductive.

Letting well enough alone proved to be the correct strategy. Dr. Fikel was flown to New York to report personally on the Apple case history to the Regis sales staff at the Plaza Hotel in Manhattan. They gave him a standing ovation; he was treated like Albert Schweitzer.

Polly Moon showed no signs of any recurrence or complication.

For Simon, there would be side effects but not all that bad, not for years.

9

"Curious, but the thing I remember most vividly is the *boom boom boom*," Brian Beem said, leaning close to Simon's ear. "*Boom boom boom.*"

"You lost me," Simon said.

"All will come clear. First, get the picture of Brother Lucas: Plum-colored face. Pug nose. Caterpillar mustache riding a fat upper lip. Bald head patched with globs of rusty hair spread like the continents on a world globe. Gray eyes holding candle flames in their pupils. Pear-shaped body. White robe. Black sandals. Are we talking Central Casting or what? Lucas looked like he slid off a wine label." Beem sucked in air until his cheeks bulged and turned red. He held two fingers in a V from the top of his skull mocking the horned god, Bacchus. "Changing lifestyles is one thing but this was something else. I've put a ton of people in the Witness Protection Program who ended up more recognizable than that lovable sonofabitch. I'd heard rumors about what he'd done to himself when he left the Agency but I had to see him to believe him."

"I know what Brother Lucas looked like," Simon said. "I murdered him, remember? They did have the courtesy of showing me his pictures at the trial."

"Lucas and I had been through plenty together, Simon. Marvelous adventures. Epic. It seems so long ago. When he quit the team it hurt me. I felt abandoned. But you don't give a damn about all that."

"You're right. I don't." Simon said.

"When Luke waddles over to me, I say to him, 'Who'd have thought you'd turn into something cuddly.'

" 'People change, Brian,' he says. 'I want you to meet my extended family.'

"I tell him I don't think that's the best idea.

" 'The meditation session is over for my blessed brothers and sisters,' Luke says. 'This is our busy season. My flock will be going back into the fields.' "

"The killing fields," Simon said. "Not that I mean to sound judgmental."

"Luke takes up a pose alongside an arched stone doorway. Like he's the Pope. I hear a chorus of voices singing about bounty from inside the monastery. His Holy Order of Digital Shadows," Beem said.

"It is a catchy name," Simon said.

"They had some beautiful setup. At least fifty prime acres on a lake. A building that looks like a castle with towers, parapets, even a little moat. Some widow willed it to the Order. She died under mysterious circumstances. Probably under Brother Lucas. I'll bet he showed her plenty *boom boom boom*. Don't worry, she got her money's worth."

"Could you stop making those sounds?" Simon said.

"I'm trying to give you an accurate account," Beem said. "The *booms* seem relevant. A sound track to spice up the scene. But if you want me to censor . . ."

"Tell it your way," Simon said. "Keep the *booms*."

"Anyhow, out come the singers in a single line. Some hold shovels, some trowels, some spades, some carry big bags of cow shit on their shoulders. Brother Lucas nods to them as they file past. They nod back with their bald heads shining. It was a terrible turn of events. Entirely unexpected. They couldn't help seeing me," Beem said. "*Boom boom boom.* Away they go, marching toward the arbor. 'So those are your Digital Shadows?' I say, 'Well fuck me, Brother Lucas.'

" 'Not on the premises,' Luke says. 'We abstain during harvest season.'

" 'Stain or abstain,' I say to him, 'it's your religion and no skin off my ass. But must the artillery keep blasting? *Boom boom boom.* My eardrums are splitting.'

" 'Those cannons fire at programmed intervals during autumn,' Brother Lucas says. 'Their thunder keeps greedy birds from devouring our ripening crop. If you look around, Brian, you'll see thousands of winged creatures waiting for the signal to migrate. It's a long, hard trip. They sense the need for sustenance. Given half a chance they'd strip our vineyards bare. Which is why our vineyard is surrounded by Howitzers from World War Two.'

" 'The neighbors must love you,' I say to him.

" 'The guns do bother some of the locals,' Luke says, looking pleased with himself. 'Brian, I myself enjoy their thug sounds. They conjure visions of the imploding souls of those who refuse to acknowledge the terror that surrounds us and the rapture that awaits.'

" 'Rapture or rupture, too deep for me,' I say. 'Bottom line, you're firing blanks.'

" 'Listen,' Luke says, 'if you're here as a friend, you're most welcome. If you come as an emissary of final solutions, please understand that I would refuse any assignment they have to offer no matter how urgent or lucrative. Nothing can alter that decision. The past is yesterday's fog. I've quit the business.'

" 'Talk about imploding souls, you were the best, old buddy. One up on the Angel of Death.'

" 'I was good,' he says. 'I was great. But that was in another country and besides the stench is dead. All that went before was preparation for a spiritual rebirth.' Then I see he's crying, Simon. Actually weeping. He points at the sky. 'See that tiny bird darting through the air?' he says. 'Brian, my former life is as remote to me as that distant dot. You must sample a glass of our Merlot before you leave. It tastes of echoes.'

" 'Let's get real,' I say. 'I hear tell the Holy Order of Digital Shadows is not averse to accepting small contributions.'

" 'Our wines do nicely but we aren't wealthy. Not yet. We do suspend pride from time to time in the cause of survival and accept generous offerings. But no dirty money, Brian.'

" 'Of course not. But if I were to extend a generous offering on behalf of the Agency in exchange for a few days of your time . . .'

" 'I told you, absolutely not. Besides, the Holy Order will be obscenely rich and powerful in just a few years. Ours is not a passive assembly celebrating vows of poverty.'

" 'You expect this windfall from the taste of bottled echoes?'

" 'No, Brian, our fortune will not come from grapes. Would that it were so simple. I'll let you in on a little secret. War and pestilence is about to swallow what we call civilization. Chaos will give birth to a second Middle Ages. Fear and fire will rule. A perfumed toxin of secondhand smoke and mirrors will descend upon peoples eager to find security. The masses will inhale that poison with gusto, happily choking on the fumes. At first they will submit to perfect conformity. A welcome malaise will settle over the planet.'

" 'At least you're not thinking small, Luke,' I say to him.

" 'Next, those who rejoice in a global coma—the willing acolytes to unfailingly successful Target Marketing—will experience the creeping horror of spiritual bankruptcy. They'll cry out for guidance. Our Holy Order of Digital Shadows will be perfectly positioned to provide solace to the comatose Children of the Microchip. In that deliciously corrupt utopia, we will offer redemption with stability. And the Chippies will pay what we ask for their salvation.'

" 'So, bottom line, you deal in happy endings,' I say.

" 'New beginnings,' Luke says.

" 'And Brother Lucas is God's gift to the new world order?'

" 'Father knows best.'

" 'I have a slightly less optimistic view of the future,' I say.

" 'Poor snide, cynical Brian Beem,' he says. 'So many assholes, so little time.' Luke slaps a ladybug off his forehead. 'Just for the record, old friend,' he says, 'tell me, are you here to make me an offer I can't refuse? Some fabulous fortune to help you tumble a government or save your leader from a teenage girl who gave him a blowjob under the Washington Monument? What?'

" 'I am, yes I am. Something that might help you over the hump before you climb the golden throne. And the job we have in mind requires no compromise of your principles, Brother Lucas. It has nothing to do with your lifting a hand against any living thing.'

" 'What, then? For how much? And why me?'

" 'It has to do with human sacrifice.'

" 'The Digital Shadows deal in sacrifice,' he says.

" 'Then you are about to become Saint Lucas,' I say, and pull out my Glock. Lucas knows that gun. Hell, he gave it to me way back when. His body shrinks like a balloon. I can hear the air hissing out of him.

" 'There's no point to this, Brian,' he says. 'If it's the nonsense about my writing my memoirs, forget it. I have no intention of embarrassing myself or the Agency. You know you can trust me on that.'

" 'Memoirs or not, there is a point to your termination, Luke. But it would take too long to explain. Does the name Simon Apple mean anything to you?'

" 'No. Should it?'

" 'No,' I say. 'And by the way, don't worry about final expenses. We'll see to it that the Digitals can pay for a first class sendoff.' Then I fire a round into his cherubic face. *Boom.* That must have scared the shit out of a few birds. His mouth drips salty wine. His eyes open wide watching his salvaged soul soar up to where those birdies are. Maybe he's thinking of migrating. Some part of him might get to spend the winter in Miami. Who knows what happens after the final curtain."

"How did you get the body away from there?" Simon said.

"A sleek new Cadillac hearse comes bouncing across the arbor. Two men lift Brother Lucas, box him and slide the box onto a rack. I get into the hearse next to the driver's seat and off we go. I make one call on my cell phone. I tell the ear on the other side what had to be done is done but there's a slight complication. I was seen by at least fifty chanting monks, so let the pixels fall where they may. Simon, it's sad but those Digital Shadows had to play follow the leader; they had to die because, lousy luck, we had no choice."

"*Boom boom boom,*" Simon said.

10

Ingesting large doses of *Nonacripthae* had a profound effect on Simon Apple's physical and mental development. The drug not only reversed the infant's awful decline, it precipitated a renaissance that caught wide attention.

Simon gained an enormous amount of weight, some thirty pounds in three short months. The added poundage was not the usual baby flab. It was muscle and bone. His eyes widened and brightened. His hair took on a radiant gloss.

Premature, Simon had been a skimpy sort; his debilitating fever and the early assault of chronic skin eruptions left him sadly depleted. Dr. Fikel's notes compared the fading child to a collapsed plastic bag. Now that same boy evolved into a mini-Hercules who Robert J. called "my power tyke."

When Simon went out in his stroller—he'd outgrown his carriage—strangers stopped to stare at him in awe; some crossed themselves spontaneously. His face had the eerie quality of toddlers in classical European art and Early American primitives, that wise, old expression misplaced on a child, the look of a religious icon. Victoria was enchanted with the changeling. She took quiet pride in what she considered to be her private miracle, the answer to her urgent prayers to Poland's own Black Madonna.

For Dr. Henry Fikel, Simon's transformation was definitely a triumph of medical science. He wrote detailed reports on his patient's astonishing progress complete with meticulous statistics on measurements, agility, cognitive ability, etc., along with lengthy descriptions of Simon's extraordinary language skills. Before he could speak a coherent sentence, Simon sped through texts far beyond *Goodnight Moon, Ant and Bee* or *The Little Red Lighthouse;*

he was browsing works by Rabelais, William Blake, Jack London and Herman Melville from his father's library and seemed to understand them. He scribbled what appeared to be attempts at free verse with thick crayons.

Dr. Fikel tested and retested Simon with the diligence of a Tibetan searching for a new Dalai Lama. His studies were sent by Federal Express to Regis Pharmaceuticals along with photos taken by Robert J. documenting Simon's explosive growth. Dr. Fikel credited *Nonacripthae* with creating a prodigy.

There were certain deliberate omissions from the doctor's reports of observations he felt might sound negative; since the Regis people were paying him well for monitoring Simon Apple's reactions to such a promising medication, Dr. Fikel felt it prudent to accentuate the positive, at least until there was absolute proof of any serious complication. At the moment, his qualms were merely vague suspicions.

From the hour Simon woke until he collapsed, exhausted, every evening, he ran, jumped, somersaulted and cartwheeled through the day. He couldn't sit still for his feedings. He had to be forcibly restrained during diaper changes. Victoria's soft lullabies, and the daily rides alongside Polly Moon's pram, calmed him.

Only when Victoria sang and Polly quit her howling, would Simon cease to resemble a frantic wind-up toy and lapse into a languid, meditative trance. That passivity was a prelude to volcanic action. Suddenly, without warning, he would snap alert and leap from his stroller, literally flying toward Polly's pink carriage. Fritzel, a trained athlete, would intercept him like a football and hurl him back into place. "Keep your piglet in his pen," Fritzel yelled at Victoria, who stroked Simon's frenzied ancient face until his color returned to normal. "Not yet, my little sausage," Victoria would coo, "but don't worry, you'll get your chance soon enough."

Like her husband, Francine Apple might have gloried in her son's quick flowering but her own life faced sudden turmoil. She too experienced a wrenching renaissance.

Victoria Wyzowik took a half-day off every Sunday to attend mass at Blessed Queen of Angels and work as a volunteer at the church food bank. During Victoria's absence it fell to Francine to care for Simon since Robert J. kept Quikpix open for weekend business. Francine waited out those heavy hours pushing Simon's stroller around and around the block or down to the local shopping center, trying to look maternal.

On one of those interminable Sunday mornings, Francine stopped her strolling to peer through the window of Fay's 7-Day Beauty Salon. She watched her neighbors having their heads baked under green, cone-shaped driers that made them look like giant crickets. On that fateful day, while Francine stood daydreaming, Simon escaped his mother's casual surveillance. He thought he saw Polly propped on a stool at the Sweet Tooth Ice Cream Parlor across the street.

When Francine Apple heard a passing stranger shriek like a smoke alarm she whirled to see her Simon hop off the curb and run into heavy traffic. Only the tuned reflexes of the driver of a Jaguar convertible saved Simon from becoming a stain on the road. The Jaguar swerved, missing Simon by the width of its bumper. Francine dashed toward her offspring and gathered him up, slapping and kissing his face in a tangle of mixed emotions. The Jaguar's driver got out of his car to check for any damage to the child or his fender. The man was about to curse out the crazy kid and his delinquent mother when he recognized Francine Apple.

"Francine Nadel? Is it you?"

"Sam Zane? You?"

The flash of recognition transported them both to the backseat of a Ford Fairlane sedan where they'd lost half their virginity sharing the qualified bliss of partial penetration. The very next day, Sam Zane left for the University of Pennsylvania. He and Francine exchanged a few letters, then postcards until their correspondence ended.

Life went on. Francine heard from mutual friends that Sam had become a Philadelphia stockbroker, married, and fathered two boys and two girls. From his sources Sam learned that Francine had become Mrs. Robert J. Apple, a match that surprised him greatly since he thought of Robert J. as a cipher, a paparazzo of pap, a loner who went around snapping pictures of weddings and babies while the nation hummed with opportunity. He didn't know she and Robert J. had produced a son.

There on the sidewalk Francine and Sam filled in the blank spaces; if Simon's existence was news to him, his dirty divorce was news to her. While they talked warmly of days and nights gone by, Simon made another break for freedom. This time it was Sam who chased down Francine's "handful." While he wrestled Simon into the stroller, Sam asked Francine if they might see one another again. Flustered, she gave him the address of Quikpix.

She never expected Sam to show up but he did, at noon the next day. Francine was alone in the store. Robert J. was shooting a Kiwanis Club meeting on assignment for *The Glenda Express*. It being lunchtime, they sent out for pizza and root beer. More memories were exchanged.

Chewing at spongy crust, blotting hot tomato sauce from her lower lip, Francine blurted that her life was a soap opera, that she was trapped in a hollow marriage to a man without drive or ambition. Caught up in her monologue of misery, she heard herself admit that she didn't particularly like her own son. "You must think I'm some kind of witch bitch," she said. "But that's the way of things. So sue me."

Sam told her that for ten years he'd been sleeping next to a woman without passion, that, worse yet, his sons and daughters were 99 percent Xerox copies of his ice-wife and 1 percent recognizable human beings. When he realized he was a family man in the wrong family, he bolted. Sam waved his pizza slice at Francine and yelled, "Great God Almighty! Free at last!"

"I know what you mean," Francine said, biting into an anchovy.

Three nights later, Sam Zane and Mrs. Robert J. Apple met at the Rooster Motel five miles outside Glenda. They bathed in a heart-shaped tub, drank a bottle of Dom Perignon, ate custard éclairs and fucked on a zebra rug. Sam invited Francine to kick off her traces and move to Philadelphia. That same night she told Robert J. she was leaving, that it was best for them both.

Though her husband knew there were crevices, even fissures, in their marriage through which he'd occasionally peek at Rowena Trask's teenage breasts or Victoria Wyzowik's pendulous ass, he thought of himself as a happily married man. Francine's brutal announcement left him flattened. He wept while his wife packed essentials and filled boxes with possessions she asked him to forward via UPS when she had a new address in Philly.

When Francine lifted her favorite figurine of a porcelain jester out of their curio cabinet and plucked audiotapes from their rack, when she marked pieces of furniture that once belonged to her mother with red stick-on dots, when she set scent on certain appliances including a blender, juicer, a chrome-plated Westinghouse toaster and an RCA stereo, Robert J. felt as if he was being torn and skinned by a metal claw.

He didn't oppose Francine or question her property rights. The objects she chose, like the ones she chose to leave behind, were drained of any value. There was no fight in Robert J. The look in her eyes—dead, hard and distant—froze him. "Take what you want," he said. "Use it in good health. We'll work out a fair financial settlement."

"You're a good person," Francine said.

"There is one thing I'm putting on the table," Robert J. said. "I will never surrender the right to visit my son. I want Simon with me on certain holidays and during summer vacations."

"Not a problem," Francine said. "Simon is 99 percent you. He looks like you. He has your mannerisms. He belongs with you. You can have full custody. I'm leaving him here."

At that moment, Simon came whirling into the room like the funnel of a tornado. His momentum caused him to trip over a Hummel horse his mother had placed on the floor near one of her boxes along with six requisitioned Limoges demitasse cups and saucers. The horse, cups, and saucers were smashed. Simon cut his nose on the glass.

Seeing his own blood flow from the gash left him hysterical. Francine yelled to Victoria, "Hurry, bring the bottle of Librium and a Band-Aid."

11

If the sky rained fire over Glenda while an earthquake splintered the town, it would have been less frightening to Simon Apple than watching his father cry.

His mother's tears were no novelty; Francine wept rivers over onions, romance novels, at movies, weddings, funerals for far distant cousins.

Simon's own eyes were ready faucets. Every frustration led to a tantrum; every tantrum drowned the world. Victoria rocked him when he slobbered, chanting what she called her Simon Song:

> *If tears would turn to diamonds, how rich this boy would be!*
> *He'd buy the earth and sun and moon and give some stars to me.*

Sometimes, for unfathomable reasons, she cried along with him. Simon learned that for women tears breed tears the way fire breeds fire. He hated being a hydrant. His father was a dry well immune to leakage. That simple fact was a touchstone for Simon, the Gibraltar of his infancy, the sign that he was safely protected against the blood-sucking vampires, snot-eating goblins or flesh-ripping giants that populated stories Victoria whispered to him at bedtime.

Robert J. did not wet the bed and did not cry. Simon thought of him as dripless. The water his father drank had only one permissible exit and a single destination. Simon potty-trained based on that conviction.

After patching Simon's bloody nose, Victoria carried him to his room, got him into pajamas, praised him when he swallowed his dose of *Nonacripthae*, then tucked him into the junior bed that had replaced his crib. The night his mother spoke of divorce, loud voices were raised in the Apple home. Screaming was usually Francine's weapon but this time Robert J. yelled back. Sounds of his parents fury made Simon tremble.

Victoria held his head against the ocean of her generous chest. He clung tightly to her, a paper boat rising and falling with her every breath. Simon heard the outside door slam shut. The shouting stopped. It was replaced by the blessing of silence, a balm that soothed the sense of dread that still lingered in the house. Simon listened to the steady drumbeat of Victoria's heart, felt a wave of love for his protector, then fell asleep.

He woke from a sugary dream of drifting clouds, surprised to find himself alone, frightened, bathed in sweat. His bladder was empty, he wasn't thirsty, he didn't feel sick, his night-light gave a comfortable glow. There was no excuse to call for Victoria.

Then he heard sniffles and little choking gasps float through the walls of his room, drifting like the clouds in his dream. Simon left his bed, careful to be quiet as a shadow. He followed those wet, swampy sounds into the dim hallway. They drew him toward the master bedroom, his parents' sanctuary.

Simon dropped down on all fours and crept along like a stalking cat. The door to that sacred temple had been left half open. Simon saw Robert J. sprawled on the king-size bed, convulsed with sobs. His father's arms were wrapped around Francine's puffy pillow, his legs kicked like a swimmer's, his face pressed against the padded headboard covered with the same fabric as the picture-window drapes. Francine was gone. Robert J. Apple was crying. Simon felt a hideous emptiness, a subtraction of self.

He wanted to go to his father but his hands felt nailed to the carpet. There was a smell in the air he recognized as stale cigar smoke but Simon had the thought that he was smelling time. He watched the hands on his mother's bedside clock jerk through another minute, and yet another.

Then he saw Victoria come out of his parents' bathroom carrying a towel. She knelt to sponge Robert J.'s neck. Simon's horror was confirmed; his father's face was a puddle. It got worse. Victoria sang to him, her special song about tears and diamonds. Simon felt his feelings change from amazement to sorrow to contempt to outrage while he watched Victoria take off his father's shoes, slip off his socks, unbutton his shirt, click open the silver cowboy buckle of his belt, slide off his pants, pull the LET QUIKPIX HELP YOU DEVELOP T-shirt over his head, yank away his boxer shorts. Robert J. was naked, still crying. He never stopped crying when he gave up Francine's pillow and grabbed for Victoria's hair. He cradled her cheeks, dared to move his fingers over her breasts. Victoria helped him with that sacrilegious exploration, her hands guiding his.

In seconds she was as bare as he was, the two of them clinging together. Robert J. kissed her nipples, then sucked at them while she moaned. She pulled away, blew air across his belly, moved her head between his thighs, took his nozzle into her mouth. Robert J. wriggled around, found Victoria's sex and tongued slowly as if he were lapping at a saucer of milk.

While Simon felt himself on the verge of throwing up, he wondered if his father had swallowed Victoria's penis. No question, it had certainly vanished. Whatever happened, at least it stopped Robert J.'s crying. Then something snapped in Simon's brain. He was released from paralysis. He stood, howled, and attacked the defiled bed swinging a fist at Victoria's face while he grabbed for his father's balls and squeezed.

Victoria Wyzowik left early the next morning, forever banished from the Apple residence. It wasn't clear exactly why she had to go but at some level her exodus made sense to Simon who missed her more than he did his mother. He wished a thousand times that he'd stayed in his own room, locked in a dream.

There was no replacing Victoria. Robert J. hired a long series of pseudo-Victorias but none came close to the original. Simon's feelings for those women were as distant and formal as his cold relations with his broken father.

After Victoria left, the "power tyke" had regressed to diapers. His ersatz nannies forced him to spend endless hours on cold toilet seats until "he got the message." They commanded his bowels to run on time. They tried to seduce him to use the plumbing with history's most successful lie, *arbeit macht frei*, but none of their transparent tricks worked.

Victoria had insisted on using cloth diapers; Simon's dirty laundry was stored in a bin until, once a week, a uniformed stranger came to collect it as if it were a gift to the gods. That gave Simon a sense of worth and purpose. Victoria's pathetic replacements used disposables. What remained of Simon's ego was tossed out with the garbage. He refused to accept the demeaning change.

Still, for all his domestic misery, the Apple child looked like a winner. Dr. Fikel's bulletins to Regis Pharmaceuticals remained deservedly upbeat.

12

"Shall I continue with this flashback?" Agent Beem said. Simon nodded a wan yes.

Beem reached into his pocket and pulled out a batch of folded papers, unfolded them, smoothed them against his pants leg.

"I get the creepy feeling that my whole life is passing before your eyes," Simon said.

"Do you want me to stop? Want to talk about the weather?"

"How did you choose Brother Lucas for Simon Apple to kill?"

Agent Beem lowered his voice to a whisper. "There were valid reasons for the Bureau's concern. Luke did have meetings with several publishers. But it turns out he wasn't peddling an exposé. He was trying to sell recipes for homemade laxatives. Regularity for the retentive. Whole grains. No additives except for faith."

"Fiber optics. On a clear colon you can see forever," Simon said.

"Even though there was no evidence that Lucas was considering a tell-all book, the consensus was better safe than sorry. We felt that a preventive strike was not out of order. Luke's profile strongly suggested a powerful urge to purge. Today, organic laxatives, tomorrow who knows what? One way or another, he had to go and the timing was right. We needed a corpse."

"Sometimes things fall into place," Simon said. "Rarely, but sometimes."

"These papers are official documents. Strictly for the archives." Beem lifted a pair of gold-framed reading glasses from a leather case and positioned himself under the eternal light in Simon's cell. He kept his body between the paper and a surveillance camera set in the steel ceiling. "I hate people reading over my shoulder," Beem said. His voice dropped an octave. "Event Reconstruction File RX 3266780. Top Secret."

"I'm flattered," Simon said.

"Please, Apple, no wiseass remarks and no interruptions. This might be the ultimate bedtime story."

"Here we go loop-the-loop," Simon said.

Beem cleared his throat and read from the file: "On the very night of Brother Lucas's disappearance, all members of the Holy Order of Digital Shadows were gathered for their annual Vesting Ceremony. As things stood, the event presented us with an unusual opportunity to tie up some embarrassing loose ends relating to the possible identification of Agent Brian Beem."

"Protecting your ass. What a unique idea. Please read on."

"Brother Lucas's devoted followers were puzzled by the absence of their missing leader, especially since their Vesting ritual was so crucial, a basic doctrine of the Order. All postulants, on the occasion of their ordination, were granted stock options in the mother corporation (Future Perfect, Inc.) that owned and operated the monastery, i.e., all its buildings, lands, the winery, products, the gift shop, web site and all subsidiary properties including books, pamphlets, CDs, videos etc. in this or any future world. It was understood by the Digitals that, at the proper moment, to be determined by Elder Shadows, the Holy Order of the Digital Shadows would go public with a listing on the NASDAQ exchange. Those Elder Shadows were empowered to offer converts much more than just posthumous rewards."

"They got stock options?" Simon said.

Beem continued reading: "Brother Lucas often told potential believers that Digitals didn't pass around empty baskets every Sunday pleading for charity. 'Instead,' he said, 'we offer cosmic and financial cornucopias, waiting to be emptied.' He kept a sign on his desk that read, VOWS OF POVERTY ARE CHAPTER 11 IN A DIGITAL'S BOOK OF LIFE. Near the sign he displayed a ceramic hippopotamus he'd jokingly named IPO, an acronym for initial public offering.

"The Vesting Ceremony was quick and simple but very emotional. Male and female Shadows gathered on one side of their chapel, acolytes on the other. Traditionally, the text of a brief but passionate sermon—Cybertime, The Hour of Underglass Revelation— was read aloud by Brother Lucas himself. His sermon reminded the Digitals of their vital role at the time when most of life's business, pleasure, science and art would be virtual, conducted online."

"I'm thinking of converting," Simon said.

Beem lost his place on the page, then found it with a finger and kept reading. "Of course, there would be opponents to the new world order. It was then that the call would be sounded and the Shadows would come boldly forth to fight the great fight. The pinched, parched, obsolete spawn of an apocalyptic past would be denied all hope of grace unless they accepted the doctrine of the Rom Triumphant, the Cybervoid, a shining new vision of Site Solemnity, Internet Immortality. In short, unless they joined the Order after paying an initiation fee as yet to be determined.

"The Blessed Vested would serve as exorcists, merciless reamers, expunging pulpy soul-waste and replacing the fetid mess with Serene Celestial Connectedness to the Pulsating Quantum. The goal of every Digital Shadow is to experience Electronic Nirvana, Pixel Paradise—a sensuous realm where Secure Commerce Penetrates Essence, when the Blessed Alliance Between Business and Belief is openly celebrated."

"Inspiring," Simon said. "Regarding heaven as a profit center. Hallelujah."

"There's more," Beem said, rattling the report.

"I'm all ears," Simon said.

Beem wet his upper lip with his tongue. "As a snide swipe at the past, that sermon was written on a parchment scroll like the Hebrew Torah, peppered with footnotes openly acknowledging certain contradictions in Digital theology. Luke anticipated frontal attack from Christians, Jews, the Islamic crowd, Hindus, Buddhists, the whole shebang. So he asked the questions he knew would come flying at the Order.

"How, for example, could even a devout Shadow reconcile embracing and profiting from an organized, digitized world while recognizing its hollow, robotic assault on the soul, that misty essence of triumphs and pratfalls once hailed as mankind's better nature? Brother Lucas is pleased to remind his brethren that every religion is seasoned with seemingly impossible contradictions which conceal doorways to larger truth. He firmly states that any doubts will be replaced with specific details crystallizing into generic revelation. Meanwhile, waiting for answers, the Gospel of Brother Lucas urges his Digitals not to sweat the small stuff."

"Amen." Simon said.

Beem cleared his throat and went on. "After the Vesting sermon came the singing of Plasmas, hymns composed by the more musical Shadows, during which Brother Lucas would confer certificates legalizing the stock options granted to the chosen. That explosive climax was tempered by a cooling down, a Poweroff, an hour of deep meditation when all present were encouraged to seek peace wandering through Inner Meadows Where Wildflowers Bloom, taking time to Navigate Calm Seas At The Center Of Being And Becoming before Rebooting."

"Excuse me," Simon said, "but how in the age of screwed up software did anybody swallow that garbage? Didn't any of those people ever lose a file on Windows?"

"We still enjoy freedom of speech in the good old U.S.A. so let's not be too judgmental here," Agent Beem said. "Those Shadows gladly gave their worldly possessions to the Order. Of course, the majority of them had lost a high percentage of those worldly possessions in the dotcom fiasco of the late nineties. The majority of the Digitals were recruited among the walking wounded from Silicon Valley. We're not talking about dunces—these people had huge jobs before the collapse so the idea of recouping some of those terminal losses in the market had profound appeal."

"Could you skip the theology and get to the part about how I murdered an entire Holy Order?"

"You weren't accused of murdering them. Only of aiding and abetting their violent extermination," Beem said.

"Excuse me," Simon said. "I didn't mean to take too much credit."

13

Agent Beem ran his finger down the document like a pointer, flipping past pages he considered irrelevant. Beem was sympathetic with Simon Apple's impatience to learn as much as he could before such concerns became moot. On the other hand, there was no need to overload Simon with too much information on the day of his death.

Nobody could say for sure how the universe worked or what happened when a traveler crossed the border to eternity. Was there some kind of celestial debriefing? In the face of such uncertainty, a sensible position for the Bureau was to keep God on a need to know basis.

When Beem was ready to resume his litany, he cleared dry webs from his throat. Simon offered him a glass of brown prison water to lubricate his vocal cords but that sludgy cocktail was waved off. After a few minutes of gagging, Beem quit coughing, found his voice. He read in the same raspy whisper he'd used to thwart the electronic ears that were surely listening.

"The Vesting ended with an elaborate feast. Cocktails of home-made wine and soy milk were followed by a mesclun salad dressed with canola oil and vinegar. The main course was stuffed blowfish, fugu, a Japanese delicacy personally prepared by Brother Lucas's own sushi chef, the beloved Jiro Kiuki, famous for his handling of that delectable *but* dangerous dish. Kiuki described his fugu as edible haiku, the gastronomical equivalent of multiple orgasms. The blowfish had to be freshly taken from safe waters and expertly rendered. In the hands of a novice, fugu can be deadly poison.

"Of course, Kiuki knew his way around a blowfish. He was a tyrant when it came to selecting and cooking the fugu served at a Vesting, especially since he himself was a member of the Order, fully vested at the highest level. While his knife worked miracles, isolating lethal blowfish bladders, Kiuki recited ancient poems about the exquisite titillation of balancing terminal risk against transcendent pleasure. By way of example:

> *I lick the fuzz on Death's moist thighs,*
> *I smile at the menace in her eyes.*
> *She beckons me to taste her flesh,*
> *I say, "Your dew is taste enough."*
> *Fugu, fugu, fugu, fugu*
> *Can any dish compare with you?*

"Emily Dickinson?" Simon said.

"Pearl Harbor," Beem said. "Keep focused."

"Sorry. Do proceed. This might be enlightening."

Beem read: "At the hour prescribed by precise computations of astrological confluences, the ceremony proceeded. Absent Brother Lucas was replaced at the podium by a certain Brother Rochelle who'd resigned his position as Marketing Manager of the prestigious Ordelan Winery in Burgundy to join the Holy Order as a novice and quickly became one of their most respected Shadows."

"Didn't anybody question the whereabouts of their misplaced mentor?"

"I'm getting to that," Beem said, turning a page then picking up the narrative. "Despite an undercurrent of restlessness, even apprehension, over the missing Brother Lucas (as detected in the Bureau's analysis of various audio and video tapes recovered from church security systems, etc.), the prospect of tasting Fugu Kiuki kept the crowd more cheerful than concerned. Brother Rochelle enforced the sense of normalcy, remarking that Brother Lucas's disappearance was no accident, that their leader wanted his children to regard him less as divine and more as mortal and replaceable. Rochelle pointed out that it was exactly like Brother Lucas to deliver that message in a dramatic fashion and that it should surprise nobody if their beloved mentor appeared suddenly to expound on the subject of inevitable succession. These comments evoked shouts of No! Never! and were followed by the spontaneous singing of "Go Softly Forth Dot Com" (a favorite Plasma). When the song ended, dinner was served." Agent Beem twisted his head left to right, then bobbed it up and down to loosen a muscle knot in his thick neck.

"Don't stop reading now," Simon said. "What's for dessert?"

Beem rubbed at a sore spot below an ear. "The first signs of paralysis became quickly evident; there was a universal reaction of disbelief, then gasps and stifled screams, as the fugu's poison took effect. In a matter of minutes, the cacophony of fear was replaced with a harmony of silence. The diners, flushed beet red, died where they sat.

"The next morning their rigid bodies were discovered by a salesman of screw caps who'd hoped to convince the vineyard to abandon traditional corks in favor of his more economical product. The first corpse he found was that of Jiro Kiuki who'd fallen beside his prized wood-burning stove, a few flecks of tainted blowfish clinging to his startled blue lips.

"Local authorities, influenced by memories of Jonestown and Heaven's Gate, first assumed that the death of the Digitals was just another cult suicide, an attempt to transport, en masse, to some blissful afterlife. But that early assumption was quickly challenged, considering the highly positive fiscal outlook expressed in Digital doctrine, the prospect of a bountiful grape harvest for their monastery, and by the very fact that Brother Lucas was not found among the deceased.

"There was still the chance that the cause of carnage was nothing more than food poisoning. The possibility of foul play hardly entered the equation since there was no indication of malice or motivation for mass murder." Beem closed the report though Simon saw there were a few unread pages.

"What about the neighbors crazed by those cannons," Simon said, "or disgruntled relatives of the Shadows? Weren't they at least suspect?"

"No evidence, no nothing," Beem said. "Our boys did a nice, clean job for a change. The investigation was flat on its face and it stayed there until we were ready to bring Luke back into the picture. And Simon Apple, of course." Beem folded the report and slipped it into his jacket's inside pocket.

"There seem to be more pages," Simon said.

"Only a list of caper credits and kudos," Agent Beem said. "The usual hugs and kisses for those involved and certainly deserved. Irrelevant for your purposes."

"You got a medal?" Simon said. "Congratulations."

"My work was recognized."

14

"Mrs. Fikel is very excited about meeting you personally," Dr. Fikel said to Regis Van Clay in the backseat of a stretch limo. "You're one of her heroes. She must have read your profile in *Fortune Magazine* a hundred times if she read it once."

"Nice to hear," Regis said. Days earlier Belladonna had clipped a tight ring around his penis to keep his erection in play, and even Trilby Morning's soothing tongue failed to heal that irritated wand. Regis shifted in his seat trying to find a comfortable position.

"See that house there? The one with the green shutters? That's where the girl I call Placebo lives," Dr. Fikel said. "Polly Moon, one of my patients. She's been in close contact with the Apple boy since they were infants. The illness that led us to administer that first dose of *Criptalhalizine* to Apple and his subsequent crusting did infect the girl but it was handled by her immune system. Placebo just went on her merry way. She bit Simon once after he was put on *Nonacripthae*.

Actually broke the skin. She showed no effects from either his illness or its antidote. I thought about reporting the information to Regis Pharmaceuticals but, well, say I thought better of it."

"You're depressing me," Regis said. "I despise children like that."

"You don't mean it."

"Of course I don't mean it. God bless the little bitch. May she live a thousand years without spending a dime on so much as a spoonful of cough syrup. How long before we reach your house, Fukel?"

"Fikel. Two minutes. It's just down Poplar Avenue."

"Poplar Avenue," Regis said. "Why do they name streets after trees? Answer me that. Give me one good reason. It really burns my ass."

"You're putting me on," Dr. Fikel said.

"No, I'm quite serious. Streets should be named after numbers."

The limousine and two smaller sedans filled with a clot of Regis Pharmaceuticals executives pulled up outside Dr. Fikel's neo-Victorian residence. Honey Fikel, the doctor's exuberant spouse, was waiting on the porch.

"That wing holds my office; the rest is home sweet home," Dr. Fikel said, pointing out the separate areas.

"Very efficient, very convenient," Regis said.

The doctor and Regis Van Clay entered the sprawling house followed by the Regis team. After introductions, Honey showed them where to hang their coats, then led the group into the living room where she'd set out an assortment of tiny sandwiches and home baked cookies.

There was a large silver samovar filled with steaming Earl Grey tea. When Honey noticed Regis Van Clay examining the samovar's decoration of nymphs and satyrs, she bubbled, "There's an interesting story attached to my centerpiece. Dr. Fikel's father was a prominent surgeon here in Glenda. During the Great Depression he often bartered his services. I think the samovar came from a Russian Jew in exchange for a gall bladder."

"What did he get for a kidney?" Regis said, checking his distorted reflection in the gleaming silver artifact.

"I know he got a gravy boat for tonsils and adenoids," Honey said, passing around embroidered linen napkins.

"Lovely bit of history," Regis said, draining his cup of scalding tea without a wince. Belladonna often filled his navel with thimbles of flaming brandy. "Now, can we get on with things? Is the child ready?"

"In my office," Dr. Fikel said, "with his father, Robert J. Apple. Which reminds me. Mr. Apple is something of a photographer. He'd like to take a few pictures of you and your associates for our local newspaper."

"No pictures," said a young man who Regis introduced as Ellis Rose, Director of Public Relations. "No publicity. I thought we made that clear."

"Glenda has a small town mentality," Honey said. "A visit by someone as important as Regis Van Clay is big news for us and hard to keep quiet. If you'd allow Robert J. to . . ."

"Get this stupid twit out of my face," Regis said.

"You're talking about my wife," Dr. Fikel said flatly.

"Maybe Mrs. Fikel could go upstairs and read a book. Watch *The Price Is Right*," Ellis Rose said.

"Honey?" Dr. Fikel said.

Honey Fikel snorted and headed for the kitchen. Dr. Fikel led the Regis delegation through the door that connected with his office where Robert J. waited, camera in hand.

"Simon is in the examining room playing with your stethoscope," Robert J. said. "My son is curious about everything."

They found Simon Apple naked on a table listening to his own heartbeat. "What a fantastic specimen," Regis said. "And this was a sickly child before *Nonacripthae*?"

"Unbelievable," said John Openheim, Vice President for Product Development. "A young god."

Regis Van Clay patted Simon on his head. "So you're the little lad who forced us to attach warning labels to every bottle of *Cripthalizine*," Regis said. "You owe me thirty-seven million dollars." He chuckled. His people laughed. "Look at you now. *Nonacripthae* has turned you into a marvel. Gentlemen, observe this cherub. Dr. Frankel, everything you indicated in your reports was not only accurate, it was understated and we thank you." Regis reached out his hand.

"Not Frankel, Fikel," Dr. Fikel said, grasping the hand as Robert J. photographed the moment. The largest of Regis's bodyguards reached out a third hand the size of an udder and slapped the Nikon out of Robert J.'s grasp. His camera split open against the Spanish tiled floor. Before Robert J. could react, Dr. Fikel patted him on the shoulder. "I meant to tell you. Mr. Van Clay is camera shy."

While Robert J. bent to retrieve his Nikon's body parts, Regis grabbed Simon Apple and swung him toward the ceiling. "Those government bastards pressured us to brew up an antidote to save your sore-ass, boy, and oh how the Lord doth work His magic. Now we have ourselves a product every moppet in the Free World will beg for. Mr. Apple, Simon here is on the glory trail."

"As long as he's healthy," Robert J. said.

"Your son has been chosen as poster boy for the drug we've christened *Hercumite*, the largest advertising campaign in pharmaceutical history. Of course, before the big drum begins to beat we're required to conduct intensive product testing but I am confident that *Nonacripthae* is destined to be another aspirin, a drug for the ages. I think a prayer is in order here."

Regis released his hold on Simon who dropped to the ground near the remains of his father's fragmented camera. "Sorry, bambino. I forgot I was holding you. And look here, not a scratch on the child, not a mark, not a drop of blood. And not so much as a peep out of him." Regis bowed his own head and shut his eyes. "Dear God, all of us at Regis Pharmaceuticals thank Thee for yet another blessing. Amen. Now, gentlemen, I think we are entitled to rejoice!"

Regis tugged at the blue silk tie of a top-shaped man with a bald, round head and a smiling face. "This is Sam Heineman, our Chief of Legal Services. He'll remain here in Glenda for as long as it takes to work out terms and conditions of a contract, all the necessary crap that goes with celebrity. I have no doubt that everyone involved will be more than satisfied. Regis Pharmaceuticals is prepared to pay generously for the exclusive rights to Simon Apple's name, image, persona, the whole ball of wax." Regis slapped his palms together. "I think that concludes our business today. Dr. Fekal, I ask you to apologize to your lovely wife for my outrageous behavior. Explain to the chubby cow that the heat of battle brings out the worst in a man. Please convey my thanks to her and remember to say that her tits are world class and her raisin cookies were memorable down to the tiniest crumbs."

"I'll pack a few for you to take along," Dr. Fikel said. "For the road."

"Tits or cookies?" Regis said. "Just kidding. I'd accept but I have a thing about puking in my car. Now, before we leave, let me kiss our angel goodbye."

Simon, who'd been playing with a broken portrait lens, jerked back his head and began to yap like a puppy. "What in hell is that all about?" Regis said as Simon crawled across the floor and climbed the shelves of Dr. Fikel's library.

"He's a bit hyperactive at times," Dr. Fikel said, "it comes on suddenly. Nothing alarming. Excess energy. And he dotes on attention."

"He caught my attention," Regis said. "He climbs like an ape."

"A power baby," Robert J. said.

"Our living testimonial," Regis said. "A power baby. I like it. Make a note of that, Sam. And make sure that Mr. Apple receives a top-of-the line Hasselblad with every accessory known to man and a lifetime supply of film."

"Not necessary," Robert J. said. "The Nikon . . ."

"And throw in a tripod," Regis said. "Jesus, I feel good about this. I feel like I just fucked a butterfly."

15

"The thing is," Agent Beem said, "we had a real problem with Brother Lucas's body. Every calculation of winds and currents said it would turn up somewhere in the Hamptons. I told them never to trust an ocean but nobody listened. They wanted the Hamptons because it's a class area. The media loves anything that happens out there. Attention must be paid. I said to them why in hell would Apple shlep the corpse across Long Island instead of dumping it near the Digitals' vineyard on the North Shore, say Mattituck or Jamesport but no, they had their hearts set on East Hampton, Southampton, Bridgehampton, Westhampton, like that, some trendy South Shore sand pile. I suggested a compromise, say, Sag Harbor or Shelter Island which made more sense but I was overruled."

"Why not dump Brother Lucas in a ditch?" Simon said. "Wouldn't that have made for an easier autopsy?"

"No question, Simon. You're absolutely right. Salt water could have easily corrupted any evidence, not that evidence was a factor since it was added later." Beem traced the body's voyage over an invisible map. "As it was, the body somehow took the scenic route, drifted from Hampton Bays, curved around Montauk then came in on high tide and ended up in fucking Greenport. Back on the North Shore, exactly where I suggested, not two miles from Luke's monastery. Jesus, Greenport. Strictly blue collar.

"At least the cadaver was intact except for the usual wear and tear. Some shark could have loused up our whole scenario. We would have had to start over again. Let me tell you, it would have taken a miracle to get the New York press to pick up the story of a floating monk in Long Island Sound. It's ironic, but if the whole enchilada of Digitals hadn't been eliminated, which was never part of the original blueprint, Lucas would have ended up as a two-inch paragraph on the obit page. You might still be walking around free. That is, until we came up with some other way to nail you."

"Perish the thought."

"I'll drink to that. The way it turned out, a little girl found him. When she saw Luke bobbing in the surf she thought he was a beached whale or some kind of walrus. Then she waded out to get a better look. His bald head was powdered by sand diamonds. His robes were still attached, like wings. She decided he might be an alien who fell out of a flying saucer. Cute kid. She prodded old Luke with a coke bottle she'd carried down to the shore to toss to the waves. It had a note in it with her name, address, and a love letter. When she saw what was left of Luke's face she tossed the bottle into the breakers and yelled for help. Smart kid."

"So you had your body."

"And we had you by the short hairs."

"But I never set eyes on Brother Lucas. I never went near that man."

"So how come three witnesses saw the two of you together at a local motel? And how come your DNA was found in that motel room? And how come you used your credit card to pay for the suite with the heart-shaped hot tub? And how come Simon Apple's DNA was found up Brother Lucas's consecrated ass? Is that what you're going to ask me?"

"Rhetorical questions, I suppose," Simon said.

"You wouldn't like the answers," Beem said.

"I never even had a credit card. Nobody would give me credit," Simon said.

"How in hell did you live without a credit card?" Beem said. "That always puzzled me. No Amex, no Visa, no MasterCard, no Discover, not even Diners Club? When your lawyer tried to make a thing about that, I think it put off the jury. He should never have accused the prosecution of conjuring a card out of thin air. You could see distance creep into those juror eyes. A man who pays cash? In this day and age?"

"Guilty as charged. By the way, how much credit did I have?"

"I think we got you ten thousand at 9.9 percent for balance transfers and a 14 percent APR for purchases." Beem said. "There was an additional fee for transfers, 3 percent of the total amount but not to exceed a maximum of fifty bucks. And 21 percent for cash advances."

"Thanks for nothing," Simon said.

"Don't mention it," Beem said. "So, Simon, did you change your mind about the lobster?"

"No. I'm standing pat on that one."

"I didn't think you'd give in. Face it. You're just not a team player, Apple."

16

In the months that followed Regis Van Clay's visit to Glenda, *Nonacripthae* aka *Hercumite* was given a cheerful pink color and the taste of chocolate pudding. It was tested on generations of lab rats and on infants in Zambia and Nicaragua. Results of the tests were entirely positive; there were no negative findings aside from rare reports of nausea, diarrhea, constipation and esophageal spasm which might easily be attributed to nutritional, environmental and psychological factors.

Dr. Fikel examined Simon Apple regularly. Results of those examinations were forwarded to the Regis Pharmaceuticals New Jersey headquarters. Simon's progress continued to amaze. The "power baby" grew rapidly into a power boy. His code name at Regis was, understandably, Clark Kent.

When it was certain that *Hercumite* would easily pass FDA muster, Simon was spirited to Minneapolis where Regis's advertising agency, Bleier, Larkin & Koblenz, arranged for him to be photographed by award-winning still and cinematic professionals. The photographers worked under the supervision of the agency's senior art director, Nevins Littlejohn, an acknowledged genius whose credits included classic portraits of Shirley Temple and the zeppelin *Hindenberg*. A happy Robert J. was present at those intense studio sessions, even permitted to snap his own pictures with the foolproof camera that replaced his shattered Nikon.

Back home in Glenda, Robert J. was privileged (as stipulated in the contract written by his lawyer, Marvin Klipstein, Esq.) to examine proofs of magazine and newspaper advertisements and to view early cuts of television commercials for *Hercumite* featuring Simon supposedly interacting with a zodiac of sports heroes. Along with those ads came store displays—life-sized, self-standing, cutouts of Simon dressed in various team uniforms. Those materials arrived in packages marked CONFIDENTIAL! FOR YOUR EYES ONLY!

Because Robert J. had signed a nondisclosure agreement, he was forbidden to display those items at Quikpix or in any public place until *Hercumite* was officially introduced to the American public. But Robert J. was not discreet; soon everyone in Glenda knew their own Simon Apple was destined for blazing celebrity.

Predictably, Simon was invited to attend Munchkin Academy, the most prestigious nursery school in town. The offer, which included a partial scholarship, was accepted.

On his first day, shaking from separation anxiety, Simon was welcomed at Munchkin by a special assembly of students and faculty. He was handed a bouquet of helium balloons, offered a glass of what the dean called "Simon Apple juice" and a tray of cupcakes decorated with his initials, and entertained by a magician who pulled roses from his ears.

For all that hoopla, the best welcome came when Simon discovered that Polly Moon was to be his classmate. His first reaction, seeing Polly, was traumatic. Simon felt suffocated by the memory of his lost Victoria which seemed to have its own clinging perfume. That typhoon of loss passed quickly; Polly looked so delectable in her Munchkin uniform (white blouse, plaid skirt, long red stockings, blue sneakers and Munchkin beanie), his thoughts of Victoria's desertion were replaced with rainbows. The last time he'd seen Polly they were both toddlers confined to carriages or strollers. Now, by some miracle, they were self-propelled. Since Simon had once heard Dr. Fikel refer to Polly Moon as "the Placebo," he thought it was a special, secret name and used it to greet her, running toward the girl with his arms ready for embrace. Polly turned away, left Simon standing with his arms outstretched, walked slowly to the drinking fountain, filled her mouth with Great Bear water, turned herself into a squirt gun and showered his face with a mix of spit and spring water. Simon had never felt happier in his life.

As things settled into routine, the days at Munchkin Academy were generally bearable. Simon endured the black hole of early childhood, those snail-paced hours of mammalian maturation, with a special advantage. He was fortified with ever-increasing doses of *Hercumite*.

Munchkin's academic regimen began with a morning march around a painted circle in the gym. The children clapped their hands together on cue while jolly songs played over the school's sound system. Next, the kindergarten set was sent outside to the playground. After that, there were lessons in ABCs and numbers, conducted with the help of picture cards and wooden blocks. Then came lunch followed by an hour of naptime.

Oddly, naptime seemed to provide Simon with his most valuable instruction though he had no idea why. It wasn't that he was sleepy or lazy, quite the contrary; in that hour he was more alert than ever. Simon lay down on a mat decorated with Mickey Mouse and Donald Duck, pretending to shut his eyes but observing the world through a narrow slit. When it felt safe to take the risk, he twisted his head, pretending to be possessed by a dream, to catch a look at Polly.

She rested just three mats away, so near and yet so far. On good days, her skirt hiked up over her thighs. Browsing the patch of uncovered skin between the hem of her skirt and the tops of her stockings made Simon go crimson, like a figure in a coloring book, with a rush of pleasure and guilt. He was certain that if the teacher who presided over naptime even suspected those feelings, he'd be strapped to the large Rand McNally world globe that sat on a desk under the American flag and rotated to death like a barbecued chicken; a dead child would be returned to Robert J.

After his ersatz nap came art class. Some of Simon's mates drew beautiful images of animals, birds, trees, flowers, happy images of domestic life. Simon drew flat-faced clocks with eyeballs marking the hours and human arms and hands measuring time. His clocks crowned towers of castles perched on mountaintops. He drew tower after tower, clock after clock. What began as gentle teacherly urgings ended as sharp commands to try other subjects but Simon couldn't think of anything else to draw.

What bothered Simon more than his teacher's entreaties to broaden his palette was her insistence that the sky above his clock towers should not hang from the top of the page like a dangling blue roof. She said the sky should come all the way down to the ground. That seemed to him like madness. It made Simon question all her proclamations. The teacher was so exasperated by Simon's hanging skies, she took him outside to show him how the sky works and explained the horizon line but he discarded those lessons as excessive, even deliberately confusing. He saw what he saw and he knew what he knew: that sky and clouds belonged up where he'd put them and he felt huge contempt for the kids who went along with her dumb instruction.

At first, the beautiful Placebo drew skies the way Simon did, as a blue rectangle holding the sun, moon and a few birds. But Polly heard the teacher's treacherous words and compromised. After a few days, her skies came halfway down, a vision that made Simon queasy. He sensed he was losing her to pedantic abuse.

During free play in the yard, Simon tried desperately to communicate his sense of dread, to warn Polly that soon her skies would touch the earth if she continued to yield to pressure, but the girl never allowed him to finish a sentence. Sometime she'd kick him in the shins or tip his milk cup. At other times, she pretended to be deaf and dumb, jumping around with her hands over her ears, eyes closed, and her mouth zipped shut. When her behavior reached critical mass, Simon lapsed into one of his furious tantrums; it took two adults to hold him down. The terrible tantrums were never reported to Robert J.; Munchkin Academy was glad to have a future celebrity on its roster. Dr. Finla, Dean of Admissions, had confirmation that Simon Apple was to be the global symbol for *Hercumite* from no less a source than his father.

It was Polly Moon who first noticed that Simon was growing antlers. Her discovery came during a dancing lesson when the two were purposely paired.

17

Marvin Klipstein, Esq., liked to say he wore his face on his sleeve, that his feelings were transparent as window glass. Marvin was no poker player; you could read his cards in his eyes and in the way his mouth and nose curled and twitched. Under severe stress, his ears wiggled and a tic trembled his left lid.

When he came to see Simon Apple, his message of bad news was telegraphed before the guard opened the cell door.

"Was that Agent Beem I saw outside?" Klipstein said. "Has he been harassing you?"

"It was Beem," Simon said, "but, no, he wasn't harassing me. He was filling in a few blanks."

"He was firing blanks, you mean. Don't trust anything he tells you. And don't answer any questions. It'll end up being used against you."

"A little late for that," Simon said, waiting for Klipstein to say what he came to say. The ticking and twitching were eloquent enough.

"Don't take this too hard, kid," Klipstein said. "The Supreme Court turned nine thumbs down. A unanimous verdict. I thought I had one or two of them on the cusp. I thought my arguments were strong. I came on like gangbusters. I was good, Simon."

"There was no way they were going to grant a stay."

"Don't be so cynical. This wasn't some cockamamie governor. This was the United States Supreme Court."

"Remind me to salute," Simon said.

"Never in my wildest dreams did I ever think Marvin Klipstein would have the opportunity to plead a case before the highest court in the land. I was shitting green in the beginning but when I heard my voice soar, it carried my soul along with it. I wish you could have heard me. It's amazing how the right set of circumstances can bring out your best. I'll never forget that it was you who got me to that courtroom. I felt like an eagle, Simon. I'll bet those austere bastards had a moment of pause before they reached a decision. They'll think about this one for the rest of their lives."

"How long did it take them to rule?"

"Fifteen minutes," Klipstein said. "That was ten minutes more than anybody expected. I could have sworn I had the black and the broad in my hip pocket."

"So, that's that," Simon said.

"There could be a Presidential pardon."

"There could be an alien invasion," Simon said. "But there won't be."

"I'm sorry," Klipstein said. "Heartbroken. Let's face facts. You're going down. In a few hours Simon Apple will cross to the other side. He will meet his maker."

"I get the idea," Simon said.

"In a way I envy you," Klipstein said. "No more sweating the daily indignities. A few gasps, a rattle of bones, one door closes and another door opens. You'll be in on the big secret. You'll have the final answer to the ultimate question."

"It sounds terrific," Simon said. "I can't wait."

"And you go knowing you're guaranteed a posthumous Congressional Medal of Honor. It won't be publicized but it will happen the minute you're officially pronounced dead. Even if they bury the medal with your remains, you'll join the nation's most elite fraternity of heroes. Believe it, I'll make damn sure they live up to that promise. Are you ready for more news?"

"Nothing can top that last bulletin, Marvin."

"We got Arlington Cemetery. Not the best plot but not the worst. You'll sleep in illustrious company. The deal is, your tombstone will be left blank, classified, for at least fifty years, but you can bet the grass will be clipped and watered. You're guaranteed perpetual care for as long as the stars and stripes wave over the land of the free and the home of the brave."

"Klipstein, you did what you could. You have my gratitude. You win some, you lose some. Now go away. Get the fuck out of here before I break your fat ass."

"I respect your need for solitude," Klipstein said. "But there is something else."

"Don't tell me you're going to bill me. I thought the Regis crowd was paying the freight. I always suspected your deal with them was more *pro* than *bono*. You know I'm a pauper."

"This isn't about money, Simon. It's about loose ends. It's about a personal favor. It's about the slim chance that those stories we hear about how the freshly deceased see a tunnel and an eerie glow of white light, how they hear classical music and see a whole crowd of gorgeous creatures waiting to usher them into paradise. If those stories are true, Simon, say a tiny bit true, in that case I'd like you to deliver some information to a few select souls you might run into on the other side."

"I'm not Western Union. I'm not the pony express," Simon said.

"I brought some pictures," Klipstein said, flipping open his wallet. "To help you recognize certain faces. This is my father, Hyman. This is my mother, Lily. Give them my love, etcetera, etcetera. Improvise. Tell them I miss them, that I'm doing well, making a living, like that. And this is my cousin, Serena. Tell her, concerning a certain delicate matter, I'm sorry for what happened but I wouldn't trade the experience for a pound of platinum. Make sure that when you tell Serena you don't trumpet the news to the rest of the family. And this one with the sideburns is my friend, Arnie. Tell him Sharon came on so strong, so wet and hot, I couldn't help myself. I tried, tell him I tried but you know how it goes and it was only a few times while he was away on business and we talked about him while we were doing it. The bald guy is my Uncle Max. Say I always intended to pay back the loans and I'll make donations to charity in his name in the full amount plus interest. And you better say that what he heard about me and Aunt Rebecca was absolute bullshit. The one in the bathing suit is Aunt Rebecca. She was some piece of work for a seventy-year-old woman. If you get the chance, tell her that what happened between us makes me wince to think about but I wouldn't trade it for a million dollars. Between us, Simon, it was only a blowjob in the laundry room and a million dollars is still a million dollars but how can it hurt to stretch the truth a little? And this is . . . I don't remember her name, but we met at Kutcher's Country Club on a singles weekend and the lies, oh, the lies. Did I know it was her first time? Did I know she wasn't on the pill? I was a different person in those days. A potato pancake was enough to turn me on. And this one holding the vacuum cleaner is my wife's best friend, Celia, a compulsive cleaner. We were in the kitchen alone doing dishes when out of the blue she slaps me on the groin with a damp sponge, I—" The lawyer raised his arms toward Heaven and screamed, "Oh dear God! The things we do, the trail of—"

"Klipstein, get hold of yourself," Simon said. "I hate to disappoint you but I plan to travel light. I'm not even taking an extra pair of underwear. I can't carry your messages."

"Would it hurt you to do me that small favor? Is this your idea of how to show gratitude?"

"All right. I'll plead your case for a general amnesty," Simon said. "But it's probably not necessary. I think we know everything the minute we die. It all comes clear. Maybe the minute before we die. Maybe that's what kills us."

"God forbid," Klipstein said. "Should I leave the pictures with you or what?"

"Put them on the cot. Under the pillow," Simon said.

"Bless you," Klipstein said. He patted his eyes with a Kleenex and threw his arms around the condemned man. "And just in case you run into anybody who knew me, mention that I argued a case before the Supreme Court. Slip it into the conversation somehow. Me. *The Supreme Court.*"

18

The faculty at Munchkin Academy couldn't help noticing Simon Apple's infatuation with Polly Moon and her reflexive response of cruel rejection. Such behavior could leave permanent scars on both young psyches as several teachers knew only too well. In conference, a decision was made to attempt conflict resolution through the healing power of forced proximity. As a start, the two children were paired during dancing lessons.

After singing "Where Is Thumbkins?" while wiggling their opposable thumbs—a rhyme Simon liked since he knew exactly where Thumbkins was at any given moment—they sang "Do You Know the Muffin Man?" a lyric that terrified the boy.

Simon's mind belched the image of a large, animated muffin with stubby legs and arms, pocked with oozing blueberries, staggering like a zombie down Drury Lane, where the song said the creature lived. That frightening thought caused kidney spasm; it took much of Simon's energy to enforce tight bladder control. The idea of peeing on Polly Moon's Mary Janes was unconscionable.

During "Muffin Man" the dancers had to take their partners by the hand, skip across the floor, spin around twice, then bow or curtsy to one another depending on gender. The complicated choreography confused Simon, who was anxious enough feeling his partner's small warm fingers trapped in his grasp; he often twirled prematurely and sent his beloved Placebo flying into empty space or another couple. When that happened, her revenge was to grab at Simon's long hair as if it were a lifeline—*Hercumite* nourished hair follicles like plant food—and give his head a hard yank in whatever direction she happened to be tossed. This happened so often the dancing teacher spoke to Robert J. several times about getting his son a protective trim. It was wasted advice. Simon's father was prohibited from taking him to a barber or altering his appearance in any way without first getting written approval from Regis's advertising people.

After one such episode, Polly Moon came away from the encounter with her hand badly cut, screaming that Simon Apple had rats living on his scalp. To quiet the hysterical girl, Simon was ordered to sit in a chair while their instructor probed his bushy mop under a standing lamp. While she looked, the teacher chanted "so silky soft and nice, no cooties and no little lice," then suddenly changed her tune to "Sweet Jesus!"

That night, Robert J. got a call from Munchkin's dean suggesting immediate investigation of two sharp lumps behind the frontal lobes on Simon's skull.

Simon and his father immediately rushed to Dr. Fikel's office. The bad news was confirmed. A pair of bony growths definitely resembling stalks of raw ginger or deer antlers had begun to sprout. The doctor used a caliper to measure those protuberances, took a series of blood tests, then pressed a naked Simon against the cold plate of his fluoroscope. Dr. Fikel did a quick survey of his insides and found nothing unusual, but there was a suggestion of some abnormality near the base of Simon's spine.

"We'll have to do a series of X-rays," Dr. Fikel said, "but I seem to detect a thickening of the coccyx."

"Meaning?"

"I can't make a final diagnosis but my hunch is that in addition to the cranial event, your son is budding a bit of a tail. It's probably nothing of concern, an adjunct to his extraordinary growth spurt. I'm left wondering if I should call Regis Pharmaceuticals."

"And say what?"

"We do have a potential problem here. Our agreement with Regis stipulates that any suspicious aberration in the child's physiology must be reported and documented. They're very sensitive to anything that might be construed as a side effect associated with *Nonacripthae.*"

"But this may not have any connection to that drug," Robert J. said. "I was a heavy smoker for twenty years. I smoked two packs of Camels a day. Couldn't secondhand smoke be the culprit here? The baby was exposed to those fumes. I'll testify to that."

"A point well taken," Dr. Fikel said. "I'll mention it. Except that in my opinion those secondhand smoke studies are a crock of shit based on junk science. Of course, if this can be traced to tobacco we're off the hook. Horn and tail growth could even be traceable to psychological stress. Has Simon been under unusual pressure? Are you abusing the boy in any way?"

"He must still miss his mother. And when our housekeeper, Victoria, left so suddenly, he was traumatized. All that happened a while ago and he seems to take nicely to the Munchkin Academy. I can't point a finger to any specific irritation. The only thing he complains about has something to do with the sky coming all the way down."

"We'll make a list of anything that could be a factor here," Dr. Fikel said. "The last thing we want is to leave stones unturned. So far, all we have are a few bony aberrations. The lad feels no discomfort. I would say there's room for prudence here before we go frightening the Regis people. I suppose I could wait a few weeks before blowing whistles. This whole thing might be a storm in a teacup."

"In a few weeks the *Hercumite* advertising campaign kicks off," Robert J. said. "It would be sinful to deny Simon such opportunity because of a condition that might be caused by something utterly trivial like a tight hat or belt."

"Absolutely," Dr. Fikel said. "Let's not forget that nature does have a way of correcting herself. Of course, I'll watch the boy like a hawk. I'll do everything possible to reverse this condition. We do have the patient's welfare to consider."

"Above all else," Robert J. said. "But you might want to reduce the dose of *Hercumite* in the meanwhile."

"We'll cut down to every other day," Dr. Fikel said. "Better to taper off gradually. I'll phone the Munchkin people. Assure them that there's no danger of contagion. Remind them to button up about all this. We don't want the entire population of Glenda aware of anything out of the ordinary. In my opinion, Simon Apple is a healthy boy, give or take. A twice-blessed boy."

The Munchkin Academy agreed to inform Robert J. of any significant change in Simon's appearance. He was immediately excused from dancing class, an activity Simon had begun to enjoy. Now he only saw Placebo from a safe distance.

19

Simon's emerging tail was easy to conceal inside slightly altered shorts. His antlers, or horns, presented a special problem. Dr. Fikel suggested that he be allowed to replace the usual Munchkin cap with a knitted hat because of a chronic scalp inflammation and that it would be merciful to order every classmate to do the same. Munchkin's dean refused to discard the school's famous cap for fear of offending nostalgic alumni who contributed to Munchkin's endowment but allowed Simon Apple a medical dispensation.

Keeping Simon's hat in place proved impossible since pulling it off became a favorite student pastime, especially for Polly Moon who took diabolical pleasure in humiliating him and nursed a powerful curiosity, even a secret envy, about Simon's tantalizing transition.

Simon himself enjoyed the attention at first but gradually developed self-conscious feelings of inferiority though he never understood what all the fuss was about. He resented his daily visits to Dr. Fikel's office where he was subjected to a seemingly endless assault of weighing and measuring, bloodletting, needle pricks, X-rays and scrapings. Dr. Fikel's sour look and the mask of concerned disappointment on his father's otherwise placid face convinced Simon that he was doing something very wrong but he couldn't pinpoint his sin. When he asked questions, the answers were always evasive, badly designed to change the subject.

When a Munchkin football team was recruited to play in Glenda's new Little League, Simon was chosen as a third-string running back. The school psychologist, Melvin Lint, who was also the coach, felt that team play with its inevitable bonding would prove excellent therapy for the Apple boy though there was no plan to use him in an actual game. Aside from evaluating Simon as a fearful child with little interest or ability in athletics, Coach Lint had been quietly informed in so many words that Apple was too valuable a commodity to risk in a contact sport. Robert J., whose nose had been permanently bent by a flying bat in a second grade softball game, signed a permission slip allowing Simon to join the team but stipulating that the boy would be restricted from leaving the bench even during practice; his job would be to suit up and sit down.

The Munchkin Marauders played their first game on Glenda

Green. They ran onto the field outfitted in red and black uniforms, white Keds, and orange helmets all donated by local stores including Quikpix.

The Marauders were welcomed by an enthusiastic crowd of parents, relatives and friends. Cheerleaders in leotards, led by Polly Moon who'd learned to twirl a baton with considerable skill, energized the players and onlookers with passionate yells and impressive gymnastics.

Munchkin Academy versus Spock Prep was a big event for Glenda, important enough to attract not only local but national media attention. A clever press release drafted by the Glenda Chamber of Commerce headed TYKE TITANS TUSSLE caught the attention of a producer for *The Speed Sage Report*, a late-night cable talk show. Covering a football game played by tumbling tots in America's heartland would work well to soften Speed Sage's negative image as a cold-hearted, right wing bulldog.

Sage and his production crew drove to Glenda Green in a Chrysler van topped by a microwave dish pointed toward a relay that would send live coverage, via Minneapolis and Chicago, to a network of 232 stations. While a reporter from *The Glenda Express* watched—from his modest vantage of a folding chair and a bridge table holding an old Olivetti portable—Speed Sage, wearing earphones and a concealed microphone, supervised the strategic placement of his camera crew and sound engineers, then took position looking down at the makeshift field from a portable aluminum platform.

When Munchkin's cheerleaders went into action, cameras were already rolling. "Move over, Dallas Cowgirls," Sage told his invisible audience, "for this bevy of milk fed pre-pubescent cuties. And get a gander at the game faces on those players. I'd swear those mini-gladiators are psyched for the NFL. Is this Middle America or what?"

The game was divided into four five-minute periods. The first three were predictable mayhem. Passes were thrown in the wrong direction, runners tripped and fumbled, every tackle was followed by a long time-out while a bloody nose was wiped, tears were blotted, somebody's mother was cleared from the field.

The coaches from Munchkin and Spock yelled encouragement

from the sidelines. Screams from the crowd mixed high praise with curses and complaints that floated through the air like slaps. "The mommas and the poppas are really getting into this," Speed Sage said. "Did somebody forget to pass around the tranquilizers? Hey folks, lighten up. Those are your kids out there. Be thankful they're toilet trained. This ain't the Superbowl so relax and have some fun. No, what the hell—let the killer instinct run its course."

Simon sat glued to the bench uncomfortable under the extra-large helmet they gave him. Most of his attention was focused on Placebo who was easily the star of the Munchkin Maidens. Her "GO-TEAM-GOs" flew from her mouth as if she spun silk. When she did splits, tiny hairs tingled on Simon's neck and he felt his new tail curl. The first time he heard his coach yell, "Apple, get in there and get us some points," he thought he was daydreaming. "Move it, Apple. Get with the program."

It was in the last minutes of the final period when Simon was pushed across the boundary between safety and suicide. There was no score in the game. Coach Lint had no choice. He needed his last substitute to replace the maimed and dispirited.

Deal or no deal, Simon Apple had to play. Later, the desperate coach would explain to Robert J. that the real issue was mental health. The Marauders were a man short. Ignoring Simon's presence in the face of such obvious need was more risky than allowing him to touch the football. Simon's wounded teammates would never forgive a coward and Simon could never forgive himself.

On his first play the fat, puffing center squeezed the ball between salami legs and sent it spinning into Simon's churning belly. Simon stood holding the ball until he was flattened by the Spock defense. The thud from that hit made the crowd gasp. Robert J., who had spotted his former employee, Rowena Trask, accepting a hotdog from one of Speed Sage's crew, looked back at the game and realized it was Simon getting up off the ground. "You stupid asshole," he yelled at Coach Lint. Simon assumed his father was commenting on his own performance. His eyes welled as he got up off the turf.

"Talk about crunch time, the boy with the big orange helmet just saw more stars than a planetarium," Speed Sage said. "But he's up and ready to go. That kid's got moxie!"

Simon's orange head was blank and buzzing. He crouched, listening to the Munchkin quarterback call signals, wondering where he was and how he got there. He felt his father's eyeballs burning holes in his cheeks.

The fat center, newly energized by a Hershey Kiss, snapped the ball with frenzy. It flew over the quarterback in a high arc. Simon chased it, grabbed for it, stared at its dumb squashed-egg shape. He heard Coach Lint's voice command him to "runnit, runnit."

Simon knew he couldn't run with the heavy helmet holding him rooted in place. He tore it off with one hand, cradled the ball with the other, lowered his head and charged at the monsters from Spock Prep.

"He dumped his helmet. He's a little locomotive," Speed Sage yelled, "but he's gonna be derailed because here comes the enemy! Hold your horses, folks! Wait just a minute. What is that kid wearing on his head? Whatever it is, it can't be legal."

Simon didn't feel the first collision or the second. He ran through obstacles that cracked and buckled. He heard sounds like the beating wings of dark angels.

"That Munchkin is going to score!" Sage roared. "He's in the Red Zone! He's in the End Zone! Touchdown! Good God, his headgear is caught on the goal post crossbar they lowered for kiddie kicks—he's spinning like a pinwheel! And he left a trail of comatose kiddies behind him. I hear groans. I see blood. Is this baby football or a hockey game? We came here expecting a comedy of errors, not carnage. What's going on here in Glenda?"

In the ballroom of The Parker Meridian Hotel in Manhattan, the Regis Pharmaceuticals Board of Directors, a group of major stockholders, and a cadre of Wall Street analysts were gathered to celebrate news of the FDA's unconditional approval of *Hercumite*.

Regis Van Clay was in the middle of a speech extolling the talents and dedication of the scientists and salespeople whose long hours of selfless work had catapulted a small manufacturer of generic aspirin, guaranteed organic herbal supplements grown in a hothouse on a former landfill in Jersey City, and a line of discount vitamin pills into a major player in one of the world's most lucrative growth industries.

"How many among us can honestly say that we prosper from improving the quality of human life?" Regis said. "Lately, there have been rumblings from the disgruntled and misinformed criticizing everything from our marketing methods to our motives. Those same critics can expect longer, more productive lives, and use more of those years to badmouth our efforts, exactly because companies like ours have endured immense risk amounting to billions of dollars, dedicated thousands of expensive hours to searching out and perfecting amazing products like *Hercumite*. I can't tell *you* what to say but I, for one, can only say God bless us, every one! And while I'm at it, God bless God!"

Regis paused for applause. During the pause he was handed a wireless gold-colored telephone; it had been arranged that a call from the oval office would carry a bouquet of presidential congratulations. When that call came in from Washington, D.C., the phone would be hooked up to the ballroom's speaker system.

Regis smiled into the receiver. Instead of the President, Regis heard the voice of his Director of Public Relations. "Some not so great news," the voice said.

"I'm in the middle of . . ."

"I'm sorry but I think you need to hear this immediately and in private, Sir. Condition red."

"This better be a genuine horror," Regis said. "Hold on."

Regis looked out at his audience. "Please excuse me, ladies and gentlemen. But as you know, all men are peers," then he dashed for the rest room waving the telephone.

Luckily that room was empty. Regis found a stall, closed the door, put the phone to his ear and heard a burst of static. "Lousy connection," he said, "but go on, and be fast."

"This sportscaster, Speed Sage—"

"Who the fuck is Speed Sage? Speak slower. I can hardly hear you. Is this some kind of bad joke?"

"It seems that our *Hercumite* boy, Simon Apple, is playing in some kind of moppet football game and he scored a touchdown."

"Is that what you called to tell me? That Apple scored a touchdown?" Regis yelled, "Well, hooray for us. That only proves *Hercumite* is . . ."

"Please, Sir, you should know the Sage guy is reporting that Apple gored his way to the goal line," a hectic voice said. "Gored. Speared. Literally. We're talking horns or antlers. He says he interviewed some local doctor who mentioned a certain drug, if you get my meaning."

A round little man in a waiter's uniform dashed into the toilet and locked himself into the stall adjoining Regis's cubicle. He heard a shriek from his neighbor's tiny closet. Since the waiter, newly arrived from Mexico, spoke only menu English, the words were only a clutter of urgent sounds, probably some constipated gringo talking to the air.

"And it's not just the boy's head in question. It seems there's a slight tail problem too. Mr. Van Clay? Are you following me? Hello?"

"I hear you," Regis said in a soft voice like a knife cutting through cream cheese. "Find out what you can about that Sage person. Get me his history from the time he was a zygote. Medical records, eating habits, marital status, any police record—traffic tickets to pedophilia. And dig into possible financial ties to Merck, Pfizer, GlaxoSmithKline, Burroughs Wellcome, AstraZeneca, whatever, I want his whole pharmaceutical investment spectrum from one-product suppository makers in China to Johnson & Johnson, from giants to midgets, obvious to obscure. And do it now. That's *now.*"

"This is still in the rumor stage. Even if there is a connection to *Hercumite*—dorsal, ventral or both—there's time for positive spin."

"What would you suggest for positive spin? Maybe we could put an amulet in every package. Or a phial of holy water."

Regis slammed down the phone. It rang again. "You're a hard man to reach, Van Clay. I didn't expect a busy signal." This time the voice was unmistakable.

"Mr. President," Regis said, "All hail to the chief. It's so good of you to put the world on hold to share this seminal moment with us. May I ask you to give me a moment—we've got a case of crossed wires. One of the unexpected benefits of deregulation."

The man in the next booth flushed. Regis covered the speaker while he dashed back to the hotel's ballroom.

"No, problem, Van Clay," the President said. "I'm sitting here relaxing with the First Lady watching some kind of moppet sports event from Minnesota. You wouldn't believe what . . ."

20

In the visitor's room, Simon studied the face behind the protective glass looking for some familiar sign, some fragment of recognition. The woman was trim and attractive, neatly groomed, fashionably dressed in a black blazer, black slacks and blue silk blouse. She wore pearl earrings and a gold chain necklace. His visitor had to be well into her sixties. Allowing for her silver hair and a few wrinkles under her chin she had a girlish quality like the women who sell Depends or Metamucil on television. Her teeth were perfectly white, expertly capped—symmetrical teeth lined up like the Rockettes waiting for a cue. Her eyes were hidden behind dark glasses with large circle lenses.

He wished he could see those eyes. They might trigger some sleeping memory. Even her voice failed to evoke recognition though Simon did feel a frisson of distant emotion when she spoke. But there was no upsurge of anything he could easily label love or sorrow. The protective glass kept him from smelling a telltale whiff of her perfume or reading any physical clue that might have come from the heat of even a casual embrace or a kiss on the cheek.

"You don't know who I am," the woman said. "Why should you?"

"Could you give me a hint? Twenty questions?"

"I'm your mother, Simon."

"Ma? Mom? Mommy? My biological mother? Is it really you?"

"Please don't be snide. I suppose you resent me for testifying as a witness for the prosecution," Francine Apple Zane said into the telephone connecting the prisoner with his unexpected guest.

"Resent you? I couldn't focus too clearly that day. I never got a good look at you. They had me pretty well fogged with illegal substances. I do seem to remember being surprised when they called you to the stand," Simon said. "But not resentful, not really. I am curious about one small matter. Do you believe those lies you told the jury about my calling you to beg forgiveness for bringing shame on the family?"

"You've got to realize how it was up there, Simon. All those people glaring, all those cameras with their blinking red lights. I certainly didn't want to come across like a liar. And where was your lawyer? He might have shaken my story. I was ready to sound less certain. I nearly fainted when he said no further questions."

"You can't fault Klipstein for letting you off the hook. You are my mother. If he tore into you it would have made a worse impression on the jury. By the way, how did they get you to commit perjury? Was it fear or money or both?"

"They're probably recording this conversation," Francine said. "I don't want to get into incriminating specifics. You shouldn't even ask me such questions. After all, I did make the trip to see you."

"You're right. So what are you doing here?"

"It is your last day. I would seem like a very uncaring person if I stayed home. And I do care, Simon. Leaving you was a difficult thing. But you always seemed closer to your father. I didn't want to snatch you away from your home, your friends."

"I was less than a year old. The only thing you snatched away was your breasts. I can still taste those rubber nipples."

"I was hoping we might let bygones be bygones. Why dwell on the past? As it is, things worked out for the best."

"Except for the fact that I'm about to be executed."

"I knew you'd bring that up," Francine said.

"Francine, do you feel any guilt knowing your genes share some responsibility for your son's—how shall I phrase it—untimely ending?"

"Oh, now this is my fault. It wasn't my genetics that turned you into a murderer."

"But I didn't murder anybody."

"Please, Simon," Francine said. "You left a trail of bodies. A mountain of evidence. You're going to have some explaining to do to the man upstairs."

"If my hands were drenched in blood why would they force my own mother to testify against me? Would they feed her a script?"

"Nobody forced me to say anything. And when it came to the movie rights I insisted that they include at least the suggestion that

Brother Lucas molested you when you were seduced into joining that cult of his."

"I didn't know Brother Lucas. I didn't join any cult. What movie rights? The law says a convicted murderer can't profit from his crime. There are no movie rights."

"The law says nothing about a bereaved mother earning a few dollars for telling her story. A mother deserves some reparation for all that shame and disgrace."

"Who bought movie rights?"

"A very dedicated director. He personally told me it was the chance he'd been waiting for to push the envelope of his talent. This is no one night stand on television. This is a feature film."

"Nobody is going to make a movie about any of this," Simon said. "In a week this will be forgotten. Swept under the carpet. I'll tell you who bought movie rights. The government. Or was it Regis Van Clay?"

"Nonsense. I read the plot outline. They did take a few liberties but there is a profound difference between ordinary and cinematic reality. Anyhow, the way it reads now, you were an abused child, the victim of a demented clergyman. They offered me a cameo role as a *sous chef* in the kitchen where they prepare the fish you poisoned. I'm one of the first to die."

"There will never be a major motion picture. Trust me. And take my advice, don't press them for opening night tickets. These people don't kid around."

"That is so cynical, Simon. What awful things did your father teach you about this wonderful world? Didn't he ever mention that there's much more good than bad? It was that vile collection of photographs that corrupted Robert J. Apple. He thought he could keep secrets from me. And that Rowena trollop. When I first met your father he was a God fearing, hopeful man. I should never have left my only child alone with him."

"It's time to end this visit," Simon said. "Thanks for dropping in. I'm glad to see you looking well, Francine."

"And you look marvelous, Simon. Have a good dinner tonight. You know, I was asked to say something to you about a lobster but I refused. I said if his heart is even half-kosher it doesn't matter what he swallows. Or was insisting on lobster another of your subtle little ways to punish me? Is that it? Between us, I would have thought you'd ask for a nice cut of brisket. Well, Simon, we did have some good times together. Sweet dreams."

21

On hiatus from the Munchkin Academy, sick of enforced confinement at home, Simon jiggled at the lock on his bedroom door with a coat hanger until he heard a snap and felt the doorknob turn. From downstairs he could hear Robert J.'s rhythmic snores that made Simon think of the purring of a cat dreaming of a world carpeted with small, plump mice.

Still in his pajamas and bathrobe, Simon escaped his room, tip-toed down to the front door, opened its deadbolt and dashed outside onto a rainy street. He pulled the bathrobe's terrycloth hood over his head, then ran through puddles toward the Waldbaum's Supermarket three blocks away.

When he reached that oasis of light and warmth he rushed past Produce, turned at Dairy, navigated displays of Beer and Soda then cut into the aisle for Pet Foods and Needs. It seemed the proper place to be since it was clear that he was transforming into some kind of animal. Even Placebo called him Rudolf on his last day at school. Others addressed him as Bonzo or Lassie.

The prospect of facing future life as a beast didn't particularly bother Simon. He had always enjoyed staring into the eyes hidden in furry or feathered faces. There seemed to be a peaceful wisdom dwelling there. Besides, gerbils to mongrels, the pets in Glenda lived good lives. A wide supermarket aisle entirely devoted to their nour-ishment and comfort confirmed Simon's feeling that sporting four legs or a pair of flapping wings offered distinct advantages.

While he cleared bags of Purina Dog Chow off a lower shelf, Simon swore to himself that he would be a credit to whatever species he was destined to join. He would be an asset to his new owner, content on a leash or chattering from a perch, peering out of a shell or squatting in a litter box. He wanted nothing more than a quiet life far from notoriety. Occasional visits to a vet presented a better prospect than the twice-weekly assaults by Dr. Fikel he was forced to endure.

Back at the Apple residence, Robert J. woke himself with a choking snort. He went upstairs to give his son an overdue dose of diluted *Hercumite*. Regis Pharmaceuticals had agreed that Simon should be gradually weaned from the drug while the cause of his condition was determined; abrupt withdrawal could be a dangerous path and there was no final proof that *Hercumite* was to blame for the boy's unfortunate symptoms.

When Robert J. discovered that Simon was gone, first he checked every room including the basement looking for the fugitive. Finally, he notified the Glenda police and began his own frantic search for his vanished son.

It was three agonizing hours before a detective waved Robert J.'s car to the curb and told him that a boy answering to Simon's description had been found by a woman at Waldbaum's Supermarket. The lady was shopping for a box of Milk Bone with a double coupon when she noticed Simon in his pajamas, his face looking plaintive under his hooded robe, sitting on a shelf with a price tag pasted to his cheek. When she asked him why he was hiding there he said he wasn't hiding from anyone; he was there to be bought, put into a shopping cart and wheeled out to somebody's car. He explained that he was good natured, playful and more than ready to join her household as a welcome addition. Then he began licking her hand.

She'd squired the child to Customer Services where he was first pampered, then intimidated by a manager waving a box of Mallomars until he revealed his name, address and phone number.

When Robert J. came to claim him, Simon was actually glad to see his father.

Robert J. rewarded the Milk Bone Samaritan by paying for her entire cartload of provisions. That gesture astonished Simon; such generosity proved his father was genuinely happy to retrieve him. Still, Simon wondered how much of his father's paternal joy was motivated by their reunion and how much by commerce. He'd heard himself referred to as a "multimillion dollar property" more than once by the advertising people in Chicago, certainly worth a bag of groceries.

Outside the supermarket, Robert J. gave Simon a hug and kiss, then took him to McDonald's for a hamburger, fries and a milk-shake. To Simon, who'd been fed a supervised diet of vegetables and fruit juice for a month, that meal was reason enough to suspend nagging doubts about the depth of fatherly affection. After his attempted escape, Simon was given more freedom inside the Apple home but never allowed outside. Dr. Fikel continued his frequent visits.

While Simon was being weaned off *Hercumite*, his classmates, especially Polly Moon, were closely observed for signs of antlerism. Polly had been exposed to identical environmental factors and daily contact with the victim. The chemists at Regis were hoping against hope that Polly, who had never swallowed any drug stronger than cough medicine, would develop some similar disease that might point to a virus or mold spore as the culprit. But the child Dr. Fikel called Placebo was in radiant health.

After many disappointing attempts to reverse Simon's bizarre affliction, after seven weeks of intensive research, an obscure researcher in Regis's New Products Division stumbled on *Viloxidril*, a serum originally developed to enlarge rhinoceros horn, prized as an aphrodisiac in Asia. Since harvesting and selling the horn is illegal (the rhino being classified as an endangered species) the *Viloxidril Project* was known only to very few scientists. Curiously, when applied to human bones during a routine experiment, *Viloxidril* performed in a manner opposite to its intended effect on rhino horn. A memo on the drug's odd skeletal behavior was sent to Regis Van Clay. On a wild hunch, he ordered it given to Simon Apple whose crown was no longer described as anything but an impressive set of buck antlers and whose tail hung nearly to the ground.

Within days the antlers dried and snapped off like kindling. Simon's tail showed signs of retracting. Within weeks, Simon Apple was well on the way to recovery.

Viloxidril
Trade name: *Symmavane*
Shaping the future with Regis Pharmaceuticals

Hercumite, which had already been heavily promoted on television and in better magazines with another robust poster boy, enjoyed a huge consumer response. Despite efforts by a battery of Regis attorneys, the FDA insisted that Simon Apple's odd reaction, however rare, merited inclusion in the Possible Side Effects listed on the label. Regis Van Clay himself advised the medical community that, by every statistical projection, what had become labeled *Simon's Syndrome, coccyxonasty antalastium grimmalis*, would affect less than .003 percent of users. In the event the *Syndrome* did manifest, the marvels of *Hercumite* could still be enjoyed by every infant, since the new *Viloxidril*, known to the layman as *Symmavane*, would cure the disease.

Regis's assurances were compromised when word came that an unfortunate tyke in Arkansas, a user of *Nonacripthae* aka *Hercumite*, grew antlers prominent enough to confuse a hunter who shot him. After the story of that accident broke on *Entertainment Tonight*, prescribing *Hercumite* was considered as too risky by more conservative pediatricians.

Hercumite was permanently withdrawn from sale in North America and Europe. Regis Pharmaceuticals stock plummeted to new lows. There were rumors that the company had agreed to pay a huge settlement to the Arkansas victim's family. Actually, a lively and lucrative black market for *Hercumite* developed among serious athletes on every continent, but the Wall Street analysts kept that information to themselves. When Regis Pharmaceuticals stock tanked, both Robert J. and Dr. Henry Fikel felt the pain of loss.

With his new lease on life, Simon Apple was enrolled in public school. For him, mercifully, the slate was wiped clean; every day was a new beginning. The only thing Simon really missed about Munchkin was Placebo. He hardly ever saw Polly Moon aside from transient encounters, all too brief.

Aside from occasional nausea, chronic constipation, dry mouth, acne, and excessive perspiration, Simon had no unusual side effects from *Viloxidril*.

Not for several years.

22

Perched on a stool, Regis Van Clay sat in the presence of the darling of the Museum of Modern Art, the Whitney and the Metropolitan, not to mention temples of art and private collections around the globe.

"I had an inspiration," Voltan Zerminsky said, pacing back and forth, waving bare hairy arms. Regis's eyes followed Zerminsky's massive shadow as it eclipsed an entire wall of the artist's studio. "One head is not enough. Each time I study your face I see another person. I think a triptych, perhaps an entire wall, a hemisphere, a curved universe, a galaxy of heads with a hundred bronze eyes focused on a single point, a beautiful rendition of your headless naked body, standing under a powerful spotlight. Thus the viewer becomes a participant, choosing the head of his or her choice. A fusion of essences. Interactive. Are you listening or am I speaking to myself?"

"It's an interesting idea," Regis Van Clay said while he surveyed Zerminsky's Greenwich Village atelier, a gigantic room in a former warehouse lined with shelves that held hundreds of plaster busts, a Who's Who of the century's celebrities. It was as if the room was built to hold the oversized sculptor.

"I'm talking in the realm of revelation," Zerminsky said. "I can see your mind thinking that such a sculpture would be too arrogant, a confession of excessive egotism. Or is it that you fear exposing so much of yourself, frightened by the thought of total access?"

"My wife's idea was a bust for our living room," Regis said. "Frankly, the idea of self-glorification is alien to me. I am not Julius Caesar. But I agreed to indulge her. You've gone far beyond my limited imagination. I didn't expect Mount Rushmore."

"Ah, yes, modesty. But if I may say so, false modesty. Regis Van Clay has risen above and beyond such inhibiting pedestrian gravity." The sculptor raised his voice to a near scream. "Van Clay, admit that you're worthy of a Voltan Zerminsky. You belong to the ages. Accept that future generations will want to know this amazing man who clawed his way out of poverty's muddy tentacles, who climbed the icy Everest of challenge to its topmost peak, who built an empire dedicated to the betterment of humanity. I tell you, one head is not enough to tell your story, to preserve your music, your symphony."

"A wall of heads? That does make some sense," Regis said. "It is original. But a decapitated naked body?"

"By God, you're right!" Zerminsky said, spinning 360 degrees. "What was I thinking? No, not naked. Wearing a simple business suit. In truth, that is your true skin. More naked than naked. And the fact that Regis Van Clay's body is clothed will diffuse any banal accusation of narcissism. As for decapitation, I am talking headless, not heedless. Remember that the viewer will supply a head from the multiplicity of choices. The result? Gestalt! Ultimate closure."

"I don't know," Regis said. "Where would I put all that? Certainly not in the living room. Not in our entertainment center."

"Not in your home," Zerminsky said. "I will gladly throw in a little bust for your mantle. Call it a wife-sized rendition of her loving husband. The installation I propose would not be a domestic ornament. Not even be suitable for the lobby of your company's headquarters." Zerminsky bent double, laughing. "Did I say *head*quarters? No pun was intended." The sculptor's wide face turned deadly serious. "Absolutely not for the lobby. You wouldn't want your workers to be reminded of a plateau of success they can never achieve. I see now that the installation should be a posthumous memorial. We would proceed in stages. First, I will complete a single element. We will work quietly, keep our tribute in storage. To be unveiled in a glorious ceremony after your passing. Does it make you nervous to accept the fact that one day, many years from now, even you will die?"

"I've made plans to be frozen," Regis said. "Our cryogenics people are making incredible strides. Who can say that death itself won't become obsolete?"

"Marvelous. Then let's assume that when your remains are thawed and your resurrection accomplished, you would enjoy the opportunity of visiting the Regis Van Clay Memorial in person."

"That would be a publicity bonanza," Regis chuckled.

"You blush with embarrassment," Zerminsky said. "There is nothing to be embarrassed about. Embarrassment is apology. You have nothing to apologize for. Regis Van Clay has earned his monument which is more than can be said of most so-called heroes."

"Your gallery told me a single head would cost me a million dollars," Regis said. "And maybe I should quit while I'm a head. Pun intended. How much would your wall add to the bottom line?"

"You want to bring this down to a discussion of money?" Zerminsky said. "Because I won't. Whatever the cost, consider that my art can only increase in value. The truth is, you will end up with a profit. A major work by Voltan Zerminsky? What will that be worth fifty years from today?"

Zerminsky gestured toward the plaster casts of tycoons, politicians, generals, musicians, singers, dancers, a galaxy of stars, the work that made him famous. "Did they count pennies? Believe me, Voltan Zerminsky takes no credit for his genius—a gift that came directly from Above. But he does recognize that, in crass, secular terms, its value is measured in the obscene language of dollars and cents. Or Pounds. Or Euros."

"I guessed that," Regis said.

"I would be proud to sculpt your essence in exchange for nothing but a crust of bread. That I must make a good living to affirm and gratify my earthbound psyche is incidental. Adding up my income is like taking my pulse. I need to know I am alive."

"Listen, Voltan, let me think about your proposal. I think we can come to terms. As you might have noticed, I'm a bit distracted today. I haven't been sleeping well."

"Tell me about it. I want to know you better than I know my brother. Knowledge translates into intuition." Zerminsky flexed his fists. "Intuition guides these fingers." His large, dark eyes darted toward a table where a blob of formless clay was held in place by a metal armature.

Regis envied the artist's magical ability to outdo nature, to seek out a human soul and preserve it for posterity. Zerminsky could duplicate face and form to perfection. Then Regis wondered if the artist's alchemy was so different from his own ability to fabricate a generic drug from a formula just past patent protection, now in public domain? Or from supervising the development of a product like *Hercumite* from molecules elusive as quicksilver, brilliantly camouflaged, shy of discovery as any spy or virgin?

Was Zerminsky's blatant flattery—his attempt to multiply a million dollar deal into a billion dollar extravaganza—was that so different from Regis Pharmaceuticals' artful marketing of a gut-busting new laxative? Yes, Voltan Zerminsky is hailed by critics, celebrated in fashion magazines, lauded by the *Arts and Leisure* section of the *Sunday Times* as an icon. A Zerminsky creation inspires automatic reverence. Zerminsky accepts his role as palpable evidence of the Supreme Being's divinity, a celestial celebrant while Regis Van Clay must be content with write ups in *The Wall Street Journal, Fortune, Time, BusinessWeek, US News*, where his achievements are documented for

MBA undergraduates who see him as a phenomenon of free-wheeling capitalism, someone to emulate, then emasculate and dethrone.

But is a Voltan Zerminsky really superior to a Regis Van Clay? If Zerminsky's glorious prostate swelled, how long would it take him to trade his blessed hands for a cure from Regis Pharmaceuticals? The time it takes to sculpt an ant.

Those thoughts left Regis feeling better, on a level playing field. "I think we can come to a satisfactory arrangement. At least on Phase One of the project."

"What is it that disturbs your well-deserved, refreshing sleep?" Zerminsky said.

"Forget that," Regis said. "It's unimportant."

"Tell me," Zerminsky said.

"A dream that cuts like barbed wire," Regis said, surprised that he bothered to answer. "I dream about a child, a boy, who gouges out great globs of my intestines with a fork."

"Evisceration," Zerminsky said. "Disgusting. But I don't mean to be judgmental."

"The dream is recurrent. I can't shake it. I stay up watching stupid television shows because I'm afraid to close my eyes."

"So? Another face to consider for the wall. A tortured face."

"Fuck your wall. I'm talking nightmares. Why would I be having nightmares?"

"You must talk with Victoria."

"Who the hell is Victoria?"

"My wife," Zerminsky said, squeezing at the fetal clay. "My Victoria reads dreams the way I read faces. She frightens me. A woman who has wandered through ancient caves where bats hang upside down coping with their own inverted dreams. I love her completely. She understands the grueling demands of living with genius. But I admit, the woman is a witch."

"Your wife is a psychoanalyst? I have news for you. My company is turning psychoanalysts into pharmacists. Regis Pharmaceuticals has cured more schizophrenics than the Republican Party."

"Victoria is no psychoanalyst. She never finished grade school. Her skills are intuitive. They are brewed from air, fire, water and estrogen."

"I don't think she can help me, Voltan. I learned long ago that demons are best faced alone."

"Our session is finished for today," Zerminsky said. "I am going to take a long shit and smoke a cigar. Let me send Victoria in here. What have you to lose except a few minutes?"

Regis looked at his watch. Belladonna was expecting him. He was looking forward to an excruciating hour. But he'd allowed himself enough time for a quick lunch before his appointment. He could give that up. "All right," Regis said. "Why not?"

Zerminsky bent his large body until his hands touched the floor, righted himself, rubbed his back, turned and left the studio. Regis spun around on the stool that Zerminsky used to park his subjects. He browsed the casts in Zerminsky's gallery. With their white plaster skin the bunch of them looked like zombies. Then it came to Regis that trumping the death card was what all this art business was about; he decided to place his bet on cryogenics. Regis shivered.

He decided to trade Victoria Zerminsky's counsel for a Cobb salad and a glass of Pinot Grigio. Regis was buttoning himself into his camel hair coat when the sculptor's wife appeared.

Victoria Zerminsky was a formidable woman. No ravishing beauty but presentable enough, good peasant stock with a body strong enough to tolerate the nightly pounding of a 6-foot, 250-pound, self-confessed genius. Regis liked her smile.

"So tell me," Victoria said.

"Tell you what?"

"Your haunting. Your phantoms."

"Did your husband tell you I was haunted?"

"He did. Voltan said you were a man possessed."

"That's a bit of an exaggeration. I mentioned an irritating dream."

"About the boy with the spoon and your intestines."

"Not a spoon. A fork."

"Describe the child."

"A boy. I'm not sure of his age. Maybe six, maybe ten, I don't know. Ordinary features. Reddish brown hair. Blue eyes."

"More. I need more."

"What can I say? He seems to be athletic. Very active. Never in one place for long. Dressed in jeans and a T-shirt, sneakers, no socks. He confronts me, says a polite hello then reaches into a pocket and comes out with that fork. I try to fight him off but he keeps jabbing at my belly yelling *pie, pie, pie.*"

"Pie? Any special kind of pie? Apple? Blueberry? Peach?"

"Just pie, pie, pie. I say to him, stop it, you stupid nit, but he keeps attacking."

"A stupid boy who says pie, pie, pie. Are you certain no particular pie?"

"Wait a minute. One time he did mention a particular pie. Apple pie"

"A nasty boy who wants a slice of apple pie," Victoria said. "You said he is a stupid boy. Is his name Simon? Like Simple Simon in the poem?"

"Simple Simon met a pie man," Regis said. "Simon could be his name. By God, it is his name. I know exactly who's haunting me. Simple Simon, Apple pie. Simon Apple. That little motherfucker. Of course it's him. How could I have missed those signals? Who else would he be?"

Victoria clasped her hands together as if she were applauding herself but there was no applause. "Simon Apple of Glenda, Minnesota? The boy whose father owns the Quikpix?" Victoria said. "Don't call Simon Apple a stupid boy. He's a smart boy. A beautiful boy. A gifted boy. A star-crossed boy."

Regis Van Clay finished buttoning his coat and left the Zerminsky witch blowing her nose and weeping.

23

Simon Apple was miserable at the Glenda Middle School. By age thirteen he had accepted that the sky came down to earth, a crushing sky that flattened any inclination toward optimism. He rolled through the halls like a hoop; he had no center.

Simon felt separated from the other students by a wall impenetrable as the barrier that kept King Kong from eating his neighbors.

That wall was made of hardened sludge and slime, tangled foliage impossible to breach, too slippery to climb.

He hated the music, movies, sports and TV shows he was required to enjoy. He spent his free time reading a random selection of books from the school library and liked some of those but even while he read he was plagued by the guilt of separation. It took an enormous amount of energy to keep those feelings private. He wanted to be popular. Simon honed a talent for lying; he feigned enthusiasm for everything Top Ten.

At night, instead of doing homework, he memorized the moment's constellation of overnight sensations—actors, athletes, mostly the reigning gods of rock 'n' roll. He specialized in the most obscure musical groups on the charts: Black Oak Arkansas, The Hues Corporation, Stealer's Wheel, The Love Unlimited Orchestra, 10cc, The Blue Ridge Rangers, Commander Cody & His Lost Planet Airmen—the "artists" who signaled a refined sensitivity far beyond the obvious passion for Dylan, Lennon, Jagger, Franklin, Gaye, Flack, Knight and her Pips. Everybody knew the biggies, no trick to that.

The litmus test of a dedicated hipster wasn't just knowing that Jim Croce died in a plane crash. It was in knowing that Pig Pen McKernan of The Grateful Dead died on March 3, 1973, when his liver quit, that Bongo Rock was on the MGM label. Simon realized that, in a disposable world, ultimate triumph belonged to trivia. He absorbed and discarded the essentials of American Pop, swallowing and defecating the information that would make him one of the boys.

Simon sweated to keep up with what he considered the blizzard of crap that saturated Glenda's air and stuck to the flypaper brains of his contemporaries. His strategy didn't work. When he dropped a name it didn't bounce. It was nobody's fault that Simon Apple couldn't find the password to belonging. He had nobody to blame but himself. He set off alarms of an alien presence easily detected by the clever antennae of the in-group. He wasn't convincing because he wasn't convinced.

When Simon dared the leap from the flying trapeze, his designated catcher yawned and let his hands go limp. The would-be flyer ended up squirming in an unwanted safety net that kept him from smashing to pulp and ending his misery. Rejection turned to self-pity seasoned with self-hatred; the brew slowly crystallized into snobbery and obnoxious arrogance. He became a pain in the ass.

He ripped down the posters of Marilyn Monroe and Elvis that covered his bedroom walls and replaced them with photos of wart hogs, reptiles and carnivorous plants. He dressed in hideous combinations of blacks and browns. He let his fingernails grow until they curled. He spiked his hair and dyed it green and purple. He wouldn't shower or brush a tooth. He chewed garlic buds and onions before he left for school. He filled a scrapbook with newspaper clippings of serial killers, rapists, cannibals, gazed into their volcanic eyes, then stared into a mirror at his own baby blues in search of some kinship.

He read the laments of Beat poets, envied the druggies and drunks wandering through Glenda's garbage dumps and automobile graveyards. He wrote his own songs of suburban rot and curdled love, odes to bum piss on brick tenements. He listened to The Fugs crow songs like Coca Cola Douche and Slum Goddess on a scratchy LP.

He longed to escape from Glenda's predictable parade and join the march to oblivion that seemed headed in the right direction. Simon thought about skipping town but before he went he wanted his father to show some trace of concern or, preferably, agitation. It amazed him that Robert J. didn't seem to notice that his son had morphed into a kind of swamp-spawned lizard.

At least his teachers acknowledged that Simon Apple wasn't his old self. Esther Palm, the English instructor who once told Simon he had a literary bent, now crossed herself when they passed in the hallway. But, all things considered, Glenda absorbed him as if he were a ghost made of fog. His hometown was either amazingly tolerant of extreme mutation or simply indifferent. "This too shall pass away" was Glenda's motto, a soothing if horrifying mantra. On the street, a few children pointed at Simon's multicolored head, some even dared make remarks, but their adult escorts scooted them along. Everybody had somewhere to get to in a hurry, no time to dwell on a passing troll.

Finally Simon was jolted by hope of recognition. Sitting by himself, as usual, in the school lunchroom, he was approached by

Albert Essman, aka Assman, who'd formed a small pseudo-renegade gang named The Assassins.

Essman certainly didn't have the appearance of a born leader. He was a short, boneless boy with the expression of a salmon spent after spawning. Yet this flaccid Essman, who reminded Simon of day-old rice pudding, was a real personality and everybody's friend. His Assassins, with their feeble attempt at respectable rebellion, were the school's heroes.

Simon had watched Albert Essman from a far distance, wondering about the source of his charisma. The nerds and studs stood in line to slap his hand; the girls, including Polly Moon, went to butter when he appeared. It was widely rumored that Essman got laid on a trip to Disneyland; it was said he scored with a dancer in a Dumbo costume. The story was probably a myth but it added hugely to Essman's glitter; nobody else in Glenda had come close to fucking an elephant.

"You want to talk, Crap Apple?"

"About what? Cheeseburgers or knockers?" Simon said, as if he always talked to socialites.

"You know about The Assassins?"

"I heard you got some kind of club."

"Very choice fraternity," Essman said. "It's usually a closed society. But when Paulie Baner moved to Milwaukee it left an opening. Are you interested or should I just go fuck myself?"

"I guess I'm mildly interested," Simon said, sucking ketchup off a french fry. He fought off an urge to bolt; a small voice asked him if he was selling out to the establishment, if Kerouac, Ginsberg or James Dean's ghost would tag him a whore. From Simon's vantage, The Assassins were less *On the Road* and more in-the-tank, a conglomerate of complacent turds who walked the walk and talked the talk without a clue to the whys and wherefores of life lived under random bombardment by quarks and angel droppings.

Simon suspected The Assassins liked the world as it was, once over easy, that they would shit bricks if they ever met a stoned Buddhist from a parallel universe staggering down Glenda's Main Street snapping at pussy, making his dick gyrate like a cobra to music played on an electric panpipe. Simon had no idea of how he himself would behave free of Glenda's umbilical in the presence of a beatific, androgynous Beatnik god, but he was reasonably sure The Assassins would cringe and grovel.

"OK, then," Essman said. "Meet me after school at The
Ptomaine Wagon."

"Deal," Simon heard himself say, "But it has to be a short visit.
I've got to get to work."

"At Quikpix, right? My cousin, Rowena works there. Major
piece of tail. So tell me, is your daddy doing her?" After Francine left,
Robert J.'s first official act was to rehire Rowena Trask. Simon often
wondered if his father was "doing" her. "Never mind, Apple Sauce,"
Essman said, holding out his hand, palm up. Simon gave it a slap. At
long last, Simon Apple made contact.

The Ptomaine Wagon, a van usually parked outside Glenda
Middle School's main gate, was owned & operated by Isaac Glenda
IV, the great, great grandson of the farmer who'd decided that his
fields were fertile enough to grow a town. Most of Isaac's progeny had
been ruined and scattered by the Great Depression but a few of the
founder's descendants hung around, ruled more by inertia than civic
pride. Most of those leftovers served Glenda's new barons as
plumbers, carpenters and gas station attendants. Isaac IV, more
entrepreneurial, sold chilidogs, hamburgers, wedges of chocolate
pie, ice-cream sandwiches, candy bars and soda to Glenda's emerging generations. He was also a source of cigarettes and six-packs of
Budweiser to the privileged underaged.

Simon chewed on an O Henry bar while Albert Assman Essman negotiated for a pack of Camel's. "I'm handing you a piece of
paper with the address of our clubhouse," Essman said. "Swear by
Jesus that you'll never give away the information even under torture."

"Amen," Simon said.

"We meet on Saturday afternoons. Can you get off of work?"

Simon knew if he pressed hard enough he'd be granted dispensation. All such requests were honored since he'd begun behaving
like a land mine; Robert J. danced around him avoiding contact with
any lethal nipples. His father wanted peace or the illusion of peace
at any price. For Simon, it was an ideal arrangement.

"No problem. What time?" Simon said.

24

The Assassins's meeting place turned out to be the old Lombard Cinema, one of Glenda's eyesores. Abandoned in the sixties when the Magic Mall Multiplex was built just off the turnpike, all that remained of the Lombard's former Art Deco majesty was a cement rectangle with corners curved in the style of streamlined locomotives. That design was carried through to a collapsing ticket booth where Crazy Henry, Glenda's only certified psycho, was allowed to nest. Protruding from the theater's broken body was the remnant of a once-ornate marquee pocked with empty bulb sockets. On the humiliated marquee a tipsy assortment of black letters in different sizes read wE SUP pORt OUR B OyS In NAM, a sentiment of the Veterans of Foreign Wars.

Near the arched entrance was a faded poster for M*A*S*H under glass cracked into a spiderweb, held together by a rusty chrome frame. The Lombard's walls, chipped and stained brown, were covered with small-town graffiti: initials, hearts, bowling ball breasts, bent penises dangling in limbo, male and female names appended with brief résumés of various talents (hottwat, gives good-hed, shitmeister, cockteaser). A few washed-out fliers advertised obsolete record albums, local politicians hungry for votes, and a circus that once came through Glenda on a date erased by wind and weather. Taken together, the Lombard was like a tombstone in a horror movie. Simon was impressed that The Assassins had enough imagination to pick the place. He wondered if he'd misjudged them.

Walking past the ticket booth, Simon smelled frying meat. A curl of smoke came out of the little hole where the ticket lady once took orders. He peeked inside. There was Crazy Henry stirring up fire inside a pail, humming "Stardust" to a pork chop skewered on a stick. Crazy Henry never bothered anybody; he was more a thing than a person, part of the scene like a traffic light. The idea that he had an appetite left Simon edgy.

The Lombard's doors were boarded shut but Essman's note covered that; as instructed, Simon found a panel marked with an A in red paint, and pushed. He slithered under plywood and found himself in what used to be the lobby. There was enough light leaking inside for him to make out what was once the candy counter and the box where a uniformed usher once tossed ripped ticket stubs. The chilly wind of nostalgia made Simon shiver.

Simon remembered the excitement he'd felt on his Saturday matinee trips to the Lombard, holding tight to sweet Victoria's hand, her perfume smell mingling with the smell of caramel popcorn, anticipating the taste of Goobers or chocolate disks covered by dot-sized white sugar beads with a weird name that sounded like nun-pearls, especially licorice domes called Black Crows that Victoria loved to suck until they dissolved. He could still hear the voices and music of Coming Attractions from inside the theater's great shell.

On this Saturday, stepping over the spongy rot of royal blue carpet, entering the Lombard's ruined entrails, he felt as if maggots crawled inside his pants. Even past the entrance, he caught another whiff of Crazy Henry's sizzling meat.

Simon saw where the light came from; a large chunk of ceiling was missing, gouged out where a gigantic chandelier once hung over the auditorium. That gash in the ceiling made him feel better; it was some kind of emergency exit even if it was forty feet off the ground.

He was also glad to see that a few of the Lombard's seats were still rooted to the floor by thick iron pedestals. Their velvet cushions gave off a sour stink but the empty rows still conveyed a welcome sense of order. And the stage was still there too, rising behind a pit that once held a gigantic organ. The base of the stage was carved into Chinese dragons. Their yellowish hides—the tarnished transformation of gold-leaf skin—still clung to those fierce bodies. Above the dragons, a torn, splotched, screen dangled like the window shade in a cheap motel. The stains on the Lombard's violated screen seemed to have shape and substance—they could have been scenes from thousands of films crusted into a grotesque mural.

"Apple Crumb, The Assassins command you!" Simon heard Albert Essman's thin voice rise from the protruding belly of the Lombard's balcony. Simon looked up through speckles of dust floating like tiny fish in the thin tube of sunlight. "Ascend the stage," Essman ordered.

"If it don't fall apart first," Simon said, realizing that ascending

the stage meant climbing over the convex dragons. He found foot-
holds in the ridged dragon humps and made the climb. Up there, he
saw that there was hardly enough stage left to hold his weight. He
could see down into the basement.

"Now strip," Essman yelled.

"Fuck that," Simon said, balancing on a steel beam. "It's freezing in here."

"Our rituals are sacred," Essman said. "Do not defy."

"What are you, some kind of queers?" Simon said. He pulled off
his shirt, dropped his pants, kicked off his sneakers and waited in his
jockey shorts.

"The whole nine yards," Essman said. "You get my meaning?"

Simon took off his socks and discarded his underwear, feeling
idiotic. He told himself that the price of admission to polite society
might be too high, but there he was, following orders. It surprised
him to learn that enough of him wanted *in* to take such crap from a
collection of card-carrying jerkoffs. The next question was, What
kind of prick did that make Simon Apple? "*Seig heil*," he said. "Now
you want me to do a tap dance?"

"Toss your stuff off the stage," Essman said.

Simon threw his clothes and shoes at a front row seat. He saw a
figure wearing a hood over his head emerge from the gloom, harvest
his stuff and run up the nearest aisle.

"Okay," Simon thought, "if this is what it takes to become an
Assassin, then this is what it takes." Simon was sure if he made the
final cut his life at Glenda Middle School would change for the bet-
ter. The rewards were obvious. Eternal respect and admiration. Even
Placebo would be impressed. If The Assassins told him to tattoo the
Mona Lisa on the tip of his dick he would get it done.

Simon saw the one who grabbed his clothes stop, dump them
into a pile, pour a bottle of some kind of liquid over them, light a
match and set his belongings on fire. "Holy shit," Simon said, watching the flames flare, "enough is enough. Put out that damn fire."

The naked Simon had a harder time climbing down the dragon backs than he'd had getting up. His clumsy descent was helped
by hands pulling him off the stage, lifting him into the air, then
slamming him down with his face pressed against a bed of splinters.

"Listen with both ears," Essman said. "We're going to show you what we do to commie beatniks with Mohawk hair. We don't want your kind puking on America."

"I get it," Simon said, "this is part of my initiation. Fine. But you know, Assman, the truth is, I'm not a hundred percent sure I want to be an Assassin. I do and I don't. I know that might sound too complicated for you but it's where I'm at right now. I'll go along for the time being but I can't promise you anything."

"Did I hear right?" Essman said. "He's not sure he wants to be an Assassin?" Simon was flipped over and punched in the belly. "You're breaking our hearts," Essman said. Simon was kicked in the groin and smacked in the face. "I want to apologize if we disappointed you, Apple Core," Essman said. Simon's skull was whacked with a paddle. "Did you really think you could ever be one of us? You're not one of us, freak. You belong somewhere in outer space." They gave Simon a shampoo with pink paint and saved some for his pubes.

"Is this or is it not part of a ritual?" Simon said. "You've got me confused, Essman. If it's the first, I'm still in the game. If it's the second, I'll kill you."

"You're scaring me," Essman said. "I'm shaking like a leaf. I always thought you were a weirdo. But you're not. You're completely nuts." Simon took a chop on the back of his neck and blacked out.

When he woke, Simon sensed that The Assassins were gone. He stood, dripping blood and pink paint, and checked out what was left of his clothes. The only things recognizable were the rubber soles of his sneakers. He gazed at the smoldering embers of his shorts, socks, pants and Free Lenny Bruce T-shirt, still holding on to the possibility that he'd passed The Assassin's test, that they'd teach him their secret handshake on Monday morning along with other secrets of the brotherhood. But he had to admit it could be wishful thinking.

Simon covered his privates with his hands and left the Lombard. When he passed the ticket booth, Crazy Henry had his face pressed against the cashier's hole. "Do you have a pickle?" Crazy Henry said. Simon accepted that it was a serious question, and shook his head no and apologized.

He had no memory of how he got back to Quikpix. The next thing he knew, he was in his bed at home with Robert J. and Dr.

Fikel looming over him. "I might get a club jacket," Simon said between gasps. "Silky. With my name on it."

"Who did this to you, kid?" Robert J. said.

"That's for me to know and you to find out," Simon said, clinging to The Assassins' code.

His father looked relieved. Revenge was not Robert J.'s forte.

"I see no signs of permanent damage," Dr. Fikel said. "But there does appear to be some respiratory difficulty. Give him an aspirin every four hours. And plenty of liquids. Get that pink dye off him as soon as possible. Let me know how he's doing."

Simon woke in the middle of the night, his throat burning with thirst. He drained the water glass near his bed and ran to the bathroom for a refill. He swallowed that glassful and another. Between drinks, he gulped for air.

Following a powerful urge, he filled the bathtub and bent over, drinking like a horse. With his head dipped under water his breathing came easier. He thought about his ordeal. Taking a beating was one thing. Facing the facts about his repulsive acquiescence was worse. The desire to belong, the horror of loneliness, had leached every ounce of whatever dignity he once had.

Along with his clothing, The Assassins had stripped him clean of identity. Simon had nothing to hang onto, no territory left to protect, no way to define himself. He looked in the mirror on the medicine chest. His pale, swollen face was clown-like under the pink halo of hair. Oddly, he felt no antagonism toward Albert Essman, not even the desire to inflict pain. The only feeling he could find was a faraway sadness. Simon was outside the normal pull of gravity. When his chest tightened again, Simon got back into the bathtub. Robert J. found him submerged, a trail of bubbles rising from his nose and mouth. When the paramedics came they plugged him to an oxygen tank and rushed him to Glenda Memorial Hospital.

After a hundred tests and re-tests, all negative, Dr. Fikel blamed stress for Simon's asthmatic attacks. When he was left alone, the patient disconnected himself from the oxygen supply and dunked his face in the sink.

While Dr. Fikel arranged for a visit from a psychiatrist, an alert nurse noticed an unusual pattern of striping under Simon's chin and behind his ears. There were more consultations with specialists and more tests before Dr. Fikel had a new diagnosis.

"What is it?" Robert J. said.

"He's growing gills," Dr. Fikel said. "He's becoming amphibious."

"That's outlandish," Robert J. said.

"But not without some precedent." Dr. Fikel squeezed his temples with his hands, pressing his brain for a memory. "Years ago I read a paper by an eminent endocrinologist," Fikel said. "He suspected something like this might happen. *Ictopera Aqueous Resperacion*. His findings were debunked, though. I recall the article by Regis Van Clay in *The Lancet*. That whistleblower was sued up the kazoo by Regis Pharmaceuticals and then countersued claiming evidence of genetic alteration caused by prolonged use of *Viloxidril* by patients with a Middle European heritage. I forget who won that case."

"My wife's maternal grandmother was from Latvia," Robert J. said.

"Bingo," Dr. Fikel said.

25

"I have mixed feelings about inflicting the death penalty," Judge Adolph Luber said. The elderly judge stood with perfect posture, his own distinguished statue. He carefully avoided Simon's eyes while he opened a heart-shaped box. "Try some of the Godiva. It was given to me by my daughter last Valentine's Day but it's still fresh." The judge reached into the box of candy and chose what Simon knew was a caramel.

"No, thanks, Your Honor. Not right now."

"Watching your cholesterol, are you? Go ahead, give yourself a treat."

After all his years, teetering on the ledge of mortality, Simon finally learned how to lift the chocolate veil and intuit which candy was what. He wondered if the makers of those confections took any pleasure in disguising their content; sometimes the identical shape and wrapping might hide nougat, fruit, mocha, cream, something chewy or crunchy. Simon picked a nut, exactly what he wanted.

While he chewed, he thought about the tidbits of valuable knowledge he would take to his grave. Then he remembered he'd chosen cremation. All his wisdom, significant and trivial, would translate into the calligraphy of smoke.

When they'd asked Simon what he wanted done with his ashes he requested that they be scattered anyplace but the sea. Burial at sea was already a cliché, overused and over praised by too many second-rate poets. When they insisted he be more specific, Simon refused. He didn't want to know his "final resting place"—their phrase—until he got there.

"Are you with me?" Judge Luber said. "Your mind seems to be wandering. Do they have you on tranquilizers?"

"No such solace. I'm not allowed any drugs."

"Of course. I forgot. As I was saying, Adolph Luber is no friend of capital punishment. It isn't the principle of the thing. Certain crimes, like your misdeeds, are so offensive that any alternative to the most basic and brutal revenge curdles the fiber of a civilized society. Justice is sometimes a blood sport."

"So I noticed, Your Honor," Simon said.

"And my stance isn't based on the DNA business just because it might prove some poor bastard was falsely convicted and dispatched. What bothers me are the methods we employ to do the job these days. When our forebears lopped off heads while thousands cheered or hanged the guilty at public carnivals, you had what I call real closure. Even the electric chair had merit. You could identify with a high voltage bolt shot through the skull and up the ass. Witnesses used to talk about the hum of current like it was a popular tune. All the lights in town blinked when they threw the switch.

"Now the whole process is sanitized. It's like bombing villages from 50,000 feet. Cyanide gas. A hiss, a whisper, *fini*. Lethal injection. It even sounds genteel. We tuck in the bastards, no offense meant, Simon. We practically sing them lullabies. To my mind that's cruel and unusual punishment for the average Joe. And Jane. Let's not forget Jane. You forget Jane, you get sued nowadays. And the endless delays between passing sentence and finally seeing the turds squirm and die. It's not only shameful, it's expensive."

"I don't envy your job," Simon said.

"I try to do my best. Cases like yours are the worst. We condemn murderers, yet our society permits you to order the violent death of a crustacean. Ironic. Are you still having lobster tonight?"

"Yes, I am having lobster and I can't think of anything I've done to justify what you people are doing to me in the name of justice. It would have been so much quicker and cleaner if you'd brought in a hitman and not involved the courts. Is that what's giving you last minute pangs of conscience? Confusing justice with gross national product?"

"Pangs of conscience?" Judge Luber said.

"Isn't that why you're here? Looking for absolution?"

"Absolution? There was never any question about your sentence. You know damn well you had to die. What bothers me is that the process, the whole charade, was so predictable. I had to come to court every day, listen to those idiot lawyers argue, wait for the *noodnik* jury to make up its mind, deliver that self-righteous speech before I closed the book on you. No suspense, no tension, nothing to hold my interest. You recall those endless notes I seemed to take? I was doing crossword puzzles."

"I never finished a crossword puzzle in my life," Simon said.

"They help pass the time," the judge said. "I just wanted you to know, Apple, that it wasn't a walk in the park for me."

"I accept that," Simon said. "And if it matters, your remarks before passing sentence were very apt and well put. About how my brutality shocked and horrified the nation. You almost had me believing you."

"Really? Well, thank you. Did you know in England the judge wears a black cloth over his wig when a death sentence is pronounced?"

"It's a nice custom," Simon said. "Very theatrical."

"Ultimately humanizing," Judge Luber said, biting into what Simon knew was a cherry floating in syrup. "I hope you get some satisfaction from knowing how many people you'll be helping tonight. Apple, you should be proud to be part of this seminal event. Any misgivings aside, I know I am."

"Proud as punch, Your Honor," Simon said, reaching for a nougat.

26

Simon Apple's gills replaced his lungs as the principal agents of respiration; except for brief periods, he could only breathe under water.

After many sessions with psychotherapists given the task of helping Simon accept what they euphemistically described as his "handicap," and following endless consultations with technicians whose specialty was assisting the patient to survive outside the hospital, Simon made reasonable progress.

He was rigged with a specially designed bell jar that fit over his head and rested on his shoulders. Two converted scuba tanks strapped to his back pumped a steady supply of filtered liquid, highly oxygenated, up to Simon's heavy jug. Earphones attached to a box on his chest allowed him hear. He learned to speak through a microphone that amplified his words and screened out the sound of the bubbles that streamed from his mouth. He was fitted with goggles that corrected the visual distortion caused by the fluid and his curved glass window on the world. He was fed through an IV tube connected to his wrist and linked to a plastic pouch of nutrients.

It was decided that Simon best be returned to normal life and treated as a recognizable human being. He was sent back to Glenda Middle School. Aside from his mechanical aides, Simon looked and dressed exactly like his classmates.

Ironically, being confined in a container worked better than a membership in The Assassins to ensure his popularity. Instead of being tabbed a nerd, Simon Apple became as big a celebrity as he'd been in the days of *Hercumite*. It was ironic that after being unfairly treated as an Outsider, Simon, now literally beyond the pale, became an Insider; he enjoyed new status and an improved vision of himself as the center of attention.

Most of his peers were shy of close contact and stayed at arms length but their interest was evident. The less timid regularly tapped

his bottle and gave him a thumbs-up. Even Polly Moon stroked his
jar when they met. He was famous.

Albert Essman kept his distance, along with the other Assassins.
They respected Simon for keeping quiet about the Lombard incident. Give or take a few inconveniences, life was good.

Inevitably, after a few glorious months, Simon's notoriety faded.
The go-with-the-flow jokes stopped. He became just another kid with
a bottle on his head. It was this return to anonymity that forced him
to face the awful reality that he was trapped, doomed by circum-
stance to survive inside the same kind of oversized jug as the ones
used in the school's water fountains. The hopeless faces of a cadre of
doctors who examined him enforced his growing depression. He was
not optimistic about the future.

One evening, Rowena Trask came to the house for dinner. After
coffee, she and Robert J. held hands and announced they were
engaged to be married. Simon watched his father slip a diamond
ring onto Rowena's finger.

He blanched. Since his illness Simon had been getting along
very well with Robert J.; opening the door to an intruder was no
thrill. Aside from being forced to share his father's affection, the idea
of having Rowena Trask for a stepmother made Simon queasy. He'd
had his first wet dreams about that woman. Now the flesh and blood
version would be running around his house in a see-through nightgown or less.

When Robert J. and Rowena asked Simon for his blessing, he
granted it through a gush of bubbles that made him seem carbonated.

The couple tied the knot in the garden behind Dr. Fikel's
house. It was a simple wedding, no frills beyond flowers, canapés,
drinks, and a flutist playing Vivaldi. The guests were limited to a few
relatives and close friends.

When the ceremony ended, the flutist left and Frank Sinatra
records were piped through a speaker. Simon stood by, accepting but
sullen. Dr. Fikel said it wouldn't hurt to drip some Cliquot into him.
The infusion of champagne helped. Simon felt light-headed, even
buoyant.

When Sinatra sang "My Way," Honey Fikel forced Simon to
dance with her. They danced over grass while everybody applauded
as if they were watching Fred and Ginger. Honey threw out her arms

and twirled. While she spun away, Simon heard somebody's cousin whisper, "It won't be easy what with the boy around the house. I don't envy them." That remark ended the festivities for him.

Simon left Honey Fikel spinning, scooped up a plateful of chopped liver and took it down to the Lombard theater. Crazy Henry wasn't home so he stuffed it into the box office porthole.

When a blissful Mr. and Mrs. Apple came home they found Simon half-hidden behind an ivy vine in their yard. It was then that Robert J. and Rowena announced that he was going along on their Florida honeymoon. Simon refused at first but they hugged him and showed him his ticket.

The three clung together crying.

27

Arrangements were made for Simon to carry his homework to the Sunshine State along with a supply of the more exotic spare parts and batteries for his respirator. The Apples flew first to Miami, then drove to Sonesta Beach, a resort made famous because President Richard Millhouse Nixon went there to escape pressures of the oval office. Robert J. pointed out Nixon's lush retreat, only a few miles from the Sonesta Beach Hotel where the Apples had reserved a suite fit for newlyweds and, for Simon, a separate room on a lower floor with an ocean view.

The weather was excellent but Robert J. and Rowena spent most of their time in their suite while Simon lounged around the pool feeling sorry for himself. He had nothing to do but imagine what the bride and groom were doing upstairs. His imaginings left him with impossibly ambivalent feelings. To keep his mind from bad thoughts, he stared at a line of palm trees, hoping for coconuts to bomb oiled senior citizens sipping tall drinks crowned with paper umbrellas. The pool was the epicenter of activity; nobody risked the ocean because the week before a shark ate a German tourist off Boca Raton, too close for comfort.

Things got livelier when a convention of NASA scientists from

Houston and Cape Kennedy arrived to discuss the future of space exploration. During the mornings they met at a planetarium down the road. Simon wondered why anybody would build a planetarium at sea level, about as far from the stars as you could get, but there it was, complete with an observatory. An impressive telescope peered at the heavens from a polished metallic dome. Simon guessed the scope was for tourists to watch Atlas rockets launch toward the moon. Afternoons, the conventioneers sat around in small clots studying maps and star charts, jotting notes on yellow pads, downing drinks without umbrellas. A few of the braver scientists dared shark odds, venturing into the surf to get bounced around by blue waves.

Simon sensed that, along with the universe, he was a favorite topic of scientific conversation. It was hard enough thinking about Rowena and Robert J. fucking upstairs. He had to accept the fact that the boy with his head in a water cooler probably reminded the NASA contingent of an alien sent to spy on their doings.

At least the conventioneers laughed once in a while, even if they were laughing at him. They got into hot arguments about orbital velocity and windows of opportunity while other guests lay sucking up sun, waiting out the endless hours. After four perfect days and three glorious nights in paradise, Simon would have welcomed a vacation in the void, somewhere out past Jupiter.

Robert J. and Rowena did their best to cheer him up when they took time off from screwing but Simon slid deeper into the sludge of depression. He saw himself as a burden to the lovers, and nothing but a few cheap yuks to the star gazers, no more than a third-rate eclipse casting shadows over the planet.

At dawn, on his fifth day in Florida, Simon wrote a long, sincere farewell note on fancy Sonesta Beach Hotel stationery with a deckle edge. He left the note on top of his pillow, quit his room, headed downstairs, sprinted through the lobby then ran past the pool area to the hotel's strip of private beach. He squatted on a dune looking out toward the salty ocean world where things with claws, pincers, tentacles, fins, tails and spiked teeth held dominion.

It made total sense that he belonged out there, drifting with debris, seaweed and jellyfish. He could listen to the latest whale songs, ride manta rays, feel the pull of the moon. If he drowned, he would leave his bleached, empty shell to his parents, a splendid wedding gift by any standard. Rowena could keep it in her curio cabinet or Robert J. could put it on display at Quikpix for a conversation piece.

Simon took a few deep, bubbly breaths, unscrewed the glass helmet, unbuckled his air tanks, disconnected his sound system, stripped off his clothes and took a slow walk toward the breakers. He waited for a wave he liked and dove in, swimming toward Atlantis, wondering if his gills could handle seawater.

They could.

Simon Apple was jolted to a new level of consciousness. He did flips and turns, popped up and down like a dolphin, paddled through assorted tropical fish glittering like costume jewelry, then let himself sink like a stone. He sat counting oysters and clams, floated up like a cork, touched his hands to his toes then swam through random shafts of rainbow-colored light, frisky as a sardine, exuberant in his proper element.

Simon lay on his back thinking about food. It might be that he'd learn to digest plankton, sea worms, strange plants, whatever was digestible, or he could simply starve to death. It didn't seem a pressing problem but it was something to consider. He dredged up ancient tales about long-lost keepsakes found in the belly of a captured flounder or mangled inside a Great White; it was entirely possible that bits and pieces of Simon Apple would turn up at the Edible Aquarium fish market back in Glenda.

Those thoughts dissipated when Simon saw a school of creatures swimming above him, skimming the water's surface. They moved like dolphins but had neither fins nor tails. Simon detected a distinct resemblance to people but wondered why ordinary humans would be so far from land. He juggled the possibility that he was in the presence of mermaids, mermen or, more likely, some unknown species.

Not knowing what those life forms might consider food, Simon carefully rose closer to the surface. He found himself looking into Asian faces. At least a hundred men, women and children were kicking splashing or floating, some clinging to rubber tires and wooden crates. Unless the currents of time and distance were very different in his watery world, he was pretty sure he hadn't covered enough distance from Sonesta Beach to reach the Orient. Whoever they were, the whole school of swimmers passed over him in a few minutes. He chose not to be too curious but it did seem as if they followed the tide toward shore.

When they were gone, Simon allowed his head to breach and scan the surrounding ocean like a periscope. He saw nothing but whitecaps and foam except for a red dot bobbing like a buoy. Simon swam toward it despite his inclination to remain uninvolved.

The dot grew larger. He suspected it was a small boat but on closer inspection it turned out to be a rubber raft, half submerged. Closer yet, he saw that a boy of five or six hung from its side screaming incomprehensible words at a high-flying gull. When Simon popped up beside him, the kid let out a piercing yowl; he wasn't expecting company. "Take it easy," Simon said softly. "Just calm down."

The raft was sinking fast; the boy would soon be quiet enough. Simon tried to tell himself that if he were a squid or an octopus, which he practically was, one more drowned kid would hardly be worth a squirt of ink. "What the hell are you doing here?" he said. "Don't you know better?"

Simon knew it was an idiotic remark but he also knew that if he pulled that howler back to land there was a good chance he might be spotted by Robert J. and his ersatz mother who were probably out looking for him along with half the Coast Guard. "Easy does it," Simon said. "You know what I think? I think you are one lucky Chinese communist."

It took nearly an hour to shepherd the boy to land. Simon had planned to dump him in the surf and let him crawl to the beach but a huge wave tumbled them both onto warm, white sand. The child was coughing and still screaming. Simon was panting, exhausted, oxygen deprived, his head whirling, but he could see a cluster of men in black suits, some holding guns, running toward them.

At least one of the approaching faces was familiar. More than familiar. It was the number one man himself, President Richard Millhouse Nixon; Simon couldn't mistake those squinty eyes and that ski jump nose.

"Fucking Cubans," he heard the President say, "Cocksucking freeloaders."

The man nearest him said. "My educated guess is the child appears to be Chinese, Japanese, Vietnamese or Thai, sir. And instinct tells me that the gasping young man is a circumcised Caucasian. Look at his organ."

"You're right," Nixon said. "Headline: DICK DECLARES DICK MORE YID THAN YANG. Unbelievable how they push their noses in everyplace. Kissinger will love this story."

The black suits arranged themselves in a protective circle around the President as a small army came rushing over the dunes: cops, state troopers, reporters, photographers, a TV crew and then Robert J. yelling, "Thank God!" Rowena was behind him carrying Simon's life support system, muttering about miracles. Simon rolled onto his belly to hide his privates as flash bulbs blasted. The boy he'd rescued jumped on top of him and held on tight.

"What were you up to this time?" Robert J. said while Rowena pulled off the child, sat Simon up and got him back on life support.

"Nothing," Simon said between bubbles. "I went in for a swim. I saw this kid so I brought him in."

"Illegals," a hefty cop said. "We rounded up most of them. The others won't get far, I promise you that, Mr. President." Almost on cue, an Asian woman dashed from behind a clump of beach plums. Her dress was in shreds, soaking wet, her long hair a black scribble. "Shen Wa!" she blurted, "Shen Wa!"

One of the President's men tackled her flat. The slobbering boy pushed past a cameraman and ran to her, speaking a sing-song language that sounded to Simon like it came through his nostrils.

"The way we read it," the tallest of the black suits said, "a ship jettisoned a whole cargo of illegals when a lookout sighted one of our Coast Guard helicopters. They appeared to be headed for Miami or Lauderdale."

"Isn't it usually freeloading Cubans?" President Nixon said.

"Absolutely, sir," the beefy cop said. "Nine times out of ten, Cubans. But sometimes . . ."

"Spicks or chinks, what's the difference?" Nixon said.

"Mr. President, the press," an aide said.

The President turned toward a television camera, composing himself, molding his Playdo face into a paternal smile. "Today we have still more proof that untold numbers of the oppressed are ready to risk their lives and the lives of their children to come to our land of opportunity. I just wish Fidel or Mao were here to see this. They might learn something about life, liberty and the pursuit of happiness. And that young American who risked his life to save a helpless boy, who is he?"

"He's my son, Simon Apple, sir," Robert J. said. "We're guests at the hotel."

"May I inquire as to why there's a water bottle covering his head?" Nixon said.

"It's a complicated story," Robert J. said. "It takes some explaining."

"Explain," one of the men in black suits said. "The President is waiting."

"Yes, I would like to know about our proud hero," Nixon said, making V signs at the camera with the middle fingers of both hands.

"Well, we think it has to do with *Viloxidril*," Rowena Apple said, adjusting Simon's filter. Agent Brian Beem of the Secret Service slapped her hand away from the device and examined it for any sign of explosives.

"What exactly is *Viloxidril?*" the President said. "It sounds vaguely familiar."

"Simon's condition might be a side effect from the medication he takes to counteract a reaction to *Hercumite*, You know, *Nonacripthae*." Robert J. said. "*Viloxidril*. It's a wonderful drug developed by Regis Pharmaceuticals."

"There's the connection. Regis Van Clay," the President said. "Standup man. Friend of the party. Mmmmm."

"The problem is, our boy experienced side effects. *Ictopera Aqueous Resperacion*. He grew gills."

"The bad comes with the good," Nixon said. "Isn't that the way of things?"

On the television news that night, Simon saw President Nixon holding Shen Wa on one arm while he patted Simon's bottle with the other. Mrs. Nixon stood smiling at Shen Wa's mother. The President answered questions about granting asylum to the intruders, explaining that the matter was under investigation by the proper authorities. "We cannot throw open the floodgates of massive immigration," Nixon said, "but there's always room for a few droplets to slip between the cracks." Then, massaging Simon's bottle, the President spoke about the importance of funding medical research to cure "even the most obscure afflictions plaguing some of our finest citizens. One victim is one too many!" He turned to Simon. "Stay on your meds," Nixon said. "Don't forget those little magical little pills, son."

An hour after the telecast, Simon got a call from his biological mother.

"Congratulations, Simon," Francine said after identifying herself, "considering what happened today I'm sure you have a guardian angel watching over you. I'm calling because I want you to know that tonight you were Bar Mitzvahed in Jerusalem. I hired a surrogate to stand in for you. There's a sect that does what they call a truncated service for the children of mixed marriages. So think of yourself as at least half a man."

"You should have asked me first," Simon said.

"Are you turning your back on your heritage?"

"It's not that. I don't know if they're allowed to Bar Mitzvah a fish, and the guardian angel you mentioned might be a porpoise. I'm not sure what I am."

"Nonsense," Francine said. "Stop that kind of talk. People far worse off than you lead long, productive lives. Besides, God is generous about who gets into heaven."

"I didn't know you were into God and religion," Simon said.

"What has God got to do with religion?" Francine said. "There's God and there's religion. Listen, Simon, don't think for a second that your father and his new sex kitten won't try to make a hundred percent *goy* out of you. It's a power thing. Trust me, those people get more Catholic with age. After fifty, they go shopping for halos. But it's the mother who decides what you are and I'm still your mother. And you're much too immature to know your own mind about such things. By the way, happy birthday. I can't believe my boy is thirteen. A regular teenager. Mazeltov."

"My birthday was three months ago," Simon said.

"Tonight I mailed you a card with a twenty dollar bill inside,"

Francine said. "Buy something you really want. And give my regards to your new friend, the President."

Back in Glenda, Simon spent the twenty at Schneir's Department Store where the Apples were listed. He bought Robert J. and Rowena a matched set of silver-plated salt and pepper shakers shaped like frogs.

28

The Regis Pharmaceuticals Research & Development Center in Bogota, New Jersey, was invisible from the highway that led to Manhattan. The company banner, a black R on a field of red, white and blue stripes, flew at the top of a tower that held microwave transmitters and satellite dishes. The tower was flanked by administrative buildings, laboratories, a tidy zoo where birds and beasts (monkeys, pigs, cows, horses, snakes, cats, dogs) were kept for use in tests.

Near the zoo, a Quonset hut held hundreds of cages filled with mice and gerbils carrying various strains of disease ranging from the exotic to the mundane. There were greenhouses filled with plants and trees gathered from every continent. Recently, a small, rotunda had been added to house assorted life forms from the world's oceans, rivers, lakes and ponds. Fanning out from the rotunda were tanks of different sizes, a power station, a disposal unit where waste was incinerated, a cafeteria, gym and daycare center for employees, a concrete field crowded with parked trucks, cars, and a loading dock that linked to a network of train tracks.

A chain link fence surrounded the facility. Security cameras were mounted on tall lampposts. Armed guards manned a booth overlooking the single access road. That impressive anatomy was interlaced with a complex pattern of multicolored pipes threaded like blood vessels nourishing the corporate heart: a pyramid of glass and steel where Regis Van Clay ruled from an office at its pointed pinnacle.

Regis's suite was pristine—white walls bare of artwork, a white carpet, white chairs, white file cabinets, a white amoeba-shaped desk holding a bouquet of white pens and pencils and a white telephone. Small white boxes jutting from the ceiling blew sterilizing puffs of lemon-scented mist at two-minute intervals. A bank of white-rimmed TV screens built into a trim white metal cabinet displayed the latest news from Wall Street and real-time quotes from the stock and commodities exchanges in New York, Chicago, Toronto, Paris, London, Tokyo, Singapore and Melbourne; Regis called those flashing numbers "the world's cardiogram." Watching the numerals stream, even in times of severe financial gyration, was more tranquilizing to him than staring at the affirming flow of waves from the deck of his Hampton mansion.

Those video screens were the only color in the room except for Regis's rosy skin, porcelain green eyes, bluish lips and a purple vein that ran from his forehead to his right temple, his trademark double-breasted navy blazer with its monogrammed gold buttons, a celadon satin tie, gray slacks and a platinum Rolex with many dials. The blatant exceptions to the sedate orchestration of subtle hues were Regis's track shoes ornamented with zigzag lightning bolts and orange racing stripes. Regis sat with his feet on the desk moving them like metronomes. The clash of styles made visitors squirm.

When his secretary announced that Agent Brian Beem of the Secret Service had arrived for his scheduled appointment, Regis buzzed him in. While his visitor crossed the spotless carpet, Regis took a beat, swung his legs off the desk, stood to shake Beem's hand, gestured toward a chair and dropped back into his own seat. He liked Beem's look—a Gary Cooper sort, alert, clean-cut and polite, a mannequin direct from Bloomingdale's.

Regis knew there was plenty going on behind Beem's cool smile; this was the President's emissary, disarming but armed to the teeth.

"Shall we cut to the chase?" Regis said.

"The President sends his best regards and regrets. He really wanted to invite you to the White House but . . ."

"I understand his plate is full what with the Vietnam thing and that Watergate nonsense. And the Russians, always the Russians."

"He wanted you to know he was deeply moved by the plight of the boy, Simon Apple, the one with the gill problem. He wants the nation to know that despite larger issues he finds time to concern himself with the suffering of a single fallen sparrow."

Regis put his feet on the desk. Agent Beem didn't flinch. "It's arguable," Regis said, "as to which sparrow fell harder, Simon Apple or Regis Van Clay. Assure President Nixon that he and I both empathize and sympathize with the Apple child's predicament. You know we've agreed to list *Ictopera Aqueous Resperacion* as a possible side effect of *Viloxidril* aka *Symmavane*."

"I understand the FDA ordered the warning."

"We would have taken the step without the FDA," Regis said.

"And everyone agrees it was a highly responsible decision," Beem said, "but that can't be the end of the story. In the excitement of the moment on that Florida beach, the President promised America a winning effort to cure young Apple. What I'm getting at is that it would be most propitious for him to declare that Apple's condition has been reversed." Beem smiled. "It's strange that we can send men to walk on the moon and engender less media interest than we get from one oddball side effect."

"We're not even sure that we're dealing with a side effect," Regis said. "But I want you to assure the boss that our best minds are lasered in on isolating the cause and manipulating a quick cure for whatever it is that compromised Apple's health and well-being. If *Viloxidril* proves to be the culprit, we'll be the first to admit it. If there's a cure, we'll be first to find it. But the President should also be made aware that Simon Apple is a peculiar individual with an exasperating physiology. His body reacts in violent and unexpected ways to the most innocent medications. Frankly, Agent Beem, I have bad dreams about that one. He's been a pain in the ass to my company, a real danger. He's already cost us mega millions of dollars and great chunks of credibility."

"I don't doubt it," the President's emissary said.

"President Nixon should understand that Simon Apple is an anomaly, one in a zillion, a magnet for side effects, a side effects farm. With all the testing in creation, test results evaluated by the government's finest, most honest doctors and statisticians, we can't anticipate every bump in the road when we put a new product into circulation."

"*Viloxidril* aka *Symmavane* was granted rather quick approval by the FDA," Beem said. "There has been rumor of inadequate testing."

"Our industry is damned if we do and damned if we don't," Regis said, tapping the desktop. "It's true that certain reasonable exceptions to the usual delaying policies were more than justified when *Viloxidril* showed excellent potential to ameliorate symptoms possibly, but not definitely, traceable to *Nonacripthae*."

"That would be the medication trade-named *Hercumite*? One of your products, isn't it?"

"It's good that you've done your homework, Agent Beem. We've never admitted to any liability directly traceable to *Hercumite* but our *Viloxidril* did cure a few statistical deviants of their so-called side effects following ingestion of that drug. And as the Lord would have it, *Viloxidril* has also proved a boon to the cosmetic industry. Virtually every lipstick, face cream, defoliant, shampoo, moisturizer, hair dye and vaginal lubricant is now *Symmavane* fortified." Regis's face changed from a smile to a frown. "What impact the new warning label will have on the sales of those items here and overseas is a matter for serious speculation. It could be huge. A thousand television commercials and print ads will have to be modified. Packaging redesigned or replaced."

"We understand the ripple effects," Beem said. "Unfortunate. But unavoidable."

"And the potential for lawsuits?" Regis said. "How much do idiot juries award these days? What you dismiss as ripple effects are catastrophic. Every side effect is a thorn in the gonads of the gross national product."

"I didn't mean to be dismissive," Beem said.

Regis counted on the fingers of his right hand: "One . . . two . . . three, maybe five Simon Apple clones might be walking around the entire world with bottles on their heads and because of that handful how many stockholders will suffer cardiac arrest? How many people for whom *Viloxidril* is a boon will deprive themselves of its benefits out of irrational fear? Ah well, there's no use moaning."

"The President vowed that a cure . . ."

"Oh, tell the President that Regis Van Clay will bite the bullet however lousy the taste. I'll get that damn kid out of his jug in time for the eleven o'clock news."

"May I assure President Nixon that some progress has already been made?"

"I'm pleased to say you may. It just happens that our biotech unit suspects the offending agent in *Viloxidril*—if there is an offending agent, which we do not admit there is—has presumably been isolated; our genetics team is off and running."

"Hopefully not running on empty," Beem said.

"That comment was not necessary," Regis said.

"I was speaking out of place. Accept my apology. Do you think it would be premature for the President to announce . . ."

"Premature as hell," Regis said. "On the other hand, he might want to say something optimistic. And I would like President Nixon offer his personal congratulations when we zero in on an antidote for IRA—*Ictopera Aqueous Resperacion*—and may I expect that the usual decade of fumfering might be avoided before we begin human trials? I'm told that, if there is any delay, the Apple boy will be found belly up in his tank in a matter of weeks."

"Ugly thought," Beem said. "The President realizes you can hardly flush a child from the public mind the way you can flush dead guppies down the toilet."

"So we're on a fast track with the FDA?" Regis said.

"I'd say so," Agent Beem said. "We wouldn't want Simon Apple to die while you're forced to perform excessive experiments on a frog."

"Tell me something, Agent Beem," Regis said, "in addition to your regular duties, I was wondering if you might consider doing Regis Pharmaceuticals what I will call a special freelance service. Within the bounds of ethics, of course."

"Please clarify, Mr. Van Clay."

"I want Simon Apple put under surveillance."

"Toward what end?"

"I'm not sure. Let's call him a physical nonconformist. That subversive child has invaded my dream life. And I hear his father has approached an attorney about suing for damages. It won't help our defense if President Nixon continues to call him a heroic victim."

"I'll suggest to the President that in the Apple affair he bank the fires of enthusiasm."

"It would be appreciated."

"By the way, you mentioned that *Viloxidril* is being used in certain feminine hygiene products. I trust we're not facing any wider threat lurking over the horizon."

"Not one woman has shown any sign of ichthyologic mutation. I wouldn't worry about a plague of mermaids threatening the nation."

"For the sake of argument," Agent Beem said, "if a female suffering from IRA was discovered, would that mean her intimate partners might suffer from exposure?"

"Agent Beem, I doubt you'll have to trade your trigger finger for a tentacle anytime soon," Regis said. "The chances are one in a trillion. So, will you consider some discreet arrangement with Regis Van Clay? A mutually profitable symbiosis?"

"It might be possible," Beem said. "One in a trillion you say? Not *none* in a trillion?"

29

Marvin Klipstein wandered into Quikpix, produced a roll of film for developing, ordered double prints, then said to Robert J., "I feel as if I know you. I once had the pleasure of dating your lovely wife. It was nothing serious, I assure you. We went to a few movies is all, then coffee and cake. I admit I was quite taken with the beauteous Francine but I never felt the feeling was mutual. When I read that she'd become your bride I was happy for you both. I was glad she found her knight in shining armor so close to home. I don't suppose she ever mentioned me or suggested that you give Marvin Klipstein a call?"

"I'm afraid not," Robert J. said. "A shame she missed you. I'd tell Francine you dropped in but we've been divorced for several years. What was your name?"

"Klipstein. Marvin. And I've embarrassed myself."

Simon came to the front of the store carrying envelopes filled with finished orders.

"This must be our young hero," Klipstein said, smiling. "The maimed boy I've read so much about."

"No, I'm the kitchen sink," Simon said, forcing an angry air bubble.

Klipstein's chubby, gray face looked like a collage made from snippets of egg carton cardboard. His bald, polished skull was slightly pointed. He reminded Simon of a manatee. Klipstein blew his nose into a Kleenex with force enough to disintegrate the fragile tissue. That blast made Simon think of South Sea natives trumpeting warnings of approaching pearl hunters.

"Curb your dog," Robert J. said to Simon, then told Marvin Klipstein, "Let me apologize for my son. He's still a bit touchy what with all the recent hoopla. Simon is usually better behaved."

"No offense intended, none taken," Klipstein said, tucking the crumpled Kleenex into a jacket pocket. "This can't be easy for him. I think it's a triumph that Simon is holding up so well. A tribute to you, Mr. Apple. And to one or both of his mothers, as the case may be."

Driving the forty miles from his office in neighboring Freebush, Klipstein had calculated the monetary value of the Apple family's pain and suffering. All the way to Glenda he told himself that the Apples must surely be represented by some major law firm in New York, Philadelphia, Boston or Washington D.C., but there was always the vague chance that every lawyer in America had made the same assumption.

He presented Robert J. with his business card: MARVIN KLIPSTEIN, ESQ. ATTORNEY AT LAW. "I'm not in the habit of chasing ambulances, but if I'm not stepping on toes, I was wondering if you've sought legal counsel regarding damages."

"Not yet," Robert J. said. "Though it's been talked about."

Klipstein let out a long sigh and flushed purple. "You have a potentially huge case here, Mr. Apple. Huge. You should certainly consider seeking recompense on behalf of your family, especially Simon here. If you decide to go ahead with litigation, I would be more than proud to represent you. On a contingency basis, of course. There would be no expense incurred by you, not a red cent." Klipstein sneezed again.

"God bless," Robert J. said reflexively.

"Bless us all," Klipstein said. "Excuse my allergies. Please tell me, am I being too forward? I'm saying what needs to be said sooner or later. And sooner is better."

"It's just that I have an aversion to involving Simon in any legal tangle just now," Robert J. said. "He has enough stress on his plate."

"Oh, yes, I understand your feelings. But with President Nixon demanding a full investigation of that *Viloxidril* drug's rapid approval by the FDA, you're in a win-win situation here. To my eyes, Regis Pharmaceuticals and possibly a trusted agency of the United States government are clearly liable. I'd say you owe it to your son, your current wife and yourself to spin the proverbial wheel of fortune. We could be talking millions."

"I'll give it some thought," Robert J. said.

"Let me say one other thing. If my son were the victim of irreparable damage I wouldn't hesitate to sue the ass off anybody and everybody responsible for his tragedy. I'd call that a prime parental duty."

"Two things," Robert J. said. "You used the words irreparable and tragedy. The President promised to use the full authority of his bully pulpit to see to it that Simon will be cured."

"His bullshit pulpit," Klipstein said. "When did that pompous prick go to medical school? I don't mean to sound negative or to frighten you but chances are, with the Watergate mess, Nixon will be kicked out of the White House before Simon's problem takes a U-turn. Then what?"

"I gather you're a Democrat?" Robert J. said.

"Just being realistic," Klipstein said. "Facing hard facts."

"The film you brought in will be ready in an hour," Robert J. said. "Here's your claim check."

That evening, over dinner, Robert J. said to Rowena, "Klipstein drips when he gets worked up. He left a stain on my tie. Maybe we should hire him. He'd shower the jury with snot if they didn't find for the plaintiff."

"It can't hurt to set up a consultation," Rowena said.

"I don't know. Did I tell you he said he knew Francine? I can't help wondering if he ever . . ."

"Yesterday's newspaper," Rowena said and gave her new husband a long kiss.

A month later, Simon was scheduled to file a deposition in the case of *Apple v. Regis Pharmaceuticals.* Robert J. watched Rowena help him dress in a new blue suit when Dr. Henry Fikel made an unexpected house call. He told Rowena to disconnect Simon's auditory input jack. The doctor had something private to communicate.

"I have news that may change the direction of your thinking," Fikel said. "The Marine Biological Unit at Regis stumbled on a substance they call *Aquathaline Dehydrosis.* It has something to do with shrimp emulsion. They claim it grew lungs in a carp's bladder. Now the fish is surviving on land."

"That's incredible," Rowena said, brushing at a crease in Simon's lapel. "But I don't see how . . ."

"The Regis people are willing to risk allocating a portion of their supply for Simon's use. It's beyond precious. There's only one test tube of *Aquathaline Dehydrosis* in the entire world. One problem is, it's never been tested on anything but a strain of rodents highly reactive to *Viloxidril.* They grew gills. Now they're able to handle oxygen. The results are very promising though there has been a slightly elevated mortality rate in the test group."

"If it's only been tried on mice and half the mouse population dropped dead, how come they feel ready to offer it to Simon?" Robert J. said.

"It always comes down to who you know," Rowena said.

"She's so right," Dr. Fikel said. "This is strictly against accepted procedure and would be entirely off the record. What it comes down to is whether you're willing to wait five years or more for a properly supervised trial in certain Third World countries. As for risk, we have no idea if other complications will surface from *Viloxidril* or how long Simon can last in a tank. You've got to know those dead mice might have succumbed to the massive *Viloxidril* infusion or to the subsequent dose of *Aquathaline Dehydrosis* or both."

"It's certainly a crap shoot," Rowena said.

"It's all we've got," Robert J. said.

"One more thing," Dr. Fikel said. "The Regis people are demanding you agree to the same restrictions as before concerning any legal claims against the company resulting from prior or future illness related to either drug. There's the additional provision that you agree to keep utterly mum about any unauthorized experimental procedure related to *Aquathaline.* In short, you would remain in an official denial mode. You'd be willing to sign a document stating that you never heard of the drug and were never approached by any Regis representative about its existence. Only Regis Van Clay would have the authority to release you from that silent mode in the event treatment proves successful. On the upside, the Regis folks do agree to underwrite a generous term insurance policy on Simon's life covering a two-year period and exempting any prior conditions. Somewhere in an amount of at least seven figures."

"Our lawyer anticipated something like this might happen," Rowena said. "That the rumor of some secret cure might be used to get us to drop our lawsuit. Besides, Mr. Klipstein says any such agreement would be worthless, tantamount to holding our Simon hostage. That would amount to blackmail."

"Your lawyer says? Do you know who represents Regis Pharmaceuticals? Shanahan, Coran, Berkowitz and Sharpton. And that's just in the United States. Regis Van Clay plays golf with Zeus and Odin. Your lawyer handles real estate closings. Look, Regis Van Clay called me personally. He's waiting for your reply. This is no delaying tactic. Mr. Van Clay is being pressured by the White House to save Simon Apple. Oh, I forgot to mention that he's willing to pay for Simon's tuition to any accredited college if he lives long enough to make it to college."

"What about stock options?" Robert J. said, surprising himself.

"I think they might sweeten their offer with options," Dr. Fikel said. "They print plenty of paper on Wall Street."

"We could postpone Simon's deposition," Robert J. said. "I'll call Marvin Klipstein. He'll have apoplexy. He'll snort from all his openings. Get me the phone and a raincoat."

Rowena switched on Simon's subterranean ears. "What's happening?" Simon said.

"Change out of the suit," his father said. "We're on hold."

30

It was nearly five when Warden Donal came to Simon Apple's cell with a gift of mixed nuts arranged in a circular plastic tray. He found Simon trying to scratch his initials onto one of the steel walls with the tip of a ballpoint pen. "It would take etching acid," Donal said. "The days of plaintive final scrawls dug into concrete are long gone. As God is my witness, I can remember a time when your predecessors not only gouged out their famous last words with files and utensils, they wrote in blood, which was rather pathetic, and actually knocked out their own teeth to use as scrapers. Some of those outbursts were pure poetry. But they were often offensive. Incendiary, obscene or banal. Hardly uplifting for future occupants. Times change. The moving finger writes and then moves on. I want you to know that when this facility was designed, I did lobby for a slab of slate to be incorporated into each Death House cubicle but the No Frills gang laughed that off. I don't know if chalk on a blackboard would have satisfied the urge to immortality but it might have helped somewhat. Where did you get that pen? Pens are off limits in here. That was a rhetorical question. I don't expect an answer."

"I suspect trying to leave messages on the cave walls is a basic instinct. Like tattooing a butterfly on your ass," Simon said.

"Nicely put," Warden Donal said. "You do have a way with words. You must be curious about my visit."

"A bit, yes."

"I did want to say goodbye and wish you well but there is something else. Writing on the walls isn't the only tradition we've lost."

"Like a last cigarette?"

"Well, yes, but that's a health issue. I was referring to the riot. When I first began in this business it was mandatory for a restlessness to grip the inmates on the day of an execution. You could smell the stinking fog of anxiety in the halls. Everyone was tense. The mood was explosive. In the last hours we could count on the inmates to beat on the cell bars with tin cups, spoons and plates. They made what I always thought was a wonderful music of rage. I meant to record those archetypical thumps and clangs and the guttural lyrics that gave them dimension. Unfortunately, I never did. When we changed over to Styrofoam cups and plastic utensils the timbre of protest was hardly equivalent."

"It is hard to thump and clump with Styrofoam," Simon said. "You could say the whole country's thumping and clumping is pretty much muted these days."

"I don't want to get into the politics of metaphor or the

metaphor of politics," Warden Donal said. "I do admit that I always felt the Dead Man Walking riot served a definite purpose. It functioned as an escape valve for all kinds of pent-up fury and frustration. The riot had a particular form—like a sonnet. A beginning, middle and end. Of course, no execution was ever postponed because of unrest or upheaval, but the calm that settled over the prison after the death sentence was carried out was a beautiful thing. It's hard to explain. It was like the calm eye of a hurricane, spiritual weather, an opportunity for reflection and self-examination."

"What you're saying reminds me of some comments by Judge Luber. He was nostalgic for the power drain when the electric chair was in vogue."

"The dimming bulbs interrupting yet affirming the connection between the penitentiary and the town," Warden Donal said. "Lethal injection does leave something to be desired."

"Maybe the pendulum will swing back," Simon said.

"Who knows? What I would like to do, with your help, is to provoke at least some semblance of a riot tonight. It won't be what it once was, I don't fool myself on that score, but at least it would make your execution more of an event. I've toured the entire facility and sense nothing but indifference."

"Maybe it's because they know I'm innocent," Simon said. "Or because they think my crime was horrendous, past any demonstration of sympathy."

"True," Warden Donal said. "But your guilt or innocence shouldn't be the issue. A riot is definitely in order, even a small riot."

"How can I help?"

"I brought this tape recorder along," Warden Donal said, producing a Sony from his shirt pocket. "I was wondering if you'd agree to say a few words to the boys, explain to them that a few howls and burning mattresses would mean a lot to you in your last minutes. Tell them that scraping the back of a toothbrush along the bars doesn't make for a rattle but it does make a statement. A continuous flushing of toilets would cause the plumbing to whine. Let's not forget the old-fashioned shouting and cursing. I suspect hearing your request for a demonstration might make a case for disobedience."

"If I agree," Simon said, "what's in it for me?"

"I'm sorry you said that. I thought you would understand the gesture would be its own reward. You'd be doing something for others. And for yourself."

"I wouldn't mind causing a riot," Simon said. "It would give some distraction while I'm laying on the gurney waiting for the drip signal."

"Exactly. You have no idea of how loud that chemical drip can sound to a condemned man. Some ambient white noise would be a blessing."

"You think I'd hear all the toilets flushing?"

"Seven hundred toilets in unison? Certainly you'd hear them. Here's the tape recorder. And I wrote out a page of notes. Not a script, mind you. More of an outline. I want you to use your own words, draw on authentic emotions. We used a script the last time. Written by a professional author and it proved to be a total failure. When the clock struck midnight, there wasn't so much as a communal sigh. Not one of the African American prisoners sang anything gospel or even a chorus of the blues."

"Turn on your tape," Simon said, sipping some water and clearing his throat.

31

Against the advice of Marvin Klipstein, the Apples withdrew their lawsuit and agreed to sign a formal document drawn by Regis's attorneys. In addition to providing access to *Aquathaline* (delivered to Dr. Fikel in unmarked capsules packaged in anonymous wrappers) their offer of a full-tuition college scholarship and a million dollar life insurance policy valid through Simon's 21st year was confirmed in writing. After much haggling by Klipstein, the contract also granted 5000 stock options to Robert J. in trust for his son. The options, which could be exercised for five dollars each, were not for stock in Regis Pharmaceuticals but in a spin-off called EduPuss that owned exclusive rights to a system designed to toilet-train felines.

Before accepting the EduPuss compromise, the Apples were

shown an advance video of an infomercial to be broadcast on national TV. The film showed an ordinary house cat fed on a special diet. A single drop of greenish fluid was added to the animal's drinking water. After an hour, the cat's owner touched the single button on a remote control; a blue light flashed on the side of a metal bowl bolted to a short tower attached to a regular commode. A high-pitched whine signaled the cat to run to the bathroom, climb a ramp, mount the tower, squat atop the bowl and do its business.

When the cat finished, EduPuss triggered an automatic flush mechanism; the cat descended and resumed normal activity. The infomercial ended with an announcer's voice saying, "Bernard Baruch, a brilliant financier, once said that the path to success is to find a need and fill it. EduPuss does both! The litter box is a thing of the past! "

That film was impressive enough to convince the Apples that an investment in EduPuss was golden. Marvin Klipstein bought himself a thousand shares at market price the first morning EduPuss traded publicly. It opened at sixteen dollars a share and quickly rose above twenty. That same morning Regis Van Clay sent the Apples a complimentary EduPuss, a year's supply of the green additive and, for Simon, an adorable black Persian male from a litter dropped by the winner of more ribbons and medals than any war hero.

While Robert J. rigged the EduPuss in the downstairs bathroom, Simon tried hard to welcome his pet with affection. He was not a cat person by nature, but Shah (his name for the kitten) had the promise of becoming a cuddly co-conspirator, a real friend. One problem Simon had was finding his face. He could see yellow eyes blinking from inside a muff of hair and sometimes a dot of nose, but no continuity of features that fell together. Simon tried to ignore his feeling that those eyes were more malevolent than accessible. He wondered if Shah still missed his mother, a loss with which Simon could easily empathize.

When Robert J. finished assembling Shah's EduPuss the family was eager to test their newest appliance but the Persian refused every offer of its special food and ignored the chemically treated green water. A pamphlet that came with the device advised patience since pussies were different from dogs—not loyal tail waggers, seemingly immune to commands, fierce guardians of their independence or the illusion of independence in the framework of domestic dependence. Cats functioned on their own terms in their own space and time. The pamphlet said at first a cat might try hard to resist Edu-Puss's seductive electronic signal but would soon yield to the inevitable.

Shah bolted to some hidden refuge and stayed invisible despite coaxing purrs, coos and ersatz meowing; he stayed out of sight for nearly a week. Out of sight was not out of mind. The Apples had a nervous sense of a hostile animal presence, and with the EduPuss firmly in place they were forced to use the upstairs facility.

Since their cat seemed devoid of appetite, the appliance remained untried. The suggested patience wore thin. Still, EduPuss, Inc.'s share price edged up to twenty-nine which was some compensation.

One evening, when Robert J. and Rowena went out to a movie, Simon finished his homework, came down to the kitchen and opened a can of sardines. He couldn't tolerate solid food for himself but he often thought about the lost pleasures of taste, and sardine sandwiches had been among his favorite snacks. Just gazing at the headless fish made him salivate.

While he enjoyed a fantasy meal, marveling at the art of sardine packaging, he heard an ominous hiss. Simon thought it was a break in his air hose, until he saw that the source of that furious sound was his practically forgotten kitten. Shah was crouched on a kitchen chair. Then suddenly he flew onto the counter, buried his face in the sardine can, grabbed a few fish, dove down to the floor and crouched again, those yellow eyes glowering above a mouthful of needle teeth.

A quick thinker, Simon emptied the sardines into Shah's bowl and watched while the cat gobbled them down along with a dose of the prescribed EduPuss diet. After his meal, Shah lapped at the green water then vanished again.

Simon waited out the suggested hour, found EduPuss's remote control and pressed its crucial button. Exactly as in the infomercial, the machine began to flash blue light and presumably broadcast its invitation. In minutes Simon saw his pet come—dragging his bottom, fighting momentum with his claws but drawn to the ramp and up the EduPuss tower where he squatted and shat a series of pellets that fell like smart bombs into the metal funnel over the toilet bowl.

Simon marveled at the sight. It occurred to him that this was a terrific time to be alive, that technology was capable of improving on Creation itself, taming even the miniscule inconveniences of civilization. Compared to exploring the planets, controlling when and where his cat shat couldn't be called triumphant but it was an exciting example of applying space-age research to make a difference on Earth.

The furry clump was still squatting when the toilet began emptying itself with a vengeance. The plumbing in the Apple house, already skittish, gave out a thunderous boom; the pipes rattled like skeletons in an animated cartoon. Shah dived off his perch, splayed himself on the white bathroom rug Rowena had brought home from K-Mart and rolled in panic, pissing emerald colored liquid in every direction. Simon watched cat piss form a mandala of incredibly complex design. Swirls, webs, circles, triangles poured from ancestral caverns in the feline mind.

Then Simon heard a chord as vibrant as a hosanna played on a cathedral organ echo through the basement. He saw the ceramic toilet bowl split open like the bud of a tropical flower and felt water sloshing around his Reebocks. He watched the EduPuss demolish itself, imploding in a shower of sparks that formed high voltage eels prowling the flood. Shah changed to a porcupine; his fur crackled with static. Simon ran out of the house yelling for help with the traumatized kitten clinging to his shoulder.

A fireman told Robert J. and Rowena that only a miracle spared their home and only his rubber-soled sneakers saved their son from instant death by appliance. Simon tried to fault EduPuss for the near disaster but with valuable stock options resting in their bank vault, his father and step mother focused blame on him, claiming it was Simon who'd misused the product by ignoring clear guidelines in the instruction manual.

Worse yet, when the firemen left, Robert J. said, "Simon, how could you torment an innocent kitten? You're not ready to care for an animal. We're going to send it back to Mr. Regis with a note of apology."

Rowena overruled her husband. She cuddled Shah against her breast the way Simon's beloved Victoria once cuddled Robert J. The traitorous cat licked her cheek. When Simon reached for him Shah swiped at his hand. That night, Shah escaped the looming threat of a replacement EduPuss by climbing through an open window in Simon's room and disappearing forever.

Simon realized he'd grown close to his pet. Now, with Shah's desertion, he had no allies in that house. He faced the lonely truth that only a fragile blood tie kept any semblance of domestic gravity intact in the Apple home.

A concerned fireman reported the EduPuss episode to *The Glenda Express*. The story echoed in *The Wall Street Journal* and *Barron's Weekly*. EduPuss's infomercial was banned from the airwaves until its advertising was altered to include a warning about a possible fire hazard or the danger of fatal shock. Sales plummeted. EduPuss stock tanked.

32

In Glenda, the EduPuss incident accentuated Simon's reputation as a dysfunctional celebrity. His bizarre fame provoked a mix of envy and hostility from the boys at Glenda Middle School egged on by Albert Essman whose gang of Assassins had disbanded under pressure from school authorities.

Simon's infrequent classroom comments, punctuated by bubbling, provoked gurgles and fish faces from the jocks. Every few weeks some wag spray-painted graffiti on his water bottle. He found cans of mealy worms in his locker. Simon regarded those putrid gestures as twisted signs of his peculiar popularity among the chronically inarticulate.

When he discussed some recent indignity with Rowena, she liked saying, "God works in mysterious ways His blessings to bestow." It appeared to Simon that it was the only way God worked.

Simon's tainted touch of glory bothered the rutting males at Glenda Middle School. The females were compassionate, solicitous, even bewitched. Young blossoms surrounded him in the corridors, shared his table in the cafeteria where he went to keep contact with the idea of real food, offered to be his study partner. Simon was the first one invited to the A-list parties; he got unsigned declarations of love; his telephone rang into the wee hours, the anonymous callers silent except for erratic breathing and tempting giggles. Those calls forced Robert J. to pay for a private line to his son's bedroom.

Monogamous by nature, Simon's own romantic fantasies generally focused on Polly Moon. For wet dreams though, the ones he called "honorable discharges," Placebo was off limits; she was being saved for better things. For purposes of gratifying loveless lust he drew on a library of movie stars and *Playboy* centerfolds to exercise his privates.

Simon was proud of his epic masturbations, elaborate productions for which he served as writer, director, producer, art director, cinematographer, costume designer, composer of intricate scores, the whole crew. He gave himself special credit for careful casting and even did his own stunts.

As for Polly Moon, she'd emerged from childhood hibernation as part weed, part daffodil. Simon's serious qualms when Placebo agreed to draw her skies all-the-way-down in elementary school proved unfounded. The adolescent Polly had a first-class mind. She was curious about everything, eager to challenge the most accepted bromides. She wore a peace symbol sewn onto the backside of her blue jeans and a picture of The Beatles on her blouse. She sang dirty folk songs about Nixon's pardon after Watergate (when the President resigned his office, Simon felt abruptly disconnected from the nexus of power suspecting that Nixon lost interest in his case). Polly was sure of her own future victories, a whirling nebula. She was confident and optimistic enough to master the basics of electric guitar and write songs about lost love, separation, and ultimate decay.

Polly might laugh at the shape of clouds or go silent as a candle in the midst of general hilarity. Her weather was as unpredictable as April; she even smelled like early spring. Most important, for the first time since Simon saw Placebo in her carriage, she turned reasonably civil.

Over the winter—it seemed like a miracle—Simon and Polly became buddies. They went for long walks together, quoting back and forth from Walt Whitman, Emily Dickinson, William Butler

Yeats, Hart Crane, Robinson Jeffers, Matthew Arnold and the ancient Simon considered his mentor, Omar the Tentmaker. They argued about who wrote Shakespeare's plays and if Sylvia Plath might have been cured by a series of enemas. Polly ripped into Hemingway and Mailer while Simon accused her of chronic penis envy. They discussed the horror of Vietnam, the fate of the human species, submarines with bellies filed with nuclear bombs slithering under Arctic ice caps, lingering screams from victims of the holocaust and racial injustice, evolution versus creationism, social issues like Lucille Ball's frantic attempts to get a life beyond the range of Desi Arnaz's patronizing smirk.

They sat on rocks, comparing indignities, elated over being depressed. Simon took pleasure watching Polly eat bags of potato chips, slow-lick strawberry cones, tongue the chocolate jackets off marshmallow twists. They remembered Victoria's songs and Fritzel's addiction to vitamin pills and exercise. The same Fritzel still worked for the Moon family three days a week. She'd married a postal clerk but the marriage only lasted a year.

When Polly mentioned the name of an author, painter, composer, politician or overnight sensation Simon hadn't heard of, he'd run to the library trying hard to keep up with her erudition. When he talked about pitchers, catchers, goalies, point guards, quarterbacks, tight ends, Polly tried hard to look interested. What they never discussed was Simon's gills or the plurping noise he made when their conversations turned intense; Polly came to accept his liquid agitation as a kind of punctuation. Her pet name for Simon was The Carbonated Holden Caulfield.

She began smoking Virginia Slims cigarettes; he held Marlboros to his intake valve. They made smoke trails like the jet planes that flew over Glenda, speculating on the destinations of those silver birds. They imagined life in Casablanca, Marrakech, Katmandu, Lhasa (Fuck Paris, Rome, London, New York, Bermuda, the predictable peasant destinations explored by tour groups sponsored by the Lion's Club, Elks or Moose).

Simon brought news of black holes, quarks and parallel universes into the mix; he became an avid reader of *Fantasy & Science Fiction* and *Omni*. Polly drew maps of other dimensions and portraits of life forms with bulbous heads and lizard bodies, possessors of infinite wisdom come to drain humans with suction-cup lips, impregnate virgins through their elbows, giddy with superior powers, eager to kill, conquer and rule the blue planet.

"This is so cool," Polly said one afternoon. "I used to hate your guts, Simon. You turned my stomach. Fritzel made up ghost stories with you as the spook. I got rashes from the way you stared at me in kindergarten. To me you were dog shit on the sidewalk. And now for some reason I like you. Talk about a parallel universe."

"I always liked you, Placebo," Simon said. "I hope it's not my disability that's changed your feelings. I wouldn't want to be pitied."

"I suppose I do partly pity you," Polly said. "The water thing does contract your horizons. Generally, I think you handle the problem very well. I admire your attitude. Still, if I can be totally honest, when I think about us, you know, together, I can't get past that glass wall. What I'm trying to say is I want to kiss you on the lips."

She took Simon's hand and rubbed his fingers. "I want you to know that Albert Essman asked me to the prom and I said yes. I like dancing as much as I like kissing but it would bug me to watch your face slosh around whenever you made a move. Besides, you didn't ask me and Albert did." Simon knew Polly couldn't see that his eyes filled with tears but he turned his back on her just in case.

"I know the two of you don't get along," Polly said. "But he is attractive even if he is a crappy person. It's hard to explain why I decided to go with him so I won't try. If things were different . . ."

Simon discharged a string of slow, deliberate bubbles.

"Well I can't help it if you're sort of off the charts. And why do you call me Placebo?"

"It's hard to explain," Simon said. "It goes way back. I once heard Dr. Fikel . . . hey, let's forget it. Just be happy that you're an amazingly healthy girl."

Simon had never told Polly Moon anything intimate about his own medical history or shared restricted information—a contractual requirement—about his treatments with *Aquathaline*.

Aquathaline
Trade Name: Zepharia
A new star in the Regis Pharmaceuticals Galaxy

33

Twice a week, Simon went to Dr. Fikel's office where a dose of the pasty drug was dissolved in a solution of bicarbonate of soda, fortified with sugar and infused into his feeding tube. Every treatment gave him biting cramps. Dr. Fikel noted his reactions on tape.

"The subject shows signs of cyanosis. He passes copious quantities of gas while complaining of intestinal distress. There are indications of gastroenteritis. His pulse rate touches 160 and his blood pressure fluctuates significantly. Some mental confusion is evident under questioning.

"Symptoms subside in a matter of minutes. I would infer that the immediate effects of *Aquathaline* are well within the parameters defined as Normal and Acceptable in the accompanying literature (pages thirty-four through forty-six) and that no lasting damage is in any way evident. The patient sometimes experiences extreme vertigo but is otherwise unaffected. He returns to ordinary activity after receiving the mandatory caution about operating heavy equipment or indulging in excessive physical exertion.

"There are encouraging signs of improvement and reason for cautious optimism. The dorsal gill trench seems to be filling with fatty tissue even as our subject's lung capacity shows no further deterioration. His ability to breathe outside his jug has increased approximately 34 percent to nearly two minutes since treatments commenced."

Simon had mixed feelings about any change for the better. He was eager to shuck off the burden of tank, tubes and monitors before starting high school but leaving the realm of the extraordinary was not all roses. He was adjusted to things as they were.

Simon enjoyed having Rowena refill his well every night, although she complained that the job gave her the creeps. She told Robert J. it was like changing diapers and hinted more than once that it would be nice for him to take a more active role in his son's maintenance. Rowena felt that watching ball games was insufficient bonding between a father and son and that it was blatantly unfair to leave the messy jobs to her.

If Robert J. left most of those mechanics to his wife, he did enjoy showing off Simon at Quikpix where an autographed picture of ex-President Nixon was prominently displayed under crossed flags. Simon's notoriety had increased business, no question. Many customers asked for photos of themselves shaking his hand or pressing their noses against his bottle.

Simon's relationship with Polly Moon was on shaky ground since she'd accepted the prom date from Assman. He did his best to understand her position—better a jock than a freak for an escort at an event as important as the Middle School prom—but there was a residue of bitterness. His meetings with Placebo had become cooler and more casual but, pride be damned, playing brother and sister was better than nothing. But not much better.

The evening of the big dance, Polly called him to ask for a meeting at Arch of Angels Memorial Park, where the bones of passing pioneers, hunters and trappers mingled with the dust of Glenda's early settlers. Simon was still reeling from a treatment earlier that afternoon but he couldn't say no.

While Rowena and Robert J. watched *All in the Family*, he snuck out of the house and managed the five blocks to the Arch of Angels gate then headed for the grave of Jabez Pine, a licensed pirate who'd chased down six British frigates during the Revolutionary War. His ship, *Rachael*, named for his wife, was battered by a storm off Rhode Island. Rachael Pine transported her drowned husband to Glenda when it was no more than a frontier trading post. Her second husband, who sold guns and whiskey to Indians in exchange for furs, didn't object when the widow Rachael, a sentimental woman, brought Jabez Pine west along with her modest dowry. Now Rachael and Jabez rested together under an elaborate statue commissioned by Glenda's citizens—a great marble eagle preening on the prow of a stone ship, its wings protecting thirteen eaglets with open beaks. That shrine was one of Polly's favorite places.

When Simon got there he found her gazing up at a luminous sky. "I'm sorry we ever walked on the lunar surface," she said.

"Is that what you wanted to tell me?" Simon said. "Because I'm not the least bit sorry. I wouldn't mind being up there right now."

"The reason I called is to say how sad I am about going to the prom without you. I'll be dancing with Albert but I'll be thinking about Simon."

"I'm against all forms of dancing anyway. I'd have every dancer killed except for a few Rockettes to keep frozen or stuffed in the Smithsonian. So forget about Simon and have a good time."

"Simon?"

"What now?"

"Let's get naked and cuddle."

"Are you serious, Polly? In Arch of Angels? What happens if somebody comes along to hang a wreath or something? I can just see the front page of the *Express*."

"We'll skinny dip under the stars. Jabez and Rachael would love it."

"I have mixed feelings about this. How would the dead feel?"

"I know this is sanctified ground," Polly said. "I wasn't talking about anything like penetration. Just lying together and looking up at the beautiful ornaments adorning our little universe."

"You're some girl," Simon said. "You'd get naked with me and later you get dressed and go galloping with what's his name. I don't know, Placebo, I just don't know."

"Don't call me that."

"Sorry," Simon said.

Polly pulled off her NO NUKES T-shirt and unhooked her bra. There were her naked breasts swinging full in the wind like Jabez Pine's sails as she reached for Simon's belt.

"There's a lot of tubing and an auxiliary pump down there," Simon said. "Before we connect you'll have to disconnect. And later, re-connect."

"Don't be frightened," Polly said. "I have a flair for fixing things. I once did a toaster-oven I found in a dumpster. It worked like a charm." She stroked a long, rubber tube that ran from Simon's bottle toward his groin. She unbuttoned his shirt, pressed her body against his bare chest, unbuckled his belt, slid open the zipper on his fly and laughed when his jeans got caught around his knees in a tangle of wires.

"You think that's funny?" Simon said. "I'm knotting up."

Simon heard the snaps on Polly's skirt explode like popcorn

popping. She kicked off her sandals, then helped Simon get rid of his pants and shoes. They helped each other with their socks. Polly dropped her blue polka-dot panties and draped them over one of the statue's baby eagles.

"Could I slip off your tank, just for a few minutes?"

"No way," Simon said. "Just pretend it's not there."

"Difficult," Polly said. "But I'm trying."

Simon felt her fingers cup the bulge in his jockey shorts. She snapped the elastic over that last obstacle. "This is prom night," Polly said. "Let's dance on our ancestors," She hummed "I Write The Songs," switched to the music from *Jaws*, then settled on "Bewitched, Bothered and Bewildered."

They danced.

Simon felt he was embracing a creature fashioned of snowflakes. Every ounce of his blood changed course and flooded toward his sex, dragging his brain, heart, lungs, liver, kidneys, spleen and soul in the torrent. That river of blood left a meringue of love, lust, gratitude and astonishment along its banks. The only thing left of him were his genitals packaged in a throbbing pouch of burning skin.

"A magic wand," Polly said, grabbing Simon's penis. "Can you believe I never touched one of these before? He feels so swollen and angry. Is he angry?"

"No," Simon said. "Something like it, though. I don't know. This is all new to me." Feeling between Polly's long legs he said, "This is so incredible. Between you and me, I thought a lot about what went on down there but I had no idea girls were filled with honey. Or is it maple syrup?"

"Just let's lie down in silence," Polly said. She found a patch of soft grass and stretched her body on hallowed ground. Simon let out a muffled yell, flapping his arms like the marble eagle's wings. He bent to join her but suddenly felt himself losing control, about to gush, so he jackknifed trying to hold back the rising tide. He lost that battle and came, off balance, falling head first against Captain Pine's sepulcher.

Simon's glass bottle smashed to smithereens. Three gallons of distilled water spilled over him but didn't cool him down. He shook a shower of splinters out of his hair and kissed Placebo's puckered lips. Their tongues tangled. It didn't matter that in a few minutes he'd be a doomed dolphin suffocated on the dunes of Polly Moon's breasts.

Simon remembered her invitation to cuddle but things had gotten more complicated. His penis hadn't signed any contract agreeing to terms and conditions. He felt ready for another explosion, climbed onto Polly and spread her thighs apart. Instead of saying no, no, please don't but meaning yes, yes, take me, like the girls in major feature films, Polly Moon pushed him away.

"You bastard," Polly snapped. "You tricked me. You nearly raped me. And you don't have any protection. Jesus. Everything about you is a sham!"

"Meaning what?" Simon said, suddenly defensive. His startled organ went limp along with his startled heart.

"There's nothing wrong with you, Simon Apple. You can breathe like the rest of us."

"Look, Polly, I swear I didn't know," Simon said. "I mean, I still don't know. What I'm saying is, I have no idea how long I can last on regular air. They came up with this drug, *Aquathaline*. I admit I've been taking treatments, but there were no guarantees. So where's the problem? This is good news for us, my darling. You should be happy."

"You never once mentioned any treatments."

"I wasn't allowed to. Besides, I didn't want to jinx myself. Even Dr. Fikel told me not to expect too much."

"I feel so cheap," Polly said, standing up, searching for her briefs and bra. "There I was thinking about you all alone by yourself while the rest of us carried on at the prom and all the time you were, what's the word, fully functional."

"At the moment, yes, fully functional, give or take, but that could pass in a minute. I might be dead by prom time. Polly, I'd never deceive you. Not in a million years. And why should you feel cheap? This was a marvelous experience. It was your idea."

"Fritzel was right about you, Simon. She warned me about you."

"Well, my Victoria didn't exactly love you either."

Simon watched the naked Placebo disappear into her clothes.

There was no chance for damage control. She climbed onto the bicycle she'd left propped against a wind-erased marker and peddled away.

A mountainous cloudbank drained all light from the sky. Simon had enough of a problem gathering his dangling hardware together. When he couldn't find his underwear in the dark, he left his jockey shorts in Arch of Angels and headed in the direction of an exit, thinking that if things had worked out differently he would have pressed that underwear between the pages of his yearbook.

The damp cemetery air smelled sweet. Every gravestone was a milestone in Glenda's long history. Technically, Simon was still saddled by his virginity but now it hung by a thread. He marveled at the thought that virtually every person buried under his feet had experienced the astonishment of fusion and now he practically belonged with that crowd.

Robert J. and Rowena were ecstatic when they discovered that Simon's need for waterworks was possibly a thing of the past. They phoned Dr. Fikel who told them to rush Simon to his office.

In the car, Simon wondered if the cause of his cure was *Aquathaline* or Placebo's sweet alchemy. Lying about how his bottle broke—a white lie; he said he tripped on a rock—left Simon feeling a little guilty but his sins of omission and emission hardly seemed relevant in light of the broader picture.

Once again, science had triumphed. Simon's affliction was vanquished by a drug designed to outwit a side effect caused by a product that stymied another potentially lethal side effect caused by a substance developed to thwart a canny virus whose genesis remained a mystery.

"There's the individual, there's you, and there's society," Dr. Fikel explained as he drew blood from Simon's finger, the same finger anointed from browsing Polly Moon's silky cavern. "And there's a constant tension between an individual's needs and those of the community at large. That clash of interest often leads to tragedy. We're all synchronous swimmers in this muddy pond of a world, but too often we're out of sync. It's a messy situation at best, so when a situation arises where one young man's amazing rehabilitation coincides with the public good, it's time for a party."

The only party on Simon's mind was the recent prom. He wondered if Albert Essman had cradled Placebo in his simian arms or got her drunk enough to get into her panties. Knowing Polly's taste for irony she might even have suggested a visit to Jabez Pine's monument after the ball was over. If that happened, Simon prayed that Assman slashed his smug dong on a pile of glass chips.

A week later, Robert J. showed Simon a clipping from *Parade* recounting Simon Apple's Florida adventure and celebrating the pharmaceutical industry's fast track response in finding a cure for Simon's malady. There was a quote from Regis Van Clay about American ingenuity and stick-to-it-iveness.

At the tail end of the story it said the smuggled Chinese, including the child rescued by Simon Apple, had been deported after lengthy hearings by Immigration and Naturalization. Allowing them entry was deemed a slippery slope.

There was a smiley face photo of Dr. Fikel, Robert J., Rowena and Simon standing outside Quikpix. Simon wore the blue suit he'd gotten for his canceled court appearance. The headline read:

MEDICAL MARVEL AS BOTTLE BOY IS CURED
Nixon Given Credit for Research Breakthrough

"You should write a few thank-you notes," Dr. Fikel said. "One to Regis Van Clay and another to former President Nixon who'd probably appreciate a pick-me-up."

"I'll do that," Simon said, and he did.

There was no reply to Simon's gracious thank-you notes, but he did begin receiving letters from the Republican National Committee soliciting contributions and a free sample of *Surge*, a new aftershave cologne "from the caring folks at Regis."

34

"It was good of you to come, Rowena," Simon said. His stepmother looked a little less juicy than the fuzzy peach she'd been when the fruit was on the vine but she still made a terrific impression. Simon saw how the guard salivated when he gave her the once over.

"This isn't easy for me. I know we were never very close but that wasn't entirely my fault."

"Absolutely not. I kept myself surrounded by a moat filled with boiling oil. But you were always supportive and you made a new life for my father. I'm the one who should be apologizing. It can't have been easy dealing with the media dragons lo these many years for you or your twins."

"Your brother and sister aren't kids anymore. Zack and Rebecca just celebrated their twenty-fourth birthday."

"Yes, I meant to send a card. One of the worst things about being locked up on Death Row is that you become disgustingly self-centered. Everything is me, me, me. So, how are Zack and Rebecca taking to all this? How do they feel about losing their vicious half-brother?"

"They're coping," Rowena said. "The publicity complicated their lives, of course, but Rebecca is in rehab going the methadone route and thinking of going back to college. She's interested in communications. I tell her that isn't the most practical occupation but you can't tell your sister anything. Zack is still into developing those video games. His last one, Kingdom of Putrid Pus People, seems to be catching on but the market is really tight since the economy tanked. You know he's getting divorced."

"I heard the marriage was troubled."

"I'm glad he's finished with that dysfunctional bitch. I warned him about marrying an actress. You know how they are. Like chameleons. She waited until her implants and the dental work were bought and paid for before she torpedoed poor Zachary. I don't mind telling you, Robert J. and I footed a major portion of those bills. And that was after her anal surgery."

"Right, the birth defect. She had two anuses," Simon said. "I knew about that."

"Actually, three," Rowena said. "But the surgery was entirely elective. Multiple anuses are fairly common. She had the gall to tell us the anuses were negatively affecting her career. That's how she put it. Never said anything about a lack of talent, never mentioned to Zack that her mother had several anuses and her grandmother before her. Not that it would have kept him from chasing her from coast to coast."

"Love is a relentless magnet," Simon said.

"If you call that love. And now she's asking for half of any Pus People royalties. And watch, she'll get what she wants. Well, at least we have an adorable granddaughter. Lucy Alice Apple."

"Zack is a daddy? That's fantastic," Simon said. "Nobody told me. Good for him."

"Not Zack's. Rebecca's. We kept it quiet. She ended up pregnant after her year in Las Vegas. She doesn't have a clue as to who the father is. Probably some white trash cocaine dealer. Lucy Alice has the cutest eyes and pitch-black hair; she's a doll, a real little mongrel. I should have brought a snapshot."

"Congratulations," Simon said. "Though it's hard to think of you as a grandma." His mind flashed to the portrait of a topless sixteen-year-old Rowena Trask his father kept for occasional reference. Simon found the relic hidden in a book about Mt. Rushmore; Rowena's image seemed to belong there.

"That's my news," Rowena said. "Except that I found out I was dyslexic. Can you imagine? If I'd known that, it could have spared me all kinds of anxiety from trying to read books right to left. Otherwise, just the usual complaints that come with age. I had a bone density scan. It shows some osteoporosis but nothing major. And I have an arthritic knee. I might need arthroscopy but not yet. You look well, Simon. Any word about a reprieve?"

"Denied."

"Oh, you darling boy, I am so disappointed. It's on for tonight, then?"

"Yes."

"Why didn't I insist that Zack and Rebecca come with me? Maybe they'll drop in with your dad. He said he'd definitely pay his last respects."

"I'd like that," Simon said. "But it's not necessary for Zack and Rebecca to schlep themselves out here. Zack must have his share, what with the actress, and my sister must have her hands full with Lucy Alice. Just tell them goodbye and good luck for me."

"I will," Rowena said. "Did Francine put in an appearance?"

"She did," Simon said. "Though I'm not sure she knew exactly why she came."

"Don't be too hard on her," Rowena said. "She fell in love with another man. It happens all the time. And not every woman has maternal instincts. I'm sure she cares very deeply for you."

"She did send me a birthday present when I turned thirteen."

"There you go," Rowena said. "God, when I think about the old days, who would have thought things would work out the way they have? I guess you never know."

"That's what keeps life interesting."

"You should have considered your family before you killed that person, whatever your reasons, which I'm sure were good."

"I didn't kill anybody," Simon said. "Robert J. must have told you."

"He must have," Rowena said. "Another joy of aging. I can't remember what I had for lunch. Things just slip out of my head."

"I won't have that problem," Simon said.

"You always did accentuate the positive," Rowena said. "I admire you for that. I wish more people had your attitude. Especially in this kind of world when you don't know if you're standing next to some crazy with a bomb in his pants. Oh, I brought you a box of Mallomars. I know how much you love them. The guard confiscated the package. He said they had to search the box. Can you imagine? But he promised they'd be delivered to your cell in plenty of time." Rowena reached for a Kleenex and blotted a teardrop from her cheek. "I know I was a lousy excuse for a stepmother but I tried. I loved you. Love you. I'm trying to say we'll never forget you, Simon."

"The feeling is mutual, Rowena. You were certainly the best looking stepmother in Glenda. *Are* the best. Present tense."

"The present is certainly tense," Rowena said. "Here's to future perfect. Well, Simon dear, I seem to be out of words."

"We reach a point when we fall off the Cliff of Words into a puddle of music," Simon said. "Hugs and blessings."

35

Sandwiched between graduation from Glenda Middle School and the murky terrain of Glenda High, Simon spent his summer working at Quikpix by day and watching TV shows like *The Bionic*

Woman and *The Six Million Dollar Man* at night, listening to records by Springsteen, Simon & Garfunkle, Dylan, The Eagles, and Pink Floyd, reading *Rolling Stone, Penthouse,* and *Hustler,* crapping around, eating junk food, worrying about the fucked-up world, wondering about the meaning of life.

Returned to health by all objective standards, Simon felt anxious, pointless and bored. He was told more than once that his cure was a gift, a sign from above that he'd been saved for a purpose but the purpose eluded him. He saw himself as entirely useless, twitching in limbo like his frenzied scrotum.

Simon's only solace was in jerking off on his own *Fantasy Island,* imagining encounters with assorted film stars past and present. It was easier for him to deal with a Marilyn Monroe, Farrah Fawcett or Elizabeth Taylor (living or dead, in color) than it was to seduce a Jean Harlow or Carol Lombard (definitely dead, in black-and-white) knowing those vibrant girls had long since gone to dust and ashes, but there was something especially seductive about their lingering ghosts. After his voyages to celluloid necrophilia, he was left with a queasy feeling as if he had robbed a grave, which in a direct sense, he had. He quieted that angst by telling himself that postmortem masturbation was a form of prayer, a combination of recognition and resurrection, like reading a book by a dead author. It was what his mother, Francine, in her rare dips into Yiddish, used to call a *mitzvah,* a true act of charity. Simon read that dead celebrities still employed agents, or their executors did, and he wished he could send a check somewhere rather than indulge in such arcane soul searching.

The leading ladies Simon cast in his bedroom extravaganzas, current or departed, had one thing in common: they were openly gracious and grateful for his ardent attention. And it wasn't Academy Award or Emmy winners that scored highest on Simon Apple's nightly phantom-fucking scale. Surprisingly his best wet dreams were inspired by Robert J.'s portfolio of local celebrities. Doing the women he recognized from his father's collection of erotic outtakes (he'd stumbled on that hidden album while chasing a bug into a file cabinet marked Tax Returns) gave him new respect for the mysteries that lurked behind Glenda's locked doors and drawn blinds.

Using those photos as fuel, Simon's swollen dick effected a spiritual bond with his neighbors. There was the lady who worked at Woolworth's checkout counter baring a world-class breast; there was Honey Fikel in a transparent nightgown, sporting a neatly trimmed triangle tempting as a poppy; there was the clerk from Berman's Bakery mooning a Kodak with a luscious ass that grinned vertically—the selection in that fleshy catalog was deliciously diverse, a gathering of beauties and beasts. As for the beasts, it puzzled Simon that it was often the plainest of the plain who made him pant the hardest and last the longest before he came and then, spent and languid, welcomed sleep.

He liked the feeling of largesse that came from pleasuring the especially needy; dispensing his favors was definitely an aphrodisiac. If a Mrs. Kripeldorf (the tailor's wife who looked like "The Roadrunner") knew she'd been chosen to spend the night featured in a Simon Apple production, winning out over a superchild like Twiggy or a harem full of Lauren Huttons, she would have sung a song of gratitude.

Simon often wondered what would happen if Robert J. put his picture collection on exhibition at Town Hall—whether Glenda would implode, explode or just look the other way. If his father were another kind of man he could have gotten rich through blackmail. Some of the most revealing photos were less than flattering; even latent exhibitionists would have paid to keep them hidden like *The Dead Sea Scrolls* if only to avoid confronting savage reality.

Simon would have liked to hear his father's thoughts about the Quikpix collection but that conversation was impossible to hope for; Robert J., custodian of the archives, would stay mute under torture, an honorable protector of Glenda's bright façade.

Simon thought it was both a sorrow and a mercy that in the span of a century the dyes in every color print ever made would fade to invisibility. A few years later, the monochromes would also decompose. Eventually the album's linen pages would go blank. So Glenda's best-kept secrets were safe, but was safety a fair tradeoff for loss? All those fleshy photos would corrode like the wind-whipped tombstones in Arch of Angels Memorial.

Alone at Quikpix one evening, Simon browsed Robert J.'s illustrated history looking for the image he would sneak home in his mind's pocket for productive nocturnal use. He settled on an anonymous lady bending over a washing machine holding a box of Tide detergent, stark naked under her apron. She was no starlet but she had frisky eyes, a luscious, promising mouth and serious cleavage. Simon knew she would do very nicely as a midweek companion.

His shameless indulgence in what he called *Glendadelecti* ended abruptly when the Quikpix door chime tinkled announcing the arrival of a customer. Simon slid the album into its plain brown wrapper, put it back into its violated crypt, put on a cordial smile and greeted the newcomer; this man wasn't a regular customer yet he looked vaguely familiar.

"Good afternoon," Simon said. "Can I help you?"

"You can, Simon Apple."

"You've got the name right. Should I know you?"

"We met once before under unusual circumstances."

"We don't have many unusual circumstances around here," Simon said. That face did occupy a niche somewhere in the past, but where, when, why, who and how? Simon's brain tried to spit out the answer.

"We didn't meet anywhere around here. Think about the great state of Florida."

"Nixon's men," Simon said. "That afternoon on the beach. You were one of the black suits."

"Right on. You have an excellent memory, lad. My name is Beem. Brian Beem. Agent Beem, formerly of the Secret Service, now with the FBI." He reached out a hand. Simon shook it.

"I'm impressed with your credentials," Simon said. "Does this have anything to do with the cemetery business? Because . . ."

"This is a social call. A reality check. Just touching base. I see things have changed for the better. No more portable aquarium? I heard you were cured."

"What can I do for you?" Simon said. "Our special today is double prints for the price of one or a free replacement roll of film, your choice."

"I dropped in to see how you're getting along. That *Aquathaline* seems to have done the trick. You know, it cost millions to cure you. *Aquathaline* was what's called an orphan drug, a medication that cures an illness so unusual, so rare, there's no way a cure can ever be profitable. As it turned out, the combination of *Viloxidril* and *Aquathaline* proved golden as a cosmetic ingredient but nobody could have anticipated that. You see, I'm talking about a labor of love here. A tremendous investment only because so many good people are genuinely concerned about your welfare. Tell me, son, how've you been getting along?"

"I'm tip-top," Simon said. "Thanks for asking. Who exactly is concerned about my welfare? President Ford? Maybe the United Nations?"

"Don't forget the folks at Regis Pharmaceuticals. We hope you hold no animosity toward any person or persons who might have been involved with your recent ordeal. What happened to you was no more than a freak accident of nature. A case could easily be made that your unique body chemistry was as responsible for the unfortunate but temporary gill episode as any amount of *Viloxidril*. When it comes to an unfortunate side effect, it takes two to tango."

"Or tangle."

"There shouldn't be any reason for you to harbor conscious or subconscious thoughts of revenge."

"Revenge? I'm just getting on with my life," Simon said. "I don't plan to climb a tower and shoot anybody if that's what you mean."

"That wouldn't be in anybody's best interest."

"My attitude is what's past is past," Simon said. "No hard feelings, as the eunuch said to the sultan. Tell whoever sent you that they won't have Simon Apple to worry about any more. So is Nixon the prick they say he is?"

"Let's not be a smart ass. Let's be respectful. If it wasn't for Mr. Nixon you'd still be drinking worm shakes. I like you, son. Sensible. Good attitude. You deserve a nice, quiet life."

"Not too quiet I hope," Simon said.

"Just one other thing. Your friend, Polly Moon. Have you seen much of her? How are things with Polly?"

"I've seen plenty of her," Simon said. "But not lately. Why are you asking me about Placebo?"

"What did you call her?"

"Skip it. What has Polly Moon got to do with anything? Is this about the cemetery thing because if that's why you're here—"

"What cemetery thing?"

"Never mind. Look, I've got ten exposed rolls to deal with before we close. So if you're done with me—"

"I hope I'm done with you," Beem said. "Believe me, I want to be done with you. We all want to be done with you."

36

"Apple, you have another visitor," the guard said. "He looks like he crawled out of a toilet. They wouldn't let him ring the bells at Notre Dame. If you're feeling social, OK, but we suspect he might be a reporter or some kind of kook. Says his name is Cecil Blee. Says he's a close personal friend. Do we keep him or kick his ass out of here? Your call. Just remember your conversation will be monitored. No interviews."

Simon couldn't place any Cecils and he had no close personal friends. If his visitor was a camouflaged reporter he'd be from some radical weekly with two readers but whoever it was had taken the trouble to come so what the hell. "Cecil? Yes, I'll see him. Good old Cecil, the poor slob."

"You'll have to go to the visiting area. I can't allow him access to your cell. Usually we only admit relatives, lawyers and clergy on the last day. Nobody else. But the warden made an exception in your case. I hope you appreciate that."

"I do," Simon said.

"You must have pull."

"No comment."

Cecil Blee waited behind a thick glass partition in the visitor's room. He crouched on a metal chair with his legs folded under him, absorbed in massaging his earlobes while he touched his tongue to the tip of his nose. The man looked like a hairball, all beard and eyebrows under a battered baseball cap. He wore what was left of a brown suit over a sweatshirt splashed with ketchup and mustard stains. Half a bow tie dangled from his neck. He squatted on army boots laced with rope over feet with no socks. His boots seemed to come from opposing armies.

Simon tried to connect Cecil Blee with some cogent memory. Nothing clicked. He sat across from his visitor and picked up the intercom phone. For a moment Cecil Bee looked befuddled but got the message from Simon's gestures and did the same. Simon heard him blowing into the receiver.

"FYI, I want you to know they'll be listening to whatever we say," Simon said.

"*Wuh. Wuh.*"

"So tell me, how've you been?"

"*Wuh. Wuh.*"

"Good to hear," Simon said. "It's great to see you. A real surprise."

"*Wuh. Wuh.*"

"Marvelous. Could you be a little more specific?"

Cecil Blee put down the phone and fumbled with his jacket pocket. His hand disappeared, then surfaced holding two pieces of torn cardboard. He pressed them against the glass. Simon squinted to read something printed in faded type. Before Simon could make out the letters the guard was there, grabbing the fragments to examine them for any dangerous content. Cecil Blee began weeping. He wiped away tears and snot with his sleeve. The guard made a face like vomit and returned the confiscated cardboard. That calmed Cecil who held them against the glass again.

Simon strained to focus. They were ticket stubs. From the Lombard Cinema in Glenda. One half said ADMIT ONE. The other said GONE WITH THE WIND. Cecil Bee was on the phone again.

"Starren Vivenlee an Cagobble."

Simon had an epiphany. Vivenlee an Cagobble. Vivien Leigh and Clark Gable. Cecil Blee, the visitor sitting across from him, was Crazy Henry, the man who lived in the Lombard's ticket booth. Cecil Blee, who was in his own protected witness program for reasons unknown, had come to offer Simon Apple a nice parting gift, a complimentary ticket to the hottest movie of 1939.

This time it was Simon whose eyes filled with tears. Cecil Bee tried to push the ripped ticket stubs through the glass partition as if it was some kind of membrane. Frustrated, he gave up the effort, left them on the small shelf at the barrier's base, clapped his hands, unfolded his legs, and ran for the exit door.

On the way back to his cell, Simon asked the guard if he could have the ticket Crazy Henry left behind. The guard told him not to press his luck.

37

The class of '78 at Glenda High staggered through its formative years like gorillas in the mist, absorbing the skills and knowledge that would carry them to the new millennium and beyond. For all the lectures, books and field trips most of what was learned came to them outside school: lessons from sitcoms, films, infomercials, commercials, music from hi-fi speakers and boom box radios, dinner table gossip, family arguments, loving gestures, little triumphs, massive tragedies, the invisible academia of acquisition and denial.

The students were nicely prepped to enjoy the full bounty of the American Century. They were taught to be optimists, urged to think like astronauts riding rockets powerful enough to arc over any limiting horizon. They had their youth, dreams of glory, and The Pill. They had cigarettes, pot and beer. The luckiest even had cars.

There was no war to worry about except for the ever-threatening nuclear one, and that was an equal opportunity destroyer. The prospect of evaporation caused transient anxiety in some but for most it communicated a welcome sense of urgency. There were rumors about lousing up Planet Earth's ozone layer and melting its ice caps but what with recycling paper, glass bottles and aluminum soda cans, it seemed there'd be plenty planet left to go around.

The 50s in-your-face Beatniks had long since died for the sins Jesus missed. Hippie ashes from the 60s blew in the wind leaving traces of flower petals and magic mushrooms. For the most part, Vietnam vets swallowed their rage and kept quiet about what they'd seen and done. The new breed of prophets hinted that racism, sexism, poverty and injustice could be erased, that the present could apologize to the past and the apology would be graciously accepted. With a little effort the shock troops of the enlightened 70s would make peace with the offspring of slaves, embrace Native Americans (formerly Injuns), build ramps for cripples, lower elevator panels for the vertically deprived, train Seeing Eye dogs for the blind, discourage lurking assassins, shuck off webs of guilt. Any slate could be wiped clean by confession. The road ahead was a six-lane highway, the Force was with you for the asking. Even God—Himself/Herself/Itself—was ready to be more tolerant of assholes. The new American mantra was: make money, eat right, exercise and live forever.

Simon Apple wondered—in that moment when everything was moving along ahead of schedule and everybody but Simon Apple seemed on track—why the poets of pop sang of depression and despair, why the wails of the lovesick and lonely topped the charts, why so many faces of the class of '78 looked besieged, angry, frustrated, frightened, bewitched, bothered and mostly bewildered. The constipated comedy shows on TV weren't funny, give or take too few exceptions.

As Robert J. liked to say about the endless supply of complaining zillionaires, those anointed angels blathering on talk shows, the celebrity gods and goddesses explaining their pain, "Go figure."

Simon divided his peers into four camps:

First were the Focused Ones—the achievers, the contenders who already saw themselves snap neatly into place in life's jigsaw. They would grow up to be doctors, lawyers, tycoons, super-salesmen, marketing wizards. No question, they knew their place in the scheme of things-to-come; they scoffed at the very idea of failure and already planned for financial security and productive old age.

That group played sports, joined afternoon clubs, gave time to worthy organizations, storing chips they knew would be redeemable when the time came to fill out applications to the hotshot universities.

They looked ahead to the day when they'd own sprawling houses, designer clothes, trendy cats and dogs, red Ferraris; they plotted long vacations, first class all the way. They knew who they were and what they wanted. They moved purposefully along The Yellow Brick Road in the direction of Fair and Warmer. They talked about finding perfect spouses and raising shining children. They heard cash registers ring like church bells in the distance.

Those Most-Likely-Tos scared the shit out of Simon who couldn't understand why they were unconcerned with the slobbering, gore-dripping demons and devils outside their windows, waiting to cut them down to size. Some of those Gung-Ho! fighter pilots might

actually make it past Glenda's city limits but most would end up peddling insurance, owning hamburger franchises or running stores like
Quikpix. Simon thought about the empty pages in Robert J.'s album
waiting like unfilled graves for snapshots of their private parts. Still,
he envied the motivated ones.

He had no clear map of his own future, no North Star to guide
him, not even a best-case scenario in his fantasy life. Every career
Simon considered seemed like forced labor. His own compass pointed him in simultaneously opposing directions. The prospect of holding down a steady job, of marrying and reproducing was as frightening to him as the game of golf.

The second group Simon isolated in his dissection of Glenda
High, rubbing shoulders with the movers and shakers, was a larger
group Simon called The Whirlpools. They kept time and tide on
hold, accepting teenage life as an eternal limbo where nothing
counted for much and neither action nor inaction had consequences.

Their dreams were modest, they gladly settled for C's and D's,
moving generally forward like jellyfish drifting toward shore. They
would be plumbers, carpenters, soldiers, dental technicians, secretaries, maybe own beauty parlors or auto repair shops. That crowd
dreamt about honeymooning in Vegas or Bermuda with some juicy
Glenda boy or girl, then buying attached houses, raising tranquil
families, driving American convertibles, watching television—but
later, not yet, no way, because—as the magazines and movies told
them—this was play time.

The guys argued over baseball, football and basketball stats,
issued bulletins on gropes at the Glenda Drive-In or the backseat of
a Pontiac Firebird sedan (who went down, who stayed up, who swallowed, who spit up, whose legs spread and whose stayed clamped
tighter than the doors to Fort Knox). They fueled up at McDonald's
or Kentucky Fried Chicken, alchemists, transforming sugar and
grease into volcanic zits they wore like battle ribbons, played Aster-
oids, zapped alien invaders at the Wookie Arcade, hummed REO
Speedwagon tunes about love's labor lost and found—or found and
lost. Mostly they just hung out, killed time, bored silly; the simmering Young, the smouldering Restless, ready to pounce.

The girls flew like sparrows to the Glenda Mall checking out

Jordache Jeans—wanting the look any jock would want to know bet-ter—drooling over Robert Redford's buns, defending their favorite Beatle or Bee Gee, waiting for the next episode of *Mod Squad*, fan-tasizing a night with Tom Selleck at Studio 54 in New York, New York.

Simon watched The Whirlpools spin from class to class bang-ing backpacks, swinging pocketbooks, happily clueless, content to goof around, smoke a Camel or a joint in the toilet, get through the day, in no hurry to replace their moms and dads. He heard them grunt like the chimps in Tarzan flicks, amazed that they were absolutely unaware that the world was waiting to mulch them. He was a little jealous of that crowd too. Nothing bothered them except homework.

The third contingent was, to Simon Apple, made up of the true elitists: The Sensitives who considered themselves enlightened avatars of the arts. They were the buds of poets, painters, film direc-tors, philosophers, united in their contempt of avarice; the gifted, answerable only to a Higher Power, like the makers of Hebrew National kosher frankfurters. They listened to jazz (Miles, Ella, Bix, Lena, Sarah), folk (Pete, Joan, Woodie, Judy) and classical (Wolf-gang, Ludwig, Bella, Igor), talked art (Picasso, Modigliani, Calder, Klee, Matisse) took on Cold War politics (why fiddle with Fidel, mess with Mao or piss on Nikita) went to flicks with English sub-titles, read books they didn't have to read, and magazines like *The Paris Review* without pictures.

The Sensitives were a tiny group who managed to find one another in the swirling student clot and quickly circled their wagons against attack by roaming savages. Simon was attracted to that snob-by set; he especially liked their long-haired girls with droopy eyes and peacenik jewelry. For some reason they resisted inviting him into arguments over whether Leonard Bernstein was more than 50 per-cent faggot or did Jack, Bobby, Joe or Arthur make Marilyn come hardest? Their indifference to him, Simon realized, was his own fault. He couldn't work up enough enthusiasm about who wrote *Beowulf*—Danes, Krauts or Brits—and he couldn't manage to bluff it with conviction.

Then there was the fourth contingent, The Night Crawlers,

who gathered at midnight showings of *The Rocky Horror Picture Show*, wearing white powder on their faces, painting their eyes and lips pitch black, dressing in camouflage jumpsuits, showing tattoos of bats and snakes on hairy arms and militant breasts, dangling skull earrings under orange or green hair, yawning and burping at befuddled teachers.

They called themselves Punks and Goths; there were maybe a dozen of those, and Simon felt some pull in their direction but it bothered him that the self-proclaimed outsiders, the REVOLUTION NOT EVOLUTION rebels, were, in fact, more conformist in their appearance and attitude than the Young Republicans.

When his own Polly Moon showed up one day sporting a bra she wore outside a dress made from a burlap coffee sack, one of her legs wrapped in mummy rags, the other in a net stocking, balancing on one high-heeled shoe and one leather cowboy boot, her arms covered by elbow-length white gloves, the silhouette of a bat pasted over her left cheek, Simon's heart skipped beats. He told himself he was glad that Placebo found her place in the scheme of things but he couldn't help feeling like he was going to howl.

The Polly Moon transformation confirmed to Simon that he belonged no place; he was doomed to live life at arm's length, a stranger to everyone including himself.

He understood how his personal history contributed to his sense of alienation. First Hercules, then Neptune; Yesterday's Celebrity to Today's Has-Been—heavy baggage by any standard and without much of a support system to help with the lifting. His real mother was a vague blur. Victoria's face was fading, breaking up in his memory like a rain puddle under a truck tire. Robert J., obsessed with his young wife, was there but not there. Rowena couldn't help being edgy in her role as mom to a total stranger.

All that was underscored by Simon's easy access to Robert J.'s album, the keyhole to Glenda's parallel universe. Simon's saucer eyes were made privy to truths usually reserved for the most intimate X-rays; it was no wonder Simon Apple was hard to find, a floating space walker whose tether had snapped, fighting the pull of the sun's searing gravity.

Sometimes, in public, Simon caught himself humming one of

Victoria Wyzowik's lullabies instead of the score from *Saturday Night Fever*.

He knew he was in big trouble.

38

Predictably, Simon's only friend at Glenda High was new in town, one of a handful of black students from a distant suburb, a spindly boy who looked like Sammy Davis Jr., self-contained as an oyster, defended as a fortress. His debut in the school cafeteria caused a buzz when he carried his tray to the small table where Simon sat chewing a rubber chicken slab, reading *You Can't Go Home Again*. "Hey, Huckleberry, you got anything against dark meat?" he said.

"Depends," Simon said.

The unknown quantity sat down across from him and punched a hole in a paper napkin then buttoned it to his shirt. "I can't keep the damn things from falling off my lap. They should make them with buttonholes. And they should make chopsticks hollow so you could drink soup through them. You heard it here first. I'm Chirp. At least, that's what they call me."

"Simon is my name."

"Look at those plantation Negroes over there," Chirp said, glancing at Glenda High's five other African Americans. "All huddled together. I was sent here to integrate so I'm integrating. Free at last. What's your take on the practice of slavery?"

"I'm not in the market right now. We're overloaded at the plantation. But what price do you go for?"

"Top dollar," Chirp said.

"Where did you get a name like Chirp? I thought all you guys were called Leroy."

"Either I was conceived backstage at Birdland and my dad is Charlie Parker or it came from having a squeaky voice. Take your pick."

"Charlie Parker, no contest," Simon said.

"Did you know birds descended from dinosaurs? I'm not talking overnight," Chirp said.

"I don't believe in evolution," Simon said. "If there was evolution how come there are so many pricks walking around?"

"I like a deep thinker," Chirp said. "With all the tables in this high class cafe I was lucky enough to drop my ebony ass across from you." Chirp looked up at the ceiling. "Thanks, Jesus. I owe you one."

Simon Apple and Chirp Bennet began to pal around together. They exchanged high fives in the hall and on the staircase, shared an English class and staked out a table in the cafeteria. When the weather was good they carried their trays out to a bench facing a statue of Paul Bunyan erected by the Lion's Club.

Most days after school Simon worked at Quikpix and Chirp took the bus back home where he worked evenings in a carwash. Chirp's mother was a nurse at Glenda Memorial. When her schedule allowed, Chirp could skip the bus ride and hang around until she drove him home.

If Rowena was free to fill in at the store, Simon and Chirp used their free time to shoot hoops, listen to records at Shenkel's Music, browse comic books and science fiction titles at The Twisted Mind, or just walk around downtown Glenda. They talked about everything from how to read the language of female nipples to sports cars. During one of those catch-all conversations, Simon learned that Chirp's father was long gone, living someplace in California. Chirp heard the story of Francine Apple's operatic exit from Simon's life. That information seemed to cement their tie.

The two loners gradually dropped their heat shields and opened private safe-deposit boxes filled with spiders and a few half digested butterflies. Their relationship was a tug-of-war between suspicion and trust—moving forward, pulling back, meeting somewhere in the middle. After a while it dawned on Simon and Chirp that they might be called good buddies, a major surprise.

One day, sitting in the park, Chirp reached into his backpack and pulled out a drawing pad. He showed Simon a group of his sketches titled "Life Forms at Glenda High." The drawings were incredibly detailed, almost photographic, but with another dimension; the more exact Chirp's portraits of people Simon recognized, the less real they became, as if Chirp's drawing pencils dissolved them into luminous spirits.

"These are fine," Simon said.

"I guess I can draw a picture," Chirp said. "Those sketches of yours, the ones you read in English class, they were good too. I was thinking, maybe we could come up with a term project. You do the scribbling. I do the illustrations. No bullshit allowed. We tell it like it is."

The idea of making a book of revelations had a certain appeal to Simon. "Why the fuck not?" he said, tempted to tell Chirp about Robert J.'s album. Simon had second thoughts about sharing that information.

When Chirp left to catch his ride home, Simon thought about the amazing drawings. He would have expected caricatures or grotesques with gargoyle faces to flow from Chirp's simmering brain, twisting the population of Glenda High into characters from a horror movie. He and Chirp had spent a lot of hours dissecting that crowd and scattering their leftovers for vulture food. Instead, Chirp made his subjects beautiful; not schmaltzy, not adorable, not cute. Just beautiful. Simon added that news to the box marked You Never Know.

Chirp's multidimensional vision did create a problem for Simon. It would have been reasonably easy to write a series of snotty blurbs to fill balloons rising from zombie or monster cartoon heads but Chirp's work demanded much more—a new set of inner eyes. Simon realized, in an uncomfortable flash, that he'd have to take the kids he enjoyed putting down more seriously. And before that was possible he'd have to take a long look in his own mirror.

For his trial run as an author of meaningful prose, predictably, Simon chose Chirp's quick sketch of Polly Moon. Before he began to write, Simon spent a whole weekend browsing *The Song of Solomon, The Rubaiyat of Omar Khayyam, Rabelais's Adventures of Gargantua and Pantagruel* and his prized collection of Archie Comics.

In Chirp's drawing of Placebo, she sat on a rock somewhere in limbo biting into a slice of pizza, balancing a Coke between her thighs, the expression on her face flickering between Goldie Hawn and Boticelli's Venus-on-a-Half-Shell. Her spiked, day-glo hair looked softer in charcoal, the safety pins that held her blouse together less fearsome in gray, the bat silhouette on her cheek innocent as a shadow, no more menacing than a birthmark.

In Chirp's drawing, Polly Moon's eyes were wide and dreamy, her eyebrows arched into rainbows, as if she'd just caught a glimpse of an approaching lover. Simon wondered who she was loving. Whoever it was, she was making a terrible mistake—her rightful young hart, leaping over mountains of spice, was none other than Apple the Scribe, holding his thesaurus, staring at a naked page, trolling for adjectives suitable to the occasion.

Deadline for presenting term projects to Miss Tabitha Ulman, a fixture for nearly a decade in Glenda High's English Department, was the following Monday. On Sunday afternoon, Chirp called Simon at Quikpix to say he was stuck in bed with a fever, his mother thought it was flu, and asked Simon to carry the ball.

"All I have is the one picture," Simon said, "the one of Polly Moon, and one page of copy. I thought we'd show her more stuff, explain the idea, give some details."

"You do the explaining," Chirp said. "It's an act of God. I feel like a tub of cow shit."

"Just don't die on me," Simon said.

On Tuesday, Chirp was still out of action. Miss Ulman requested an audience with Simon to discuss the material he'd submitted. He went after school expecting Armageddon, which is what he usually got.

Miss Ulman was at her desk reading through a stack of papers when Simon entered her classroom. Before she acknowledged his presence, without looking up from her labors, she gestured him to a front row seat. "Are you nervous?" she said. "I think you are since you're carrying your neck sunk between your shoulders and you're walking in a slouch. Straighten up. Think spine. The spine in a line. Proper posture is the first rule of good health and well-being. Allow your organs full reign, Simon. Alignment of the trunk is essential to relaxation and relaxation is the road to fluid expression. Please sit. I'll be with you momentarily."

Simon sat. He resented being reminded of things like spines, especially his own. He'd long since developed an aversion to X-rays with their intimation of mortality. He didn't appreciate being forced to think about his skeleton or guts. It was the same as a discussion of the ingredients in his favorite foods. The inside story was always worse than the outside story. Besides, Tabitha Ulman was an English teacher, not a professor of anatomy. Her turf was grammar and exposition, not body parts.

Simon waited, watching Miss Ulman work. He noticed that she moved her lips slightly as she read and occasionally let out a sorrowful sigh. When she jotted some note with a thick red pencil she let her own spine bend forward enough to reveal the tops of her breasts and the crease between them that flowed softly into her blouse. Simon sat thinking of the Mississippi River dividing the American continent.

He felt himself blush. He'd never had the slightest inclination to examine Miss Ulman's geography, certainly not to consider her as a sexual object, and there he was noticing how her bosom pressed against her blouse, twin hills on a landscape of flowered rayon. She was up there in age, probably nearly thirty, and even though she was no Marlo Thomas, she was a nice looking woman. He remembered that Chirp once commented favorably on her swift legs and neat behind.

"Now," she said, putting aside a folder, "about your term project. Let me tell you, Simon, that Chirp's illustration and your fragment of text left me baffled."

"It was a first draft. We were going to . . ."

"Please listen, then speak. Did I say baffled? I meant astonished. Astonished and delighted. You two, especially your collaborator, always struck me as distant, a tad hostile or is the better word uncomfortable?"

"I guess you could say a little uncomfortable," Simon said. "But when you get to know us, I guess we're pretty comfortable. We . . ."

"Hush. Chirp Bennet's sketch of Polly Moon told me more about the boy than anything I ever heard him say in class, which wasn't much. I was unprepared for such a display of refined sensibility."

"I know what you mean. When he first showed me his . . ."

"Shush. Which reminded me once again never to judge anyone too quickly. I don't profess to be an art critic but am confident that Chirp is a genuine talent and I trust my instincts."

"That's how I . . ."

"And now we come to Simon Apple's prose. Like most citizens of Glenda, I am not ignorant of your traumatic history. To have overcome such adversity and emerged with the ability to see life clearly and see it plain, as they said of Alexander Pope, is a marvelous and heroic accomplishment. You have the makings of an author."

"Well, thanks Miss Ulman but I don't know if . . ."

"Stop. Never recoil from deserved recognition, Simon. I feel that you are among the few obliged to confront the monstrous gift of talent. Talent is monstrous. It makes terrible demands. It insists on huge sacrifice. The gift can be refused or indulged. That choice is yours. But before you turn your back on such nascent—that's a word you might wish to look up—such nascent ability you must consider the possible rewards you spurn. The incredible pleasure of making the invisible visible, singing songs of enlightenment, venturing into the deepest caves of human experience clutching nothing more than a sputtering candle stub . . ."

"I don't think I'm ready to play in the majors," Simon said.

"Don't dare to trivialize," Miss Ulman said. She grabbed for her cheeks and burst into tears, trembling like a tuning fork. Simon saw her melt like the sputtering candle stub she'd described. He left his seat and ran to her desk wondering if he should yell for help. Instead, he put his arm around her shoulders.

"I didn't mean to upset you," Simon said to Miss Ulman's beehive hairdo. She tilted her head back, pulled Simon toward her and kissed him on the mouth. Her tongue pushed between his teeth. When the kiss ended, Simon pulled away and backed toward the door.

"Don't misunderstand my motives," Miss Ulman said. "I've waited forever for a boy like you. And your partner. To think, Tabitha Ulman discovered two pearls in this oyster of mediocrity. Can you possibly know what I'm saying? Someday you will. Let me be your mentor, your spirit guide, Simon Apple. You and I can work closely together if you'll commit to the effort. And I'll have justified my existence."

"You mean me and Chirp, right? He's one of the two pearls."

"I've already shown his drawing to Mr. Binwasser in the Art Department and he was as excited as I knew he would be. Mr. Binwasser's province is visual. All well and good. Mine is verbal. In the beginning was the word."

"I thought they grunted in the beginning," Simon said.

"It's a biblical reference."

When Miss Ulman said *biblical* her lips moved out on the *bib*, in on the *lic* and pouted on the *al*. "I knew that," Simon said. Old Testament. I'm half Jewish."

That night, Simon conjured Barbara Eden to help him get to sleep. She wore her *I Dream of Jeannie* harem outfit and did everything he asked of her but she kept transforming into Tabitha Ulman, a confusing development. He sent Jeannie back into her bottle and summoned Tina Louise off *Gilligan's Island*. Miss Ulman showed up in her place peeking out from behind the trunks of palm trees.

Simon got out of bed and washed his face with cold water. Sitting on the toilet, he got some relief with a Vulcan maiden he resurrected from a *Star Trek* episode, but that experience was unnerving, what with her pointy ears and mind-melding.

39

Two days later, while he walked briskly toward Quikpix, Simon heard Chirp's voice call his name. The yell came from under a blanket of music—"Some Girls," by the Rolling Stones—pouring out of a red Chevy with a white racing stripe. Chirp was behind the wheel, gesturing for Simon to get in. Simon got in. "What's this about?" Simon said. "I thought you were sick."

"Mama took me to Lourdes," Chirp said. "I am healed, hallelujah. So what happened with our project?"

"Tabitha liked it," Simon said. "She creamed."

"Tabitha?"

"Miss Ulman. She says you're a genius, showed your work to Mr. Binwasser. He thinks you're a black Picasso. I tried to call you three times, no answer. Where the hell have you been besides out stealing cars? So tell me."

"I got my driver's license," Chirp said.

"Bullshit. You're not old enough."

"That's for me to know and them to find out. Here it is—The Chirpmobile. Catch my smiling face. So what do you think, friend? Your honest opinion or at least a beautiful lie."

"You're telling me this is your car? No way."

"It's been my car for a year," Chirp said. "My little baby. A wreck when I rescued her. A '68 Camaro selling wilted flowers from the gutter. Look at my Eliza Dolittle now. She's got it. 327 V8, Cragar wheels, 4-barreled Holley carburetor, Crane performance camshaft, open headers, hood scoop, Hurst shift, and leopard skin seats—is this not a chariot of fire? Man, this vehicle rocks. Listen to that stereo. Feel the bass on your face. The door's ajar so come on in."

Simon got into the passenger seat and ran his hand over the gleaming dashboard.

"Why didn't you tell me you were still alive? I was writing your obit."

"Sorry," Chirp said. "But I was too busy living. Anyway, I can't believe it myself. Chirp Bennet is in the driver's seat. Now all he has to do is get laid before the Commies blow up the world and he'll achieve the American dream. Not a minute too soon. Hang on. We're off to see the wizard." Chirp revved the motor.

"Not now, Dr. Do-As-Little-As-Possible," Simon said. "Got to get downtown. Listen, Mr. Binwasser said to tell you he wants to see some other examples of your doodles. He's going to work with you, she's working with me."

"You're talking Tabitha?"

"I'm talking Miss Ulman."

"Who'd have thought it?" Chirp said, wetting his lips with his tongue.

"Cut that out," Simon said. "She's very nice. Very sincere."

"Excuse me," Chirp said. "But does Miss Ulman have a 4-barreled Holley carburetor?"

"I'm not sure," Simon said

Over the next months, much of Chirp's free time was spent washing the car, spraying Windex on its windows, waxing and polishing its body, rubbing its wheel hubs with Brillo pads.

Simon pressured his reluctant friend to give him driving lessons. It took a lot of persuasion; Chirp winced if Simon so much as burped inside the Camaro. The idea of allowing a neophyte to sit in the driver's seat was unthinkable at first but Chirp finally yielded to Simon's sulks, pleas and outright bribes.

When he had the money, Simon sprung for gas, kicked in for a battery that could power half of Glenda, and gave his instructor a Mick Jagger bobble-head—more chick bait to dangle from the rearview mirror.

The first time Simon ground the gears, Chirp whacked him square on the jaw but Simon had no hard feelings since he'd brought it on himself.

When they weren't taking curves on obscure country roads outside town, Chirp and Simon worked together on their school project. Mr. Binwasser met with his protégé three times a week, offering a mix of criticism, encouragement and humiliation. He spat on Chirp's favorite drawings, ripped up sketches, threw tantrums, gushed praise, lectured on the sanctity of art, forced concentration, pointed the emerging artist in what Mr. Binwasser thought were positive directions. Whatever Mr. Binwasser did, he did catch Chirp's attention. Simon could tell how their sessions went by the way Chirp drove, measured on an automotive scale from madman to maniac.

Simon huddled under Tabitha Ulman's engulfing wings. The pages he brought her were returned looking like wounded soldiers, slashed in red and battered by a black marking pen. She made Simon read E.B. White's manual on basic grammar. She force-fed him stories by Anderson (both Hans Christian and Sherwood), Fitzgerald, Hemingway, Salinger, Balzac, and De Maupassant. She gave him novels by Twain, Melville, Hammett, Roth, Bellow, Flaubert, Dostoyevsky, Tolstoy, poems by Dickinson, Yeats, Jeffers, Cummings, plays by Sophocles and Shakespeare. She made him copy whole chapters by hand, quizzed him on the mysterious transit from felt emotion to cold type, explained subtleties of style and form, forbad him to use a typewriter instead of a pen or pencil because there was no substitute for direct connection from flesh to paper.

Sometimes she poured him hot chocolate from a thermos, topped with a squirt of whipped cream, before sending him through an open door on his way to some new discovery. Miss Ulman gave him a set of rubber letters—the alphabet glued to wooden blocks, along with a stamp pad—hammering home that every book on the school's library shelves traced its heritage to those few symbols. She rhapsodized on the marvels of language and its infinite challenge.

She also gave him spontaneous erections that Simon tried to hide by scrunching in his seat or pacing her classroom facing backward. No woman had fussed so much over Simon Apple since the days of Victoria. He worked his ass off for Tabitha Ulman, tempted to glory; he respected her, adored her, lusted after her. On those rare occasions when his teacher was pleased with a sentence, a paragraph, a turn of phrase, Simon melted to butter. When she'd touch his cheek or fondle his hair to show approval, Simon noticed that her breath would quicken, her cheeks glow like traffic lights in the rain, her nipples pop up, a sight as startling as seeing crocuses burst through snow.

Then there were the silent moments that made the noblest language obsolete and meaningless. Those twenty-six rubber letters in the English alphabet were exposed as only a collection of stale crumbs. Mentor and student dissolved into smoke, drifting and mingling in the afternoon air. The eloquence of shared silence was, curiously, the best muse for inspiration.

Simon, who was fascinated by experiments that made Popsicles out of dead people in the hope that they could be thawed when cures were found for diseases that killed them, imagined what it might be like to be chipped from the tundra like a wooly mammoth, then thawed to sentience. It was like that during his after-school conferences with Miss Ulman. She brought him to life.

When their term project was finished, Chirp and Simon were forever changed. The work was marked A+ (a first for both). Miss Ulman and Mr. Binwasser arranged for its publication in the *Glenda High Annual*.

Author and artist were instant stars. The night the magazine appeared, Chirp scored with Elaine Flink, head cheerleader for the Glenda Eagles. Polly Moon sought out Simon and told him she realized he was a "real person" in a superficial world, a man with "groovy karma." In the past, her words would have been manna. But Simon was already in love and not with Placebo.

40

"We should celebrate your success, Simon," Miss Ulman said after Principal Myron Borg lauded Chirp and Simon's collaboration during assembly. Simon felt edgy being alone with his teacher in the now empty auditorium. He answered in a whisper, in case some student had left a pair of ears behind.

"You could wish me happy birthday," Simon said. "I just turned seventeen. Aren't you supposed to collect two hundred dollars when you pass puberty?"

"Happy birthday, Simon," Miss Ulman said while Simon waited for her nipples to confirm the blessing. "You know, I was thinking how nice it would be to continue our relationship. We do learn from one another."

"I have nothing to teach you," Simon said.

"Not true. This has been a symbiotic association. I was actually about to extend an invitation to dinner at my home. That could involve certain complications. You know how it is here. People talk. And what they say can be based on gross misunderstandings that lead to awful consequences."

"What could be wrong about dinner?" Simon said.

"Nothing. But I could be charged with corrupting the morals of a minor." For the first time Simon heard Tabitha Ulman laugh at her own joke.

"Well, thanks for the thought," Simon said.

"Still, it is your birthday."

"Maybe we could go someplace for a pizza. Out of town. Strangers in the night."

"I suppose we could sneak off," Miss Ulman said. "Pizza and champagne. A cupcake and a candle. A *whoosh* down the road and a wish for good things. Lovely. But I don't have a car."

"A car?" Simon said. "I can get hold of a car." Hearing his voice say that, Simon doubted his sanity.

"Really? You drive?"

"Absolutely. But I can't afford champagne."

"That's my department," Miss Ulman said.

"When are we talking about?" Simon said.

"How about tonight while your birthday is still fresh."

"Tonight," Simon said. "No problem. I could pick you up someplace nobody goes."

"It's a date," Miss Ulman said. She held out a copy of the *Annual* and asked Simon for his autograph.

Simon found Chirp holding court outside the school's main entrance, surrounded by a crowd of admirers. He asked for a private audience. "What's up?" Chirp said.

"Not much," Simon said.

"This is some kind of week," Chirp said. "I'm liking it."

"I noticed. Listen, buddy, I have something to ask you. Prepare for apoplexy."

"I was born prepared for apoplexy," Chirp said. "Speak."

"I need to borrow your car tonight."

"Say *wha?*"

"You heard."

"First of all, your daddy has a car. Your mama has a car. You got uncles and cousins with cars. Second of all, you don't have a driver's license, not even a learner's permit. Third of all, you never soloed in a moving vehicle except maybe for your stroller or on your bike. Fourth of all, I would not lend my wheels to any living thing under any circumstances for any possible reason whatsoever. Say you were late for your exorcism. I would not lend you my car. Tell me you got to pick up a heart for a transplant. I would say tough titty. No and no and absolutely no. There's no exception to this rule. I wouldn't lend Martin Luther King my car, not Jimmy Baldwin or Langston Hughes or Miles Davis. Not Jack or Bobby Kennedy. Not Jesus, not Moses, not Muhammad, not Bobby Dylan or Aretha Franklin. Do you understand my position here?"

"Is that a definite no?"

"I'd say so," Chirp said. "You know how long it took me to get that car? How much self-denial? What indignities I suffered? And when I bought the Camaro it was unfit for human habitation. You have a glimmer how much sweat I put into that machine? Ask me for anything else. But, my man, please do not ask me to lend you my car."

"I wasn't planning to drive to the Grand Canyon," Simon said. "Just a few miles on straight roads. If it was for a transplant or exorcism I'd take the bus. But this is big, Chirp. Enormous. Strictly off the record, a pizza date with Miss Ulman."

"You're joking."

"No joke. Her idea. I have feelings for that girl."

"Girl? That is no girl. That is a fully developed lady. You're walking barefoot on hot coals, Simon. Besides, how many times have you told me you're saving yourself for Polly Moon?"

"I am," Simon said. "In a larger sense. But in the meanwhile, I'm like a meteorite pulled by gravity. I can't help myself. She brought up the pizza. Maybe she just wants to talk. Maybe all we'll do is eat and share a moment together, probably nothing intimate. What have I got to give her besides gratitude? And I am grateful to her. You should be too. We owe her, Chirp."

"If anything but your cherry was under discussion this meeting would be over. Simon, if I am dumb enough to go along with this madness there are a few ground rules. You keep the sainted vehicle for two hours, max. You don't even consider trying to parallel park. If the cops stop you, your story is you got hold of my keys and sneaked the car on your own. I had nothing to do with any of it. If you eat pizza in the front seat you spread napkins everyplace including the rugs on the floor. If, God willing, you make it to the backseat you drape the Turkish towel I keep in the trunk for such occasions. If there's any kind of stain, tomato or otherwise, or even crumbs on the carpet, you not only pay for the cleanup you agree to kill yourself in a slow, agonizing manner and leave a neat note pinned to your shirt saying how you were depressed by racial injustice. Lastly but not leastly, when the car is returned it will have a full tank of gas. High test. Swear."

"I swear."

"On what?"

"My immortal soul."

"Say amen."

"Amen."

"After tonight, I own you," Chirp said.

"By the way, Miss Ulman said she wants your autograph on her copy of the *Annual*."

"She did?" Chirp said. "She really said that?"

Simon arranged to pick up Tabitha Ulman two blocks from her apartment in West Glenda. Chirp left the Camaro parked around the corner from Quikpix in a public lot that was all but deserted after business hours. When Simon found it waiting he broke into a heavy sweat. He let himself in and screwed himself into the sacred driver's seat, blotting his face with a Kleenex.

After five minutes of fear, he turned the ignition key and felt the delicious power surge as eight cylinders made the car shudder. Simon sat enjoying the vibrations. They helped calm him down. Then he depressed the clutch and shifted into first gear, pressed lightly on the gas pedal, clutching the wheel with all his strength. The car actually moved.

Exhilarated, Simon eased out of the lot and turned onto Washington Street before he remembered to switch on the headlights. When those yellow beams fired, Simon realized that he was in control, master of the machine. He shifted smoothly into second, then third, aiming toward a destination so unlikely, so astonishing, his mental gears flicked into overdrive.

He was on the road zipping past familiar landmarks, navigating through traffic, swerving around cloddish trucks, turning left, turning right, following the trail Miss Ulman had mapped in a series of precise instructions Simon had taped to the beautiful, luminous dashboard. And there she was, exactly on the corner where she said she'd be, dependable as the Big Dipper.

Simon saw that his self-proclaimed mentor carried a picnic basket. He was psyched for pizza with pepperoni, anchovies, maybe a few mushrooms trapped in melted cheese. That expectation was quickly dashed. There was no conceivable way Miss Ulman could manipulate a large, sizzling pie into that straw box. As he applied the brake, a wave of disappointment made his salivary glands go dry. He cursed himself for such a crass demonstration of pure gluttony; the important thing was Tabitha Ulman, not bubbling mozzarella with whatever array of savory toppings. That his teacher had taken the time and trouble to prepare a feast along with the promised bottle of champagne more than made up for a puddle of cheese and tomatoes on a soggy crust.

Simon smiled, reached over to open the passenger door,

grinned as Miss Ulman settled into her seat with the basket on her lap. She said, "Well, here we go."

"Where to?" Simon said. "I await your command."

"Straight ahead. I'll tell you where to turn. It's just too nice an evening to sit indoors."

Driving along, Miss Ulman sat quietly for what must have been thirty miles. Simon's blood oath to Chirp limited his outing to two hours. Forty minutes were already history. When the car was returned, aside from checking his watch, Chirp would certainly consult the mileage indicator. Simon wondered how far Miss Ulman planned to travel before she felt safe from local eyeballs.

When she pointed out a dirt road marked Seven Ponds Lane he hoped the pond Miss Ulman had in mind was first, second or third but not seventh. It turned out to be the fifth pond where she directed Simon to stop at the cusp of a crescent-shaped clearing invisible to passing cars.

"This is a wonderful place," she said. "I wanted to share it with you, birthday boy. Because I know you'll appreciate its beauty and solitude."

Simon was listening to the Camaro's Michelin tires grind against pebbles that paved the parking niche, thinking of how little stones sometimes lodged between the treads like seeds between teeth. "It is nice here," he said.

"Are you a hungry author starving in your lonely attic?" Miss Ulman said.

"Famished."

Miss Ulman handed Simon the basket. He followed her through a clump of bushes, around a large rock, past trees heavy with new leaves. When they reached a circle of grass on the bank of that fifth pond she opened the picnic basket, unfolded a thin blanket tucked under its lid, arranged red plastic plates, spoons, knives, cups, and napkins decorated with bluebirds in the blanket's center. From pods of aluminum foil she produced raw carrots, celery strips, snap peas, sliced zucchini and slivers of green pepper. There was a box of French soda crackers, a tub filled with some kind of creamy dip, two containers of yogurt, a wedge of goat cheese, a few slices of ham and a tin of smoked oysters. A bottle of New York State champagne was cradled in a plastic pouch, kept cold on a bed of chipped ice. Lastly,

Miss Ulman came up with a thick candle in a pewter holder and two chocolate cupcakes. "For my young stag," she said.

Squatting on the blanket, Simon rocked the thick wine cork, pushing at its mushroom-shaped cap with both his thumbs. Finally, the liberated cork flew into the night. Simon heard liquid fizz like a genie inside the heavy bottle. Miss Ulman used a metal key to open the tin of smoked oysters. "I never tried those," Simon said, pouring Taylor's champagne into plastic cups. Miss Ulman plucked an oyster from the tin and slid it into his mouth. His tongue tasted a smoky, fishy flavor.

"Some believe oysters have magical powers," Miss Ulman said. "They're considered aphrodisiacs. There's some medical validity since they are rich in phosphorous."

"They taste like tobacco," Simon said. He washed the oyster down, then sampled the tub of dip with a truncated celery stalk. "Guacamole," she said.

"Good," he said.

"Try the yogurt."

"I don't think so, Miss Ulman. I'm not really a yogurt person. I might be allergic."

"It's very healthy. And please, call me Tabby. We're friends now."

"I guess I have a thing about food that starts with a Y, Tabby."

"You're disappointed."

"No," Simon said. "I have these food quirks."

"Well, it's part of my job as your spirit guide to open your mind and heart to new experiences, to help you shuck off ingrained prejudice. It can be something as small as yogurt or as large as ambition. You have the capacity to cross every horizon, conquer any obstacle. When I read your lovely words I sense that you're not like the others. You are a special young man. The whole world is your smoked oyster if you have the courage to seize the day."

"Thanks," Simon said. "I hope you're right. Between us, I don't feel very special. But I do think you're very special. If it wasn't for you I don't know if I would have finished writing anything. I never met a woman like you. This might be the best birthday I ever had."

"How sweet," Tabitha Ulman said. "I'm going to confess something. I have strong feelings for you. Beyond the usual. You shine with luscious energy. Don't laugh at me, Simon Apple, but I envy your future. I think about my own wee life and of the many marvelous adventures ahead of you, Simon, and the myriad of rooms you'll enter. I think about you as if you were a ripening fruit about to let go of its branch. You're destined to make many discoveries during your voyage through the world and break the hearts of many fair maidens along the way. I ask myself, Tabby, how far will Mr. Simon Apple travel? How marvelous will be his triumphs? Will he even remember a whisper of the gentle times we spent together? I see Tabitha Ulman here in Glenda, rooted like a statue, taken for granted, a fly spec on eternity's wall while your path is unlimited. I do sound the fool. This isn't easy to say. Feel how my heart is racing."

She took Simon's hand and placed it on her left breast so that he could feel her thumping heart. Her eyes were closed, her lips parted. Simon leaned across the crudités and kissed her softly. Polly Moon's kiss had been under glass. Technically, this was his first kiss outside the family circle. Simon's head spun.

"Do you have feelings for me?" Tabitha said. "Do you find me attractive? Or am I a wrinkled old prune who belongs in a museum display? A conquest to boast about in the locker room."

"I love you, Miss Ulman," Simon said. "When I touch you, I feel *smarter*. I thought about touching you but I didn't know it would make me feel smarter. A lot smarter. Does that make any sense?"

"Are you a virgin, Simon?"

"That's a hard question to answer. Yes and no It would take some explaining . . ."

"Are you afraid of me?"

"A little, I suppose."

"It's getting chilly out here. Why don't we take our drinks and go to the car. We'll save your cupcake for later."

"The car? You want to go to the car?" Simon said.

In the backseat of the Camaro, Simon was undressed, massaged, primed, and engulfed. He heard his groans mingle with Tabitha Ulman's verdant moans. His shirt unbuttoned, his pants and shorts pulled down to his ankles, he waited while she unwrapped and unrolled a lubricated Trojan, then slipped the rubber cap over his swollen organ. She stripped off her sweater and bra, lifted her skirt, wriggled out of her panty hose and pushed him down onto Chirp's leopard upholstery. He remembered his holy promise to spread a Turkish towel if he managed to get lucky but taking time to open the trunk and find it seemed gauche under the circumstances.

Simon's qualms about accidental spatter were ignored the moment his sex entered Miss Ulman's honeyed tunnel. She moved against his thrusting, in and out, in and out, until he exploded in a deluge. "You are the fountain of youth," she said, panting. "Oh, Simon, my young prince, I thank God we came together after so many eons, through such twists and turns, and how many spins around the universe?"

"I think you turned me from a moth to an eagle," Simon said.

"I hope you realize all this was no more than a dream. Something beautiful for us to cherish forever. One perfect rose of memory sealed in crystal. A treasure nobody else must even suspect."

"Oh, please don't worry on that score. I'm not going tell anybody," Simon said.

"Not even your closest friend?"

"I promise. Scout's honor. No, this goes into a locked box. Strictly private. When we come here it's just you and me."

"We can't do this again. It would be wrong."

"Why?" Simon said. "Is it because you'd probably end up doing time if somebody got wise? Forget it, Tabby. I'm the only witness."

"Nothing to do with that," Miss Ulman said. "Too complicated to parse."

"What's parse?" Simon said.

"Oh, something like dissect. It's a grammatical thing."

"I figured," Simon said.

"You'll understand some day. Some things can only happen once."

"But why only once? Maybe twice? Like an encore?"

"We'll see. Let's get dressed now and finish our yogurt."

"I was wondering if we could stop for a hamburger on the way home?" Simon said.

"I don't think so," Miss Ulman said. She pulled up her panty hose, hooked her bra, hiked her skirt, got into her sweater, slipped into her sandals and got out of the car.

"What a glorious night," she said. "So many stars and the moon is a melon."

Simon, still glowing, coped with the condom dangling with the weight of a few million dazed sperm. Even the slightest drip on the upholstery would be a disaster. He managed to get the rubber off without incident, tossed it out the window, then buttoned his shirt and grabbed for his pants.

Something was wrong.

Simon couldn't bend.

He tried moving. He couldn't move. He was anchored to the Camaro.

"Come make a wonderful wish and blow out your cupcake candle."

Simon twisted in place, trying to push himself up with his arms. His body elevated but his bottom stayed glued to the car's rear seat. His blissful mood dissolved to panic. He searched his memory for anything read or overheard about symptoms involving the rump.

"Simon?"

"Miss Ulman? Tabitha? I'm having a problem."

When the police and firemen responded to an anonymous call from an unknown woman, they found Simon Apple fused to the chassis of a '68 Camaro sedan. He told an officer he'd "borrowed" the vehicle from a friend and driven to Seven Ponds Lane on impulse.

When a team of paramedics tried to pry him loose they discovered that what held him in place was beyond the realm of any known adhesive.

While they fussed over him, Simon Apple tried hard to concentrate on the lovely memory of Miss Ulman's tremulous body. His object was to put aside his own embarrassment and any thoughts of Chirp Bennet's reaction to the news that the right rear door of his car had been ripped off by a rescue team, that the backseat was pried from its foundation by the Jaws of Life, that the gas tank had ruptured spilling a dangerous puddle of fuel and that the muffler detached.

Miss Ulman had explained her predicament while she packed her basket and left in a hurry on foot. Simon encouraged her flight, asking only that she take time to sound some kind of alarm. He'd apologized profusely for the inconvenience she'd suffered. The marvelous woman was a real sport about the unexpected developments, genuinely sympathetic and compassionate, all in keeping with her character. True to her word, she'd summoned help. Simon worried about how Miss Ulman would find her way back to Glenda while a doctor who'd arrived by helicopter examined his nether regions.

"I've never seen anything quite like this," the doctor said. "Except in the case of conjoined twins. This boy appears to be bonded not only with the seat and portions of the trunk and frame but also the drive shaft. There may be some involvement with the transmission as well. Only an extensive scan will tell us. Make no further attempt to free the victim. He can't be cut loose. We'll have to tow the entire unit to Glenda Memorial as quickly as possible. I'll call ahead and warn them. I don't know if the Emergency Room can handle this mass. Maybe they can move some life support to the downstairs garage."

41

At dawn, inside a large tent hastily erected on the hospital lawn, Simon Apple ate a substantial breakfast of ham, eggs, toast and tea with Robert J. sitting behind the Camaro's wheel. "What the hell were you doing out there?"

"Nothing," Simon said, gulping down hot Earl Grey. "You keep asking the same question."

"Why did you tell the police you drove yourself?"

"Because I did."

"Car theft and driving without a license? Those are serious charges, Simon. When I saw Marvin Klipstein he just shook his head. He said the case hinges on extenuating circumstances."

"There was nothing extenuating about the circumstances," Simon said.

"They found a candle in the grass. The wax was still hot. And a cupcake. They're talking about witchcraft."

"I gave myself a birthday party," Simon said. "Sweet seventeen."

"You're sure you were alone?"

"I answered that."

"They found a lipstick. And a condom."

"What do you want me to do, take the Fifth? What's the difference what they found?"

"I'll get the story out of you," Robert J. said.

"When are they going to let me out of here?"

"Dr. Fikel says we're facing serious surgery."

"We?"

"They called in Dr. Martin Feibush from Chicago. He's the only surgeon in history who separated triplets."

"It doesn't matter," Simon said. "I'm dead anyhow. When Chirp Bennet hears what happened to his wheels . . ."

"Was the Negro involved in this?"

"The Negro? Are you referring to my former best friend? No, Chirp wasn't involved but he'll get involved, don't worry about that. You know how he loves this car? Shall I count the ways?"

Under anesthesia, Simon dreamed about Tabitha Ulman. He was walking in a garden when she popped out of a salad bowl filled with weeds. Her head balanced on a fragile stem. Simon bent to sniff her perfumed hair. He heard a buzzing sound. A gigantic bee circled her head. The bee had a human face. It looked like Albert Essman. Simon kept swatting at it with his fist. He was flailing his arms when he woke in a foggy daze. He heard Dr. Fikel congratulate Dr. Feibush on a fabulous piece of work.

"I thought I'd reached my peak with those damn triplets," Dr. Feibush said. "The Medicaid scale for Siamese detachments is pathetic. Six hundred dollars per detachment. That operation ended up costing me money. It's a wise man who said no good deed goes unpunished."

"The story of your skill was on the national news," Dr. Fikel said. "All three networks."

"You could say the publicity was worth something. But there was a downside. After that procedure I had the feeling I'd done it all, that nothing more challenging than a brain tumor would come along. When you called about the Apple boy it was like a shot of adrenalin. Still, I'm glad we weren't dealing with a foreign car. You realize I had to practically reconstruct the Poupart's ligament and restructure the aponeurosis of the obliquus externus abdominus, the inguinal canal, the piriformis, the pectineus and adductor longus, never forgetting the magnus and rectus femurs. The gluteus medius and maximus were no piece of cake, and neither were the sacrum, sacrococcygeus, coccyx, and innominatum, nor the required building some facsimile of a functional ilia, ischia and os pubis. Did I mention the sacral plexus and saphenous vein were wrapped around the sigmoid flexure and caecum, compromising the descending colon and rectum? But what the hell, you never promised me a rose garden."

"But what caused the fusion?" Dr. Fikel said. "There was no evidence of prior trauma."

"That's the $64 question. We may never know. You showed me his record. *Cripthalizine, Nonacripthae, Viloxidril, Aquathaline.* My hunch is that it was some residue of one or all or none of the above. That was some tangle of muscles, tendons and bone. The X-rays reminded me of an Ingmar Bergman movie."

"I've contacted Regis Pharmaceuticals," Dr. Fikel said. "They never encountered a similar case."

"Whatever the genesis, Apple's not out of danger yet. His spine is still linked to a coil from the shock absorber and there's pelvic adhesion to a sliver of brake drum. Frankly, the prognosis is dubious. I'd strongly advise against any further invasive surgery. There's every chance he'll remain bedridden for the rest of his life."

"And the periodic erections?"

"More spasms than erections," Dr. Feibush said. "They might subside in due course. I wouldn't venture to predict. I've done all I can here, Dr. Fikel. He's your patient now. But your mentioning Regis Pharmaceuticals did stir a memory. Back in the forties, when Regis was a start-up company, one of their salespeople came to me touting a drug called *Expeloton.* As I recall, it was developed to help the profession in cases where practitioners leave things like scalpels or scissors lodged in body cavities. Which of us hasn't had that experience? These days, who has the time to take inventory of every gizmo laying around the OR? They claimed *Expeloton* could nudge the immune system to disintegrate metal and facilitate its disposal in fecal matter. The patient actually hears a clank when fragments make contact with the toilet bowl and theoretically, that's the end of it."

"An abrupt ending," Dr. Fikel said.

"We did a few tests. *Expeloton* worked to a point but actual disposal proved to be a problem. Instead of passing through the digestive tract, the disintegrated metal chips burst through the epidermis. Most of the patients hadn't realized a few instruments were left rattling around their insides and we didn't exactly rush to trumpet that information; the malpractice mafia would have had a field day. In most cases we usually shut up about it and even if there are certain aftershocks it takes years for complications to show up. Long after the statute of limitations is past. The Ethics Committee determined that prudence was the better part of valor, to let sleeping dogs lie. For a patient to experience a pair of clamps or a handful of staples jumping out of his belly seemed counterproductive. So we stopped all experiments with *Expeloton*. The Regis people made some attempt to interest the military in the solvent during World War Two, but the costs were prohibitive considering the sheer tonnage of shrapnel carried around by the Purple Heart crowd. Besides, the drug worked better on stainless steel than lead. To my knowledge, *Expeloton* was shelved. I don't know if any samples were stored but you might contact their people. I'm not saying it would do any good here, but what's to lose?"

"*Expeloton*. I'll write that down," Dr. Fikel said.

A month later a phial of *Expeloton* arrived in Glenda packed in dry ice. A note from the Regis Pharmaceuticals Shipping Department, attached to an invoice, acknowledged Dr. Fikel's order noting that it had taken weeks to locate the product. Only a few hundred milligrams had survived from the original batch; those were kept only for archival reference.

The note went on to say that a copy of Dr. Fikel's request had been sent to Regis Van Clay for his personal attention (*Expeloton* had been one of his pet projects) and assured the doctor that Mr. Van Clay would be more than delighted if it proved effective in the case of Simon Apple.

When Regis Van Clay called Dr. Fikel forbidding him to administer *Expeloton* or any other Regis Brand item, including vitamins and cold pills, to the Apple boy, it was too late; Simon had ingested 50 mg, the suggested dose, and immediately lapsed into coma. After a touch-and-go struggle to keep him alive, on the third day after the infusion of *Expeloton,* all remnants of the Camaro were forcibly ejected. The spring had failed to deteriorate sufficiently and propelled Simon out of his bed to the far wall of the hospital tent. It took seven hundred stitches to repair his exit wounds but Simon was left generally intact and free of Camaro debris.

Expeloton
Trade Name: *Sepronalol*
Splinterrific! from Regis Pharmaceuticals, Ltd.

Simon was discharged from Glenda Memorial and sent home for rest and rehabilitation. Marvin Klipstein, Esq., succeeded in having all charges dropped by the court after a plea successfully linking Simon's erratic behavior to his use of *Aquathaline.* Following the verdict, that medication was required to carry a warning of possible hazard to operators of heavy equipment, drivers of passenger vehicles or trucks and women who were or might consider becoming pregnant. In addition, Regis Pharmaceuticals agreed to pay Simon Apple's legal and hospital bills and to provide Chirp Bennet with a new Corvette convertible, all without admitting to any liability or malfeasance. The substantial cost of 50 mg of *Expeloton* was absorbed by its makers after Simon and Robert J. signed a paper agreeing not to press for further compensation. Marvin Klipstein explained to the Apples that proof of *Aquathaline's* involvement in the bizarre bonding was sketchy at best and advised them to accept the Regis offer.

While he recovered, Simon was tutored at home by a series of volunteers recruited by Glenda High under the close supervision of Mrs. Tabitha Binwasser, the former Miss Ulman, who'd unexpectedly eloped to Las Vegas with the art teacher a few weeks earlier. Simon's only contact with Chirp Bennet was a letter that said:

Dear Oedipus, i.e. Motherfucker,

I am glad you're coming along nicely. Someday I hope I can bring myself to visit you in person but not yet. When I think about the Camaro may she rest in peace I get bad cramps followed by the trots. Also, I vomit. My mom put me in therapy and the doctor says it would be better to keep some distance between us until things calm down.

I still consider you my friend on the one hand but then there is the other hand. Your actions violated every oath pledge and promise which leaves me wondering exactly what honor means to you Simon—about as much as a bag of shit is my feeling. I don't know how long my grief will last but when (and if) it ends you'll be the first to know. Meanwhile I try to focus on the good times we had together. By the way my Corvette is a hoot but not the same. It's like when my dog died and my Uncle Al came up with a replacement puppy. Thanks but no thanks!!!!! if you know where I'm coming from.

Sincerely yours,
Guess Who

PS. Why you didn't use the towel as agreed upon between us I can't say and maybe it wouldn't have made any difference but I still feel as if you brought this on yourself not to mention me. But why cry over spilt milk or whatever it is you spilt? Fuck you.

42

Simon recognized the trustee who carried a portable table, a white cloth, paper napkins, a set of plastic utensils with a spatula in place of a knife, plastic party plates, a plastic glass and a lobster bib to the center of his cell.

The chubby, middle-aged convict with a limp and twitchy eyes was Milton Stanwick, formerly an Executive Vice President of Crawford, Tolley and Smythe, the accounting firm that once represented many Fortune 500 companies including Enron, Adelphia and Regis Pharmaceuticals. One of the few white collar predators actually convicted for complicity in the great corporate scandals that burst the hot air balloon of prosperity in the first years of the new millennium, Stanwick had turned state's evidence and copped a plea.

One editorial in the *National Review* called him the Wall Street Jesus, a scapegoat chosen to atone for the sins of his peers. From an interview on *Entertainment Tonight,* Simon knew Stanwick saw himself as a hero of unfettered capitalism. If he'd crunched a few numbers and shredded some documents, he'd acted in reverence to the God of laissez-faire and helped the economy thrive.

Stanwick had expected full vindication and a Presidential pardon. Instead, he was promised lush accommodations in a minimum-security facility and early parole but, media-fucked, he was forced to serve out his full term in a Federal dung hole. He was sustained by the knowledge that for all the indignities and an occasional reaming in the shower room, after a few years he'd return to his ranch in Texas. His personal fortune was intact except for a few million in fines; he'd be embraced by a loyal family and grateful comrades.

The ideal inmate, Stanwick felt his sentence was more unjust than the death penalty decreed for Simon Apple or anyone else. Simon smelled the amiable arrogance behind Stanwick's ballet of self-effacement. Still, Stanwick moved like a penitent just doing his job.

Simon waited, arms folded, while the portable table was snapped open and set with precision as if it would appear in a spread for *House Beautiful.* Stanwick patted down the white cotton table-cloth that would hold Simon Apple's last meal as if he were smoothing his own shriveled soul. He would probably bow before he got his ass out of there.

"You hate me, don't deny it," Stanwick said when he finished setting the table. "If you ask me, it's a classic case of the pot calling the kettle black. Did I force you to invest in mutual funds? Well think of it this way, Mr. Apple. In half the world it's tomorrow. You're already dead on five continents."

"There's a smudge on my coffee cup," Simon said. "Unforgivable. And I never invested in mutual funds."

When the guard came to let Stanwick out, Simon was informed that his two nieces were waiting in the visitor's room to say their farewells. Simon had no nieces he knew about and he wasn't particularly curious to find out who the imposters were. Probably kooks or enterprising reporters. But that table in the center of his cell and the lingering essence of Milton Stanwick gave Simon enough motivation to shrug, nod and hold out his hands to be cuffed.

He was led to the visitors room where one of his hands was freed after the other was securely chained to a metal bench. Through the glass, Simon saw two formidable women stare back at him.

One was built like a Sherman tank with breasts like cannons. She had skin like an armadillo and hands the size of a catcher's mitt. She wore a black leather jumpsuit with buttons like rivets. Her features were heavy but they fell together under close cropped hair in a way that made her strangely attractive, a comic book superbitch.

The other was a wraith who might have been fashioned out of spare parts from a puppet factory. Her hair was topping for a Boston cream pie, her porcelain face as remote and saintly as a stained glass portrait of the Virgin. She wore a cotton dress covered with dragonflies hovering over curled waves. Simon couldn't see below her waist but he wouldn't have been surprised if she dwindled into fog.

"He looks smaller than I thought he was," the first ersatz niece said.

"Like Yul Brynner does," said the puppet. "Or teeny-tiny Dustin Hoffman."

"My name is Belladonna," said the first counterfeit niece.

"I'm Trilby Morning," said the second.

"Why are you here?" Simon said. "You can be perfectly honest, considering the fact that you're my long-lost relations and this conversation is being monitored."

"It's a little hard to explain," Belladonna said. "It's about your Uncle Regis."

"Regis is very important to us," Trilby said. "You could say, he's our best and most loyal client. We're his massage therapists."

"You do know that I'm scheduled for execution in a few hours," Simon said. "If my Uncle Regis sent you to give me a massage, thank him, but I doubt the authorities would allow that even if I was in the mood for your services." He pushed back his chair, ready to head for his cell.

"He didn't send us. We came of our own volition," Belladonna said, clasping her hands in her lap.

"We're so worried about him. He's been acting strangely," Trilby said, shaking her head in a gesture of puzzled despair.

"He came to see us both in the same day," Belladonna said. "For intensive intervention. Very intensive. In the same day."

"The same day," Simon said. "I heard you the first time."

"He usually comes once a month," Trilby said. "And that leaves him exhausted. He is getting on. There's only so much a man can take."

"How shall I put this?" Belladonna said. "The technique I practice is a bit unconventional. It's very physical."

"I can only do so much post-traumatic healing," Trilby said. "Are you following any of this?"

"I'm beginning to catch the scent," Simon said. "If Regis Van Clay is having emotional problems, I'm deeply sorry for him."

"What about us?" Trilby said. "If anything happened to Uncle Regis it would affect our lifestyles in a very negative way. When he found me I was working in a cubicle behind a tattoo parlor."

"What can I do that would guarantee your fiscal stability?" Simon said.

"I can read people," Belladonna said. "Regis tried to convince me that he's a happy man today. It has to do with your execution, Mr. Apple. He was raving about the joy of closure. I wasn't convinced."

"Yes, he seems to believe that after this nasty business is done with he'll be free of stress," Trilby said, licking her lips. "But Regis seemed very stressed. Stress can do damage."

"If I've caused Uncle Regis excessive stress, please make my apologies," Simon said. "I think it's time to end this conversation."

"We were wondering if you'd be willing to opt for cremation and sign your ashes over to us," Trilby said in a burst, bowing her lips. "We'd treat them with every consideration. I own the most gorgeous urn I bought at Sotheby's—a museum piece. It was featured on that *Antiques Roadshow* program. It has a documented provenance. It was commissioned by Marie Antoinette, the Queen of France. The actual Queen of France. It's a classic design that would complement any décor. I was saving it for myself. But I'd be willing to have your ashes placed—"

"Oh shut up, you stupid cunt," Belladonna said. "Listen, Mr. Apple, my thought is that Uncle Regis might like to keep you where he can see you. Possibly in his office or on a mantle at home. For constant reassurance."

"Making certain you're definitely dead would surely lift his spirits," Trilby said, with a schoolgirl smile. "Of course, we'd be willing to pay for all rights."

"In cold cash to your heirs. Or to a favorite charity," Belladonna said with a knowing wink. "Bye-bye estate tax. What if you turn us down? What do they usually do with the bodies? Shovel them into a lime pit?"

"I was planning to be stuffed and mounted," Simon said.

"I can relate to that," Belladonna said. "But it's not very realistic."

"This conversation is getting gross," Trilby said, making a face. "Let's lighten up. Mr. Apple, we have all the papers with us. All you'd have to do is sign on the dotted line. Isn't it better to leave a joyous legacy than just decompose? I suppose they promised you perpetual care for your grave but never count on *perpetual.* I wouldn't."

"I need a few days to think about this," Simon said.

"I thought tonight was the night they throw the switch or whatever it is they do," Trilby said.

"It is," Simon said. "I wish you sweeties had come sooner."

43

Side effects caused by *Expeloton* proved more extensive than first supposed. After nearly a year, Simon Apple's fillings came loose and shot out like bullets. That was no major surprise; the fillings were metallic, made from a silver and mercury amalgam. But a routine sonogram showed that his gall bladder was clogged with sludge and stones the size of golf balls. An unexpected and alarming development.

Shortly after the gall bladder was removed and donated to the Heidelberg Institute for Medical Oddities, it was discovered that Simon's spleen spontaneously shrank to the size of a split pea, detached, passed through his kidneys, entered his bladder, then was excreted into a cup during a urine test ordered by Dr. Fikel.

Expeloton, never expected to produce important profits—car fusion was not a common ailment—didn't merit further testing by Regis. The drug was assigned to a company subsidiary, Luscious Nature, Inc., a top-secret facility where stores of anthrax, smallpox, ebola and plague were kept in an underground vault below a greenhouse where popular medicinal herbs were organically cultivated.

Simon's weakened condition made a return to Glenda High impossible.

His studies continued at home with excellent success. He was graduated with honors. Mrs. Binwasser, swollen with child, brought his diploma to the house. She invited Simon to pat her belly and asked him to wish her well. "If it was a boy I would have named him after you," she said. "But it's a little girl and calling her Simone seemed too pretentious for Glenda. You know how real estate people tell you not to build a palace in a middle class neighborhood? We're going to call her Virginia Brett after Virginia Wolfe and Bret Morrisey."

"Best wishes," Simon said. "And I want you to know, Tabitha, that if you feel any guilt because of what happened between us, please don't because however many parts I lost, it was an experience I'll cherish until I disappear entirely."

"Nothing happened between us," the former Miss Ulman said.

"Right," Simon said. "I forgot."

"You might like to hear that Chirp Bennet got a scholarship to the School of Visual Arts in New York. My husband had something to do with that."

"Excellent," Simon said. "Chirp and I lost contact. It was my fault. I caused him great pain. He came to visit me once but we had nothing to say to one another. He just sat there glowering."

"That's an old, sad story," Mrs. Binwasser said. "Ships that pass in the night."

"Speaking of passing ships, do you ever see Polly Moon? I was expecting her to drop in for old times sake," Simon said.

"Another expatriate. She and the Essman boy formed a rock band. They call themselves Rumplestiltskin's Revenge. I heard they went west."

"Interesting," Simon said, feeling his blood pressure surge.

"And you, Simon? Any plans for college?"

"I'm undecided," Simon said. "The story of my life. Maybe I will head for some college when I feel up to snuff. The honest truth is I'm impatient to sink my teeth into some real experience. I feel too old for school."

"You're still a child."

"So I'm told," Simon said.

"Whatever you do, I'm sure you'll do well," Mrs. Binwasser said. "I'm glad our lives touched. I hope you'll let us hear from you from time to time."

"I will. You taught me how to write great postcards."

Robert J. had Simon's diploma framed and hung it on the wall of his son's bedroom.

While he hammered in a picture hook, he said Dr. Fikel could find no physical reason for Simon's chronic malaise and attributed it to depression brought on by trauma. "What it boils down to is that you've got to muster your inner resources," Robert J. said.

"For a person without a spleen or gall bladder that shouldn't be too hard," Simon said.

"One of my customers is a psychiatrist," Robert J. said. "Dr. Herbert Trobe. His hobby happens to be photography. He takes pictures of creatures with shells and crusts."

"In Glenda?"

"We've got snails," Robert J. said. "And box turtles. All kinds of insects. Besides, he's not from here. He's on staff at Massachusetts General. He comes to visit his mother."

"I don't want to see any psychiatrist who takes pictures of snails," Simon said.

"Dr. Trobe agreed to see you. He's coming over tonight."

"Cancel him."

"Nobody is saying you're crazy. Just that you need help to get back in step. There's no shame in this. I wouldn't go broadcasting it around the neighborhood but seeing a qualified professional for some counseling is a sensible way to go. Some of the most successful people . . ."

"I have nothing to talk about."

"For once in your life, just listen. And don't hurry to blame your mother or Rowena or me for your hang-ups. If you wanted to take driving lessons you should have said so. It's not our fault that you steal cars. You had every advantage."

"That car incident happened ages ago," Simon said. "And there's more to the story than meets the eye. I never stole . . ."

"I didn't mean to bring it up," Robert J. said. "Let bygones be bygones."

"Is anything ever forgotten or forgiven?" Simon said.

Dr. Herbert Trobe found Simon sitting on his bed wearing only a Jerry Garcia T-shirt and boxer shorts. "What's this?" the psychiatrist said, "A juvenile declaration of war or are you making a fashion statement? Well, two can play at that game." Trobe stripped off his shoes, jacket, shirt and pants, folded them neatly, and flopped his corpulent body into a rocking chair where he sat swaying like a metronome.

"I hear you're giving your dad a hard time because you feel misunderstood and neglected or is it overprotected? I forget," Dr. Trobe said. "There are some things you should understand. The older one gets, the closer to death, the harder it is to take young complaints seriously. They begin to seem trivial in the face of one's own downhill slide toward eternity. You have to be there to know what I'm talking about. Robert J. Apple is a man of middle age, dancing through a psychological minefield. With the further burden of satisfying a young wife. He has plenty to think about besides you. Then there's the inevitable dimension of father-son envy I call the flip side of the Oedipus complex. You're driven by a subconscious urge to kill pop and penetrate mom, that's common knowledge. Well, Mr. Oedipus, your father is entitled to his own unconscious drive to stuff you into the disposal and screw your best girl."

"I had a friend who called me Oedipus when he meant motherfucker," Simon said. "I think it was a term of endearment. I know the theory but I can't say my subconscious ever thought much about having sex with my mother. I'm not even sure what she looks like."

Dr. Trobe smoothed down what was left of his hair and scratched at his skimpy beard. "I am a highly respected practitioner, the author of six acclaimed books and protected by tenure. I've been given a sketchy outline of your miserable history as a victim of side effects I suspect to be manifestations more psychologically than pharmacologically induced. Whatever the source of your problems, it's difficult for me to either empathize or sympathize with your turgid behavior—your so-called depression and appalling display of self-pity. In short, it's hard for me to like you. However, I am willing to make the attempt to help you for a vastly reduced fee if you'll agree to meet me halfway."

"I'll give it a try," Simon said. "Where do we start?"

"I'm more Stanislavsky than Freud," Dr. Trobe said. Like the Actor's Studio. Let me reach into my own bag of formative experiences, the kind that make you wince for the rest of your life whenever they come to mind. I did my undergraduate work at an Ivy League university in Massachusetts, a state located just under the Arctic Circle. Winters were so fucking cold up there—the prevailing conceit being that the lower the temperature the higher the academic level—that for the first time I began listening to weather reports and searching for buds like a rabid insect. My fellow students adapted to eternal winter by behaving like lunatics. They learned to ski. They climbed frozen mountains, chipping at blocks of ice. They went fishing through donut holes cut into lakebeds. Their crowning glory was to mount a carnival celebrating December's frigid solstice. Members of fraternities and sororities, already bored with the incestuous intramural fornication that supplemented a pathetic heating system, devoted the remnants of their light-deprived energy to building huge statues of snow. Those graven images were colored with vibrant dyes extracted from large pots of boiled vegetables.

"Each year's Carnival had its theme. In the particular solstice that haunts me, the theme was Fairy Land. Each refrigerated sculpture was of a character familiar from the works of Anderson, Grimm and Disney. At night the statues were lit with floodlights of the kind used outside the theater where the Academy Awards are presented or at the opening of a new supermarket. Most of those statues would have been improved by an early thaw but one, a monolithic Snow White, was gorgeous. Chalk it up to my crystallized brain waves, but I was captivated by Miss White, utterly enchanted by her polar perfection. On a night for the record books—it must have been thirty below zero—I left my dormitory, drawn by some powerful magnet, wearing nothing but a bathrobe. I found a stepladder and carried it out to where Snow White stood regally between the shoemaker with the elves and Cinderella's extended family. I dropped my robe, climbed the ladder naked, embraced that slut of disinterested sherbet and kissed her ruby lips. We stuck together. I couldn't even scream for help because our mouths were glued tight. They wouldn't have found me until spring break if it wasn't for an alert watchman.

Snow White and I had to be transported as a unit to the infirmary and melted apart with buckets of hot water. So, when I heard about your automotive entanglement, I offered my services to your parents." Dr. Trobe genuflected as if he were a priest. "A bit of body language," Trobe said, "to underline my feeling that I'm here out of compassion, empathy, nothing materialistic."

"Like money?" Simon said.

"The statement was rhetorical. It didn't require a snotty comment. Getting back to my little tale of horror, it took me months to shake off the humiliation of that conjuncture. I was trapped in lingering depression and, like you, Simon, refused to leave my room. Then, the evening before I was scheduled to be plugged into a shock treatment dynamo, out of the blue came liberating insight. I realized that I had every right and reason to be depressed. If I'd been anything less than depressed I would have deserved two lobotomies." Dr. Trobe let out a laugh. Simon actually laughed along with him. "I endured six years of intensive psychoanalysis with a traditional Freudian who kept insisting that I'd somehow confused Snow White with Mamie Eisenhower. He'd met my mother and, like you, ruled out any hidden lusting in that direction. It took an eternity to free me from the bondage of inner fantasies and outer indignities. Fortunately for you, Simon, our profession has entered a new age. Are you aware of psychotropic medications? Decades of couch time are about to be replaced by a few easy-to-swallow tablets and by a stroke of luck I've been chosen to experiment with a new example of those marvels, far beyond Miltown or Librium. It's called *Xanelul*. I'm leaving you a month's supply. I think one pill three times a day for four weeks should eliminate any chemical imbalance resulting from life's thuggeries crunching your cortex. Take these tablets seriously and take them on time. Let me know when you feel improved. Or sicker, though there have been no instances of any so-called side effects attributable to *Xanelul*. The doctor produced a small bottle of cerulean blue tablets that could have been mistaken for jewels in the window of Logan's Lapidary on Main Street.

"I want you to know, Simon, that while I may be contemptuous of a coddled complainer like yourself, I do take your discomfort seriously even though it pains me to think of all the warm young pussy waiting to welcome you back to the world while my horizons shrink with every tick of the clock. At least I have a good wife, passable children, my work, enough reason to avoid taking the gas pipe." Dr.

Trobe got back into his clothes. "It's been nice talking to you, Simon. Many of my patients are much less forthcoming."

That evening for the first time since he left Glenda Memorial, Simon Apple came downstairs for dinner. He wore the same outfit he'd worn on his date with Miss Ulman, except for the ruined pants. When Robert J. asked what he and Dr. Trobe had talked about Simon said it was privileged communication.

Before dinner, he swallowed a capsule of *Xanelul* and found himself laughing at the *Evening News* though Peter Jennings reported on a chilling crisis allegedly caused by a flock of migrating cranes NORAD had nearly mistaken for Soviet missiles.

Xanelul
Trade name: *Harpacinimon*
Bliss of mind from Regis Pharmaceuticals

"What's funny about nuclear warheads?" Rowena said. "The joke eludes me."

"It's the whole idea that birds still migrate," Simon said. "In this day and age."

Three weeks later, when Dr. Trobe called to ask about Simon, Robert J. reported an amazing change. "He's upstairs now filling out college applications," Robert J. said. "He seems hopeful, involved, optimistic. He acts like a normal happy young man. Though sometimes my wife and I are puzzled by his unprovoked outbursts of laughter."

"I'm faxing you a refill for the medication I gave him. It's expensive but well worth the price."

"Medication?"

"*Xanelul.* An energizing tranquilizer. Didn't he mention the samples I left?"

"He must have," Robert J. said. "These days my mind is a sieve."

"Keep him on the same dosage. And I would like him to check in every few months. I'm part of a major study on the drug. So far *Xanelul* seems to be remarkably tolerated except for a chronic itch and severe abdominal pain in a very small percentage of users. It could be a life-changing discovery."

"It's amazing what they're coming up with," Robert J. said.

"The irony is, *Xanelul* was originally developed in Europe as an additive to cattle and poultry feed. It was only by sheerest chance that a schizophrenic shepherd ingested a quantity and ended up cured. Some half-assed chemist in Manchester came up with the formula. Now he's making millions. In fact, his pipsqueak company was just acquired by Regis Pharmaceuticals. That's a huge conglomerate. I'm doing a study for them."

"I'm familiar with Regis," Robert J. said. "Do you name your patients?"

"I do include names and basic data on my subjects. If you're concerned about Simon's right to privacy, rest assured that the information is kept confidential. It won't be made available to any third party like an insurance company or employer. Certain government agencies and the World Health Organization might be exceptions but I can't see how that would generate anxiety. No reason for apprehension. Let's not dabble in paranoia, Mr. Apple."

44

"I didn't feel anything," Regis Van Clay said, yawning. "Unstrap me from this board."

"I don't understand," Belladonna said. "Fish hooks in the scrotum attached by piano wire to those remote-controlled toy trucks used to cause you quintessential anguish. Now you're dozing off?" She unbuckled the leather bands holding him in place.

"Try something else. Roll the pineapple over my belly," Regis said, sitting up on the wooden plank.

"That pineapple's spurs are already blunted. What about a tongue in the toaster?"

"Would it be any more effective than toes in the microwave?"

"Everything I say is wrong," Belladonna said. "Maybe I'm having a bad day. Maybe it's you. Do you want to get into the electric eel's tank?"

"That lousy eel's discharge couldn't turn on a nightlight in the nursery," Regis said. "I told you last week to get a new eel."

"You are so cantankerous," Belladonna said. "You're like a different person."

"I came for relief, not criticism. There's a scream bottled inside me. I've got to get rid of it. Hurt me. Earn your money."

"You've put yourself in a bad place for no reason," Belladonna said. "Just because some half-assed shrink in Massachusetts wrote a prescription for your precious *Xanelul* to the Apple grub doesn't guarantee catastrophe. Nothing's happened so far. You said the little incubus had enrolled at some quiet college in St. Paul. Don't make a federal case out of this. It compromises my talent when you make yourself suffer."

"We sent out a moratorium on using any Regis product for Simon Apple including cold pills. That damn shrink don't read his mail."

"What's done is done."

"I need you to lay out a worst case scenario. Tell me about how *Xanelul* will turn Simon Apple to equal parts werewolf and idiot savant. Tell me how that idiot lawyer Klipstein will relish his day in court, how the jury will find me liable in a unanimous verdict, how my stock will plummet when the FDA forces me to print a skull and crossbones on every *Xanelul* capsule. Explain how it will tumble down a black hole like *Expeloton*. Spare no details. I need to develop immunities."

"I'm not very verbal," Belladonna said.

"It doesn't matter. You couldn't rattle my confidence because when it comes to *Xanelul* we're happy in our castle, surrounded by a moat filled with boiling bilge. Based on projections following the FDA's green light—you have to understand that the Office of New Drugs and the Office of Drug Safety are safely in my corner and we're already into a positive Figure Study—*Xanelul* promises to account for 32 percent of our earnings and we expect the figure to easily triple within five years. Is four dollars a dose excessive? Not if millions are crazy enough to pay for a semblance of sanity in this cockamamie era. And do they care if a pill costs me four-point-three cents to make out of Irish cow flop? It would have been three-point-five cents if I didn't personally insist on the classy purple coloring and the rainbow-shaped dispenser." Regis swallowed a phantom pill in pantomime then grinned like Howdy Doody. "Who cares if we mix the junk in slightly rusty oil drums? Is it my fault we get a tax break for moving our factory to Puerto Rico? What was I supposed to do about some stupid rumors? So what if some shit collecting two-leaf clover says a few of our cattle went bananas in Ireland? Who'll swallow that dribble? Hell, those people believe in leprechauns."

"You're apologizing for yourself, Regis," Belladonna said. "You're more conflicted than usual. When you come here you should know what a rat's clit you are, no ifs, ands or buts. Why don't you go see Trilby Morning? Let Little Miss Fluffy Muff sprinkle glitter on her Mound of Venus and tell you how Regis Van Clay is the second coming and what a shame it is that some undergraduate pimple will topple his empire."

"No," Regis said. "I need pain, not praise. Don't fail me, Belladonna."

"I could try rubbing jalapeno paste on your foreskin," Belladonna said.

"What are you running here, a kindergarten?" Regis said.

"Why don't you just have the sonofabitch killed?" Belladonna said.

"Funny," Regis said. "That's what my wife suggested."

45

With the help of *Xanelul* aka *Harpacinimon* and long-distance encouragement from Dr. Herbert Trobe, Simon breezed through his years at sedate Celadon College in St. Paul. He absorbed the lessons of civilizations past and present with relish on his way to a degree in Liberal Arts.

No single subject interested him more than another. He chose to major in Twentieth Century American Literature with a minor in City Planning because he was required to major and minor in something. He found reading fiction the quickest path to learning and approved of the idea of cities, especially their hidden infrastructures, the pipes and wires that allowed urban life to flourish.

His writing talent, first wakened by Tabitha Ulman, matured into long reports scrupulously researched in the library and in an occasional Op Ed piece for the school newspaper, but Simon had no urge to compose anything like a novel or even a poem.

Xanelul left Simon even-tempered, in control, often smiling.

He had many friends and no friends. He dealt with people as if he were sniffing flowers in a strange garden. Simon was entirely aware of the quakes and rumblings that caused others to march, protesting or endorsing some local or national issue, of shattered romances that knotted the hearts of his dormitory mates, of the fads and fashions that popped up like mushrooms in the fertile ground of young exuberance, but he went his own way, never completely alienated but always willingly apart. Simon remembered that in his early years separation seemed a curse. Now he viewed it as a blessing. What he described as his policy of social solitude was a perfectly suitable path to peace.

Once, an alumnus who'd achieved fame as the host of a daytime television show returned to the Celadon campus as a guest speaker in a symposium on *Popular Culture: America's Greatest Export*. During the Q&A that followed his talk, one frisky coed asked him how it felt to be universally recognized here and abroad. The celebrity said he would trade fame and fortune for anonymity. "I wish I had the moxie to have my face deconstructed and rebuilt by a plastic surgeon who specialized in anonymity," he told her. "Just for argument's sake, suppose I was in this bar and met this girl. Is there any way I could take her up to my room for a glass of wine and a roll on the bearskin rug without tabloid flashbulbs exploding through the window?"

While the audience laughed, Simon sat quietly feeling nothing but sadness for the hypothetical girl and her universally recognized seducer. The experience affirmed his belief in neutrality and confirmed his affection for backup singers on music videos whose names and faces would never be known.

On trips back to Glenda, Robert J. quizzed him about a choice of profession; Rowena asked if he'd met "that someone special." Simon swung the conversation around to some book or movie, whichever came to mind. Or he talked about the intricacies of sewer systems, waste management and landfill. Simon was expert at using what he'd learned for the practical purpose of straight-arming any potential tackler before he got tangled in the pile.

Halfway through his junior year Simon got a nickname: The Ancient Mariner. His christening derived from an incident in a sci-

ence class when the professor asked his flock to predict some outlandish development that might change life in time for the new millennium. Simon talked about the possibilities of technology discovering some alternative to fossil fuel or atoms as an energy source.
Remembering back to an article in the *Encyclopedia Britannica*,
Simon predicted the development of solar cells. The professor
informed him that tapping into sun power was not exactly a new
technology. "If your generation kept up with life beyond 'Bette Davis
Eyes,' you might know something useful," the professor said. "And I
might *get some* satisfaction, from my profession. But it's probably too
late for your generation. Or is it degeneration? You're happily mired
in ignorance. The Chinese and Indians are going to cream us."

That night Simon called home and found out the family's second hand *Britannica* dated back to the 1940s.

He explained his obsolete discourse on solar energy to the professor before their next session, not expecting his story would be
repeated to the whole class with the professor's admonition that
"There's an important lesson to be learned here. Built-in obsoles-
cence isn't limited to washing machines and automobiles. Reference
books are subject to the same corruption. Mr. Apple, if you're interested in harnessing new energy sources, consider how young ladies
sitting on stools at soda fountain counters swing their legs back and
forth, forth and back. If that potential wattage could be channeled,
the entire planet would glow like a Christmas ornament. So what do
we do? We replace the soda fountains with shelves for more useless
products. How many volts and ohms are being squandered right
down the street? Please don't accuse me of sexism. I'm trying to
make a point. Creative is not a synonym for exotic."

When word of his senile encyclopedia reference got around,
The Ancient half of Simon's nickname was immediately established.
The Mariner part came when a girl whose advances Simon ignored
told her friends that he gave her hives, that his eyes drifted, that they
never made contact, that Simon Apple was like Sinbad the Sailor
looking for shore.

Simon was pleased with the Ancient Mariner name tag; it was
exactly the image he had of himself—an old sailor weathered by
gales, drifting toward some shore or other without hullabaloo. The

catchy nickname gave him enough campus notoriety to prove his existence to himself and a few others without the inconvenient startle of flashbulbs.

46

Simon realized how close he'd come to being saddled with another nickname, some terrible label like Ducky Lucky. In his freshman year he'd escaped early death several times from a series of unexplained accidents. Once a gargoyle fell from the chapel roof and missed hitting him only because he'd stopped abruptly to tie a shoelace. Not long after that, a moose head tumbled from its mounting on the wall of the library reading room spearing Simon's chair with its massive antlers. Seconds before, Simon had left his place to get himself a drink from the water fountain. A week later, an abandoned van rolled down a steep grade and crushed Simon's bicycle. Before impact, he'd jumped off the bike with the intention of adjusting its seat to protect himself from crotch rash. When flames shot out of a socket behind Simon's bed and set fire to his mattress in the middle of the night, Simon dodged disaster because he'd fallen asleep in the study room cramming for an exam. After the alarm sounded, and by the time Simon stomped out the flames on his blanket and sheet, his bed and mattress were transformed to a pile of sticks and embers.

An investigation of the fire suggested that the socket showed possible signs of deliberate tampering. The blaze went on record as suspicious. Simon was asked by the police if he had anything against the college or any known enemies. He assured the investigators he felt nothing but affection for the college and had no knowledge of enemies.

Ms. Shelby Spaulding, already a senior, founder and president of the Wicca Society, a sympathetic girl Simon respected for her thoughtful comments in a speech about *Affirmative Passivity—The New Feminism*, told him his so-called accidents might be the work of a poltergeist. "All the signs are there," Shelby said, "and we're ready to help."

"I'm not big on poltergeists," Simon said. "Not into Tarot or I Ching or Voodoo, but I appreciate your offer."

"There's a full moon tonight. I invite you to join us as we gather to greet her. It's a nice ceremony and the moon ends up owing us a favor in return for our hospitality. The Wiccans can use that favor to chase away your tormentor."

"I don't have a tormentor," Simon said. "What I have is a series of coincidences."

"There are no accidents, no coincidences," Shelby said. "There's only synchronicity. And powerful forces for good and evil at work all around us. Open your mind to new experiences, Simon. It's what secondary education is about."

That night, Simon stood wrapped in a toga made from his fire-ravaged sheet. Except for a few gaping holes and charcoal stains, that sheet was still usable. The fresh linens he'd requested from Rowena hadn't yet arrived. There was enough left of the burned sheet to cover most of the army cot that replaced the lost bed, more than enough to preserve Simon's modesty as he went to greet the moon.

Robed in white shifts, the good witches of Celadon College circled a skeptical Simon, their heads thrown back, their voices humming at a star-speckled sky. When the round moon revealed herself, sliding from behind a cloudbank, President Spaulding raised her arms as the Wicca maidens let their togas fall, joined hands, then knelt on the grassy turf. Simon took a quick survey of the variety of bodies surrounding him: thin ones, fat ones, middle-sized ones, each equipped with breasts of amazingly various shapes and sizes. Every moonchild was decorated with a unique tuft of pubic hair ranging from wispy to lavish. Simon had the secular thought that the pudenda might be a viable alternative to fingerprints for identifying unknown victims who happened to be armless.

The sweet natured Wiccans came to embrace him one by one, the last being Shelby who did a dance in the style of Martha Graham, then declared Simon sprite-free. The girls applauded, then dressed and dispersed.

"Was that so bad?" Shelby said. "How do you feel?"

"I feel good," Simon said. "That's a nice religion you've got there."

"Do you like my body, Simon?" Shelby said. He remembered Miss Ulman asking a similar question. "You know, men's eyes are better than mirrors for revealing truth."

"That's arguable," Simon said. "But yes, I like your body, Shelby." He was pretty sure he remembered which body was Shelby's, the one with the curly pubes.

They walked together to a small park where a statue of Romulus Celadon stood facing the college he'd endowed. "That sculpture is a Zerminsky," Shelby said. "You know Voltan Zerminsky? This is one of his first commissioned works. It's worth a small fortune now."

"You know everything, Simon said. "You belong on *Jeopardy.*"

"We could have sex," Shelby said. "It would probably be a good idea. It might please the moon and add dimension to the ritual. But you can't fall in love with me. Not unless you'd consider going to live in New Zealand. Because that's where I'm going. Are you aware that when the terminal war starts, wind currents will carry radiation everyplace but New Zealand?"

"You think there'll be a war?"

"With all the mental beanbags waiting to press pretty red buttons, how can you doubt it?"

"Well if you're right, one of their missiles will probably end up in New Zealand. A little miscalculation, something like that. Collateral damage."

"It's better than living in a bulls eye. At ground zero. You know we keep our missile silos only a few hundred miles from here. So, tell me, do you want to hold me?"

"Under the Zerminsky?"

"Yes, in the daisy patch."

"I never thought much about New Zealand," Simon said, balancing temptation against apprehension.

"You seem tense," Shelby said. "Is it performance anxiety? Is it because I'm taller than you?"

Simon wasn't concerned with his performance or Shelby's dimensions. His problem was more complicated: Neither Dr. Fikel nor Dr. Trobe could guarantee that he was completely cured of any tendency to postcoital adhesion exaggerated by things metallic. The Zerminsky was solid bronze. There was a definite possibility of repeating the Camaro fiasco.

Because of that uncertainty, Simon hadn't allowed himself to think about conjugating since his prolonged stay at Glenda Memorial but there was no graceful way to say no to Shelby Spaulding. A woman might choose to reject a man's advances, but not vice versa.

He did ask Shelby to change her mind about the daisy patch since the Zerminsky looked too much like his father. She was entirely agreeable. They found a nearby pallet of deep grass behind a wall of privet.

Simon Apple and Shelby Spaulding lay together under the huge moon and things went very well. "Are you set on New Zealand?" he said between couplings.

"If it gets too crowded, there's Tasmania," Shelby said.

Later, back in his dormitory, ready to gloat, Simon called Dr. Herbert Trobe long distance to tell him about the poltergeist business, his submitting to the Wicca brigade, and mostly about his multiple mergings fairly near the statue of Romulus Celadon. "I didn't even pick up a splinter," Simon said, "Not so much as a bottle cap."

"Frankly, you sound too excited," Dr. Trobe said, then doubled Simon's daily dose of *Xanelul.*

After Shelby graduated, Simon was celibate for the next three years. The *Xanelul* aka *Harpacinimon* kept him free of carnal thoughts. He couldn't swear it was the moon but he remained accident free.

47

In the balmy spring of his senior year, on the night Daylight Savings Time went into effect, Simon prepared for the time change by going to sleep an hour earlier than usual.

Because of *Xanelul* he'd become addicted to his dream life. One bonus of the drug was to transform the theater of night into a house of magic; he'd been having a series of delectable dreams in the deepest dark and did not want a whole hour gouged from that pleasure. An extra sixty minutes of daylight was hardly an acceptable tradeoff, even for one sleep cycle.

That particular night of time's abrupt advance was destined to become mythic in the history of Celadon College.

At three—formerly two—A.M. Simon found himself zipping like a darning needle across the artificial border that fractures the unity of all places, people, things. His *Xanelul* dreams allowed him to explore the infinite spectrum of time and tide. Each dream presented him with a stunning challenge he'd have to overcome before being allowed the privilege of another morning.

Simon usually settled on an identity and a quest within seconds after sleep, but on the night in question he hovered in a cloud of indecision, hesitant to commit, impatient, and frustrated by his reluctance.

The choice of a suitable role was made for him, very different from his usual exotic creations. He was himself, sitting alone in a huge concert hall looking down at an empty stage lit only by a single hanging bulb. An unknown man came striding into Simon's dreamscape, disrupting its expected symmetry. Simon sensed that the stranger was some kind of undefined threat. Dressed in a formal outfit, the man removed a curious musical instrument from a case covered in alligator skin. Simon winced when he realized that the instrument's strings were alive, twitching and swaying like stretched snakes.

The man announced that he was called The Minstrel and had been called to play and sing for Simon's exclusive enjoyment, then began to pluck at the writhing instrument. The Minstrel tweaked reluctant strings that made amazingly sweet music despite their constant squirming, snapping and loud whispers of complaint. Then The Minstrel sang a ballad about a brutal, endless war between two nations whose people were identical images of one another. The lyric explained that the enemies were actually mirrors with flesh of fragile reflecting glass.

Gray, smoky clouds left The Minstrel's mouth as he sang. Those clouds filled hollow space between the ceiling of sky and the hard, polished wood of the concert stage. The clouds gave way to The Minstrel's song; his words and music hung like a curtain.

The Minstrel's song of epic battles, with riffs that told of grand heroics, suddenly changed from a hymn of praise to a nonsensical cacophony of comical couplets. The Minstrel grabbed at his throat trying to silence himself but his rebel voice persisted in making a mockery of victors and vanquished, the wounded, dying and dead. The runaway voice flailed at the stupidity of even the most heroic and noble foot soldiers, the cupidity of their leaders, the ridiculous architectural arrogance of castles crumbling under withering cannon fire while kings and queens fornicated in puddles of blood that glowed in green phosphorescent light from catapulted flares.

Now the helpless Minstrel was attacked by the wriggling strings of his own instrument. He was being slowly strangled center stage.

Simon had enough of that performance. He struggled to find a quick exit from a dream that had become a nightmare, an especially disturbing turn of events since he'd gone to bed early with opposite expectations.

He left his aisle seat and dashed for the nearest door, rushing toward what he gradually recognized as his room lit by dawn's early light. Relieved to be done with such feral entertainment, Simon yawned, got up and pissed a bucketful.

He didn't yet know that he was the only resident of Celadon College who'd managed to get any rest that night.

At the precise moment The Minstrel made his debut in Simon's head, other sleepers on the Celadon campus were wakened by ethereal, high-pitched music unlike any they'd ever heard. It was discordant but oddly compelling; there was no perceptible melody, no easily traceable tune, no obvious association with any familiar source.

The eerie concert began gently with chimes carried like snowflakes and feathers on the gentlest breeze. Chords entwined into a harmony subtle as the echoes of fermented fruit in the finest wine. Soon the music changed to a piercing organic wail like the howl of famished wolves. Then came booming drums that vibrated the ivy-covered bricks of Celadon's gothic buildings. Branches of the maples, oaks and dogwoods that shaded its paths, swayed and bent like the limbs of modern dancers.

Lights blazed in window after window where students and faculty members, their own dreams disbursed, peered into the darkness seeking the phantom orchestra that wandered onto the college grounds. The security guards who patrolled Celadon's perimeters began a search for perpetrators of what they believed to be a colossal practical joke. When they found no sign of any pranksters, they looked for hidden loudspeakers or suspicious wires inside clusters of rhododendrons, creeping carpets of hostis, hedges of yews, and banks of puff ball hydrangea.

The music stopped abruptly at sunrise.

48

The next day, that music was the subject of every conversation between sleep-deprived citizens of Celadon College as they staggered between classes. Simon overheard several of those conversations and—not atypical for a Liberal Arts major—actually found himself participating in a few without having the slightest idea of what caused all the commotion.

He quickly picked up on the fact that some errant nighttime noise had roiled students, instructors and professors. Simon wondered if that same interference had corrupted his formerly soothing and indulgent dream life though he'd heard nothing.

"I can't believe you slept through all that," Gerald Warren, a bassoonist with Celadon's marching band whose room was across the hall from Simon's, said, "You missed an incredible experience. It must have come from some mix of wind chimes, a Moog Synthesizer, maybe a Theramin. It was beautiful and strange, entirely global, an amalgam of liturgical, klezmer, baroque, folk, and Sousa. The kind of sounds you might expect if a Marilyn Monroe was singing Happy Birthday, Mr. President from inside a garbage disposal. Authentic, eerie, hypnotic, slightly disgusting, and you could say a trifle upbeat."

"Maybe it came from a troubled owl," Simon said. "Or what they used to call the Music of the Spheres. Planets rubbing together, something like that. Maybe a hot rod flying saucer cruised over Celadon with its portholes open. You should have taped it."

"I tried. My batteries flaked out. Wouldn't you know it."

"There might be an encore," Simon said.

"It was loud enough to wake a corpse," Gerald said. "I can't understand how you didn't hear anything. You better have your ears checked. "

What had been dubbed *The Windchime Concerto* repeated that very night; the music began at the identical ungodly hour of its first performance. This time, Gerald Warren had his tape recorder ready. He ran across the dormitory hallway and pounded on Simon Apple's door.

"Ancient Mariner, your prediction was right on target," Gerald roared. "We're being treated to an encore. What the fuck does it take to wake you? Get the hell out of the sack. Stick your head out the window. Get with it. Feel the vibes."

Simon was glad to be jolted awake by Gerald's thick voice. In his dream, The Minstrel had materialized again. This time, Simon found himself bottled inside The Minstrel's skin. It had the plastic texture of a *Xanelul* capsule. Gerald's yelling split the wall that held Simon captive and let him break free. Half awake, he shook off left-over dream lint and went to the door where Gerald was pounding. "What encore?"

"It just stopped cold," Gerald said. "Only a second ago it came on like gangbusters. I caught the overture. Gorgeous. Then the minute you came to the door, nothing."

"Could I go back to bed now?" Simon said. "I didn't hear any-thing."

"Which is really peculiar because it sounded to me like Rampal, Spike Jones and the Borah Minovitch Harmonica Rascals were hav-ing a convention in your room. Are you up to some shenanigans?"

"I was fast asleep, you crazy bastard."

"Whatever you say."

A half-hour later, the music began again. This time, following a wild hunch, Gerald Warren carried his recorder toward Simon Apple's room and watched its volume needle spin like a compass in the Bermuda Triangle. When he got to the door Warren turned its knob. A groggy Simon had left it unlocked.

Inside, Warren saw Simon sleeping on his belly across from a wide-open window. His arms embraced a pillow, his body arched like a bridge with his behind at its apex.

While Simon's top half wheezed and snorted like a baby with a stuffed nose, his bottom half played The Minstrel's dulcet score. When it came time for the climactic chaos of the finale, like the last act in a fireworks display, Simon's stomach gurgled the cue for what became a series of humongous farts in merciless machine-gun cadence.

That barrage even woke Simon. He saw Gerald Warren (the bassoonist, backed flat against his bookcase) plugging his ears, simultaneously pinching his nose—an acrobatic that involved both hands. In the process, he'd dropped his tape recorder onto the floor but its spindles still spun. "All that beauty, all that majesty is *anal!*" Warren said. "No wonder your gut is rioting. You're digesting Mozart, Wagner, George Gershwin, the Rolling Stones, Philip Glass, Johnny Cash, even Vivaldi and a few lesser artists from the Baroque period."

Because of Gerald Warren's ranting and the audiocassette he offered in evidence, Simon Apple had agreed to an examination by Celadon's attending nurse. A few hours later, when his test results were in, Simon sat across a massive desk facing Dean Abraham Squandor, assistant to Celadon's chancellor, who studied a scribbled report from the infirmary.

"It seems she found nothing unusual," Dean Squandor said. "Though there was some indication of a slight deviation in the sphincter."

"I don't understand any of this," Simon said. "Why am I here?"

"There were significant disturbances last night and the night before that made sleep impossible within a five-block radius of this building. And the finger points to you as its source."

"That nurse's finger inside a rubber glove?"

"Let's avoid a defensive posture, Apple. I have no wish to sound confrontational, only to examine Mr. Warren's accusations. This is exam week. As you well know, whole careers turn on test performance, including your own. I'm sure you understand why we can't abide another interruption of what I will call campus solitude after ten o'clock."

"I never heard the music you just played for me," Simon said. "Gerald Warren is a nice guy who I hardly know. Last night I found him hysterical in my room making insane statements about my anus. It seems to me you should be talking to him. Instead of probing my sphincter, you should be examining his head."

"More than one witness stated that the music in question came from the general direction of your dormitory. And let me add that while the composition was universally admired, except by the most traditional classicists who described it as simply eclectic, many felt the melody was excessively provocative. Sexually provocative, Mr. Apple. At this juncture, I blame you for nothing. Please consider my position. I could suggest that you commit to a battery of sophisticated tests at an accredited clinic to confirm or deny your, let's call it, unique talent. If those tests proved positive, you could assert your right to special treatment as a disabled person under strict guidelines provided by the Federal Government."

"Disabled? By what disability?"

"Some perverse need to seek attention through a kind of gastronomical aberration resulting in uncontrollable rectal recital, I suppose," Dean Squandor said. "In which case, our beloved Celadon College would be required to build a soundproof facility for your exclusive use. We are not a hugely endowed institution, Mr. Apple, and the cost of providing such accommodation would be prohibitive. We're already facing serious shortfalls in construction costs for our new football stadium. As alternative to such a disheartening series of events, I'm prepared to make you the following offer: If you will agree to remove yourself from this campus, we would consent to eliminating all requirements related to your pursuit of a Bachelor of Arts degree. In short, we will give you your diploma. Cum Laude."

"I could skip my finals?"

"Absolutely. There is one more condition. We feel that Celadon College is entitled to all rights to *The Windchime Concerto*. Considering the disturbance you've caused."

"Be my guest," Simon said. "I wouldn't feel right about profiting from creative farting. If I leave now I get my degree with honors and I'd be entitled to attend graduation? It means a lot to my family."

"That would be possible. Though you should realize that Mr. Warren has not been very discreet about his so-called discovery of what he calls your intestinal genius. There might be some harassment from the less evolved."

"They might heckle me?"

"That's likely and probably unavoidable."

"I've been there before," Simon said.

"Let me know if you accept my offer before this evening," Dean

Squandor said. "We don't want further disturbance. And if you refuse my offer, remember please that I could have you expelled for encouraging lewd and licentious behavior."

"*Summa* Cum Laude," Simon said.

"Agreed."

Simon rushed out of the Dean's office and took long, deep breaths of spring air. He felt the urgent need to talk with someone understanding. He called Dr. Herbert Trobe in Boston.

"I was afraid of this," Dr. Trobe said.

"Afraid of what?"

"We've had other reports of a quasi-musical reaction to *Xanelul*. Nothing remotely as ripe as yours, Simon. At most, only a few bars, single choruses, some tunes hardly more melodic than a police whistle. But there have been incidents. I want you off *Xanelul* immediately. I'm faxing a prescription for thirty milligram tablets of a new non-resonant anti-spasmodic dispersion formula called *Solacitrex*. It should inhibit the worst of your emissions. Your colonic stereo should unplug within a few weeks. Or months. However, I do want to alert you about potential symptoms from the sudden withdrawal of *Xanelul*. Watch for mood changes. Avoid stress. And I thank you, Simon, for helping me make a difficult decision. I'm going to strongly recommend that *Xanelul* carry the warning of a potentially serious side effect—*Atonal Cacophonic Analopathy*. On that other matter if I were in your shoes, I'd accept Dean Squandor's offer."

Simon rubbed his temples. "So what do I do besides avoid mood changes and stress until the *Solacitrex* kicks in? I can't stay awake for weeks or months. If I go home to Glenda, I might give the whole town insomnia."

"I'll see to it that Regis Pharmaceuticals picks up the cost of a trip to someplace nice, someplace where you won't disturb another living soul during rehab. Someplace where they appreciate New Age sounds. Come to think of it, I can only recommend one such place with absolute confidence. New York. The city never sleeps so what's another series of sonic booms, eh? Take your *Solacitrex* religiously— I'll send you some blank prescription pages for you to use as needed for refills. Please keep me posted about your progress. And send me a copy of that tape you mentioned."

"New York," Simon said to himself as if he were talking about a dragon.

Solacitrex
Trade Name: *Silentush*
Sweet dreams from Regis Pharmaceuticals

49

Regis Van Clay sat on the cool steps of the Lincoln Memorial gazing up at the pensive pale face and sad wise eyes of the president. Regis looked around to see that nobody was within earshot.

"So, Abe, you made it onto a postage stamp, you got your face stamped on a copper penny and a paper five-dollar bill," Regis said. "The bad news is they also put Donald Duck on a stamp. A penny can't get itself picked up off the sidewalk or buy a wish in a soda fountain and you know what a fiver's worth today?"

There was a lot disturbing about the statue's body language and detached expression. It told Regis how much the marbleized Lincoln knew about the elation of victory and the awful cost of Civil War. That sullen face showed that every bleeding wound and rotting corpse, every accusing ghost of a fallen soldier shriveled his soul. The end of slavery was partial justification for so much destruction, but only a glorious future could offer sufficient reparation for all that carnage.

Regis could see that any peace Abe Lincoln's own lanky ghost might know would come from an America so grand, so powerful as to shine forever as the world's cradle of hope. "How ironic," Regis said to the colossus, "that only a mile from where you sit a huge bureaucracy conspires to mock that very vision."

Regis imagined himself sitting comfortably beside America's icon, certainly a seat he'd earned, with his arm around Lincoln's bony shoulders. He could almost hear the pair commiserate over the foibles of senators and representatives, toadies and lackeys, secretaries and commissioners, lobbyists and reporters tainted by the twisted liberal notion that salvation lay in regulation, that the minds of the best and brightest be encased in condoms of restraint. "We grownups know that the foundation of democracy is capitalism," Regis said. "Its cornerstone is profit. To inhibit profit through restrictive laws eviscerates the beautiful body of Lady Liberty. Inflicting such laws in the name of some public good is the ultimate crime against humanity.

"Take my case as a prime example. Every day I face an ultimate dilemma. Regis Pharmaceuticals is in a race to market some life saving product before some foreign competition snatches away the prize. But wait! Before we can milk the golden calf, I suppose I should say cow, we're forced to surmount impossible barriers, climb Everests of paperwork, endure endless studies, terminal testing, then retesting, then testing the testers. Before we can trumpet the news of a new balm in Gilead, offer solace to the afflicted masses at a fair price, we're further plagued by the curse of excessive disclosure. We must taint every package with a warning label that details any possible side effect, however obscure, that might, just might, affect some troll living under a bridge in North Dakota.

"To advertise everything from corn plasters to remedies for gastroenteritis, antiwrinkle creams to enemies of jock itch, vaginal lubricants to laxatives, therapies for cancer to muscle-building tonics, there must be a list of alerts and alarms displayed in print or recited in television commercials. We're compelled to squander immense amounts of time and money frightening our best consumers.

"Tell me, Mr. President, is there anything good in life without a possibly harmful side effect? Isn't progress a trade-off between benefit and risk? Take the Union you saved. Did you expect that majestic word to end up on the banner of the AFL, CIO, UMW, or, God help us, Actors Equity, the Writers Guild, the Teamsters—the list goes on *ad infinitum?*

"You and I, Mr. Lincoln, are in the same boat. You sit there looking like you just may have welcomed the bullet that gave you release. Well, Sir, don't think Regis Van Clay hasn't considered assassination as an enviable end to his own earthly bondage. But frankly, without sounding vain, my existence is simply too important to terminate. Regis Pharmaceuticals employs 246,000 workers on six continents.

"You agonize over the deaths of a handful of young warriors? Right now, in puddles of African sludge, tropical South American swamps, offal piles in Asia, lord knows what shit holes in Europe, the Middle East, those imploding Commie countries, maybe even in an ice chip from a melting arctic glacier or some meteorite hurtling toward Earth, some virus is mutating, replicating, some germ is germinating capable of wiping out the entire human species. And those little bugs don't need approval from the Food and Drug Administration to run rampant. Does Regis Van Clay get handouts from the Pentagon? Not a dime, not directly at least. And is there a greater defender of the right to life?

"But fair is fair, there is a bright side. Every one of those recumbent molecules, every one of those demonic spirochetes means opportunity for my business. The more lethal the scourge, the more chance for a stock split and a dividend increase. Regis Pharmaceuticals supports the work of more research scientists than all the universities in the world while we watch over the welfare of millions of our shareholders. The jobs generated by my company and the stock dividends we pay mean money to buy vitamins, sewer systems, food, shelter, antiseptic sprays, vaccinations, medical care, medications, beauty products, clothes, cars, houses, toilet paper, dental floss, engagement rings, suppositories, steroids, sugar substitutes—the pantheon of things that make life pleasurable, even possible for millions. And never forget, my workers and stockholders pay taxes.

"Well, Mr. President, facts are facts, there's money in disease. No apology for that. Do you really believe it doesn't hurt Regis Van Clay when something as lucrative as polio, scarlet fever, measles or smallpox vanishes as an important profit center? Yes, it hurts. I'd be a liar to say otherwise. I suppose it's ironic, even comical, that in the microbe business every cure is a catastrophe.

"No sweat because it's only a matter of time before some new plague finds a home in a monkey's gut and that the toxic ape will bite some Zulu's nose or get served to a gourmet in one of those four-star French restaurants. That ever-present, dependable threat, Mr. President, is in addition to the mayhem simmering in test tube arsenals we keep for good measure in case our hydrogen bombs leave a few people vertical postwar.

"And when the latest plague opens on Broadway, where would the world be without Regis Van Clay, Honest Abe, Mr. Stamp, Mr. Penny, Mr. Fiver, Mr. Statue? Should I be looking up at you? Who should be admiring who?"

50

A dapper gentleman climbed the monument's white marble steps two at a time. He looked like the model Regis chose for his company's ad campaign for *Predator (The Scent-Sational Men's Cologne)*.

"Regis Van Clay?"

"Congressman Eff?"

"Yes. It's an honor to meet you, Van Clay."

"The same," Regis said. "And please call me Regis. I was delighted that Agent Beem could bring us together. I've admired your spunk. I like what you stand for."

"Glad to hear it. Kind words are always appreciated."

Regis squeezed the Congressman's shoulder. "Now that we're past the appetizers let's get on to the main course. I'm here to ask a favor. I know you have the ear of the White House."

"An ear is not a testicle but an ear is an ear and I'm proud to say a cordial relationship exists between . . ." The Congressman pulled at his left lobe and winked at Regis who fought not to wince.

"Congressman Eff, if you were to uncover a sinister plot to undermine the economy of this country, I assume you would be inclined to take drastic action."

"It goes without saying." The Congressman nodded, affirming his patriotism.

"Let me begin by reminding you that our economy has been rather slovenly of late. Our balance of trade is no less than scandalous despite a shrinking dollar."

"There are promising signs of an up-tick in the GNP. Economists predict—"

"That things will turn around? The economists with jobs, you mean. We're told inflation is not a problem. Good news except for the slightly curious epidemic of shrinkage evident to every shopper with half a brain. Packaging hasn't changed, the boxes are still big enough to glut landfills but, oops!—we're paying a significant percent more for a hell of a lot less including everything from detergents to candy bars. At this rate, what's inside those packages and containers might disappear altogether.

"Truth is, we're dancing in deep shit and it's getting deeper. We're giving away whole industries, squandering our technology. America has become 'a service economy.' What in hell is 'a service economy'? Tell me who'll buy the glut of crap being manufactured overseas if nobody here is working. And what's our major export? Entertainment for idiots."

"There's something to be said for bread and circuses," Congressman Eff said. Regis ignored the comment.

"There is one bright spot on an otherwise turgid horizon. Our medical and pharmaceutical complex is thriving. Even with the oppressions of Medicare and Medicaid, doctors manage to drive Mercedes. The price of adequate health care rises respectably year after year. And drug prices have more than kept pace; they've soared like noble bald eagles. There is no trade deficit in my business, Congressman Eff. Our balance sheets are satin. Red, white and blue satin."

"Yes, I read your annual report and I must admit those numbers—"

"Can you imagine what those numbers would be without government interference? You must have some sense of how our business works. First, we isolate some ailment with enough victims to justify a huge investment in research and development. If we do discover a panacea to offer succor to the stricken, a testing phase begins. And following years of testing there's a Figure Study to affirm the results. It takes nine to twelve years before a new drug is approved for general use. A baby born when our work began is ready to give blow jobs by the time our product comes to market.

"And when approval of a new drug is finally granted we must find ways to produce it as efficiently as possible which usually means in some remote corner of the world. Everybody's doing it so what choice do we have? Of course, there can be no compromise with quality even if our product is made by a five-year-old with dysentery.

Globalization. Share the wealth. Pardon me while we go fuck ourselves.

"Next, Congressman Eff, comes the task of informing thousands in the medical profession, more thousands of pharmacists and
the multitude of patients of its existence. The gluttonous cost of that
essential phase rivals and exceeds the expense that went into entire
process of discovery. We find a catchy name and create a catchy
image attractive to as many users as possible. That means designing
a pill, ointment, cream, lotion, or suspension with universal appeal.
So, by the time a product is actually in the pipeline, we've hemor-
rhaged hundreds of millions. Do we complain?

"No. Even if the powers have decreed that after a few short years
the drug we've birthed will lose exclusivity and enter the cursed
realm of the generic. Some pissy outfit in India or Canada will have
the right to sell the same drug for a hundredth of our price. Despite
those indignities we keep a happy face. Before we lose exclusivity, we
do manage to realize a few billions in profits. Proudly, I point out
that a substantial portion of those gains flow toward our shores
through subsidiaries from around the globe. Inflow, not outflow,
Congressman Eff. Assets, not deficits."

"I am aware of the importance of—"

"Of course you are. And you're also aware of how much our
industry contributes to your party and to your campaigns. We are not
misers."

"And you know, Mr. Van Clay, how much we—"

"Allow me a few more minutes to reach my point though I know
I've taken the scenic route. Getting past R&D, the eons of wading
through red tape, the focus groups commenting on the shape and
color of a product and its package, the presentations to doctors and
nurses, the advertising and promotion, moving past all that, there is
still the matter of disclosure. Which brings us to the subject of side
effects." Regis's right hand mimicked the universal gesture for masturbation. "If I begin to sound emotional it's because I am. No herb
or potion since Hippocrates first dissected a gladiator has been entirely free of some side effect however rare, however unlikely to affect an
ordinary mortal. But when even the most obscure side effect is documented, my government requires that a warning of it be included

in all relevant literature, cited in advertising, or, perish the thought, noted like a blight on the product's label in full view."

The Congressman smoothed his silver hair. "You must admit dangerous side effects deserve full disclosure. Recent studies predict that the number of deaths caused by drugs, many of which are prescription drugs, will soon rival the figures for traffic fatalities. To jeopardize—"

"You support the notion that every wisp of alleged bad news should be displayed for each unqualified, neurotic, paranoid, overprotective schmuck to see? Is that what you're saying? Of course you are. What else can you say with the liberals circling? Now let me ask, have you ever considered what acknowledging a side effect means to my bottom line?

"Take a marvelous drug like *Xanelul*. Forget that it's been the antidote for despair preferred by millions of depressed neurotics for whom nothing more than reading the daily newspaper has meant unendurable pain and suffering. Last month alone, Regis Pharmaceuticals was required by the FDA to issue a side effect alert to every grateful user of that marvelous psychotropic because of something called *Atonal Cacophonic Analopathy*. Because of that warning, untold numbers of the afflicted will quit spending dollars, pounds, yen, lira, francs, shekels per pill for the most successful tranquilizer in the whole history of medicine. Our sales projections for *Xanelul* have gone from fabulous to dismal. You think America's trade deficit is bad now? Wait until next year when the *Xanelul* factor kicks in. I'm talking about ink redder than a mandrill's bottom. Or should I say the Kremlin flag?"

"Actually a mandrill's bottom is blue. I don't mean to nitpick—"

"The color of a mandrill's ass is not the point here," Regis said, gesturing toward Abraham Lincoln's marble visage. "Let's go back to 1860. If John Brown and Jefferson Davis, not to mention slaves and abolitionists, were on monitored doses of *Xanelul*, if that actor, Booth, had the pill, if Dr. Mudd had written a prescription for Abe and especially Mary Todd Lincoln, there might never have been a Civil War. This statue would have a grin on its face instead of that tortured look. But what if those agitated folks back then had refused to swallow a few milligrams of *Xanelul* because they'd read some gib-

berish about *Atonal Cacophonic Analopathy?* I'll tell you what. We'd
have had the war we had! Which we did! Are you following me, Congressman Eff?"

"You're shouting, Mr. Van Clay. It's not in our best interest to
attract attention. I'm still uncertain as to why you asked for this meeting."

"Congressman Eff—the Honorable Jason Weston Eff—I'm
going to tell you about one of your constituents, a young man named
Simon Apple. When you hear me out you won't ask *why?* You'll
know *why.* And you'll know *what must be done.* Not just for my company, not only for my shareholders. This is for those spacious skies
and waves of grain we cherish. This is for the nation."

51

Dean Squandor's suspicion that attending the commencement
ceremonies might be problematic was confirmed. Simon, The
Ancient Mariner, was renamed The Tailpipe Prodigy after a local TV
newscaster broadcast selections from Gerald Warren's tape of *The
Windchime Concerto* along with his questionable story of its composition.

The Minneapolis press was quick to pick up the story and managed to get hold of Simon Apple's yearbook photo. Simon, who was
back in Glenda, learned of the fuss from the chairman of Celadon's
board of directors who strongly advised him against granting interviews to the media. The warning was redundant since Simon, Robert
J. and Rowena had no intention of prolonging what they felt was an
agony of humiliation. Still, the Apples tabled any idea of attending
Simon's commencement ceremony. They limited their celebration
to a private party attended by themselves and the Fikels.

When Marvin Klipstein, Esq., read a blurb about "the new
music" in *Time Magazine* he offered his condolences. When Robert
J. mentioned the possible role of *Xanelul* in the unfortunate affair,
Klipstein offered to instigate another civil action against Regis Pharmaceuticals. The offer was refused. Simon burned his only copy of
Warren's tape in a backyard bonfire and was glad to see it go up in

smoke. Whatever had caused the musical outburst, *Solacitrex* had stifled any recurrence; Simon was glad there was no need to sleep inside a concrete cave. The incident was a closed book.

In a long-distance telephone call plagued by static, Dr. Trobe expressed his feeling that there would be no permanent damage to Simon's bowels or pyloric sphincter though he did recommend regular monitoring of his "gifted colon." That phrase and Dr. Trobe's extravagant reaction to *The Windchime Concerto* infuriated Simon. "I'm not into jazz as a rule," Dr. Trobe said, "especially when it flirts with atonal themes, but I've listened to the duplicate tape you sent me with undiminished awe. It's like listening to Thelonious Monk and Stravinsky riffing in some Greenwich Village basement. I've advised your Dr. Fikel to put you on a reduced dose of *Solacitrex* for the time being but I want you to know the truth is I can't help hoping that you're poised to give us another masterwork."

"I think I'll pass on that. I'm thinking seriously about what you said about New York."

"If you've decided on anonymity, there is no better place. And, Simon, I want you to know that I'm giving up my practice," Dr. Trobe said. "Without sounding like a quitter, I've been subjected to a series of bruising thumps since our last conversation. First it was some ridiculous inquiry about the ethical implications of sleeping with my patients. I happen to believe that penetration is the shortest distance between two animals and though it was exhausting for me I was willing to spill my seed in the interest of mental health. Then there was something about the accreditation of the medical school I attended in French Guiana. And so on and so forth. It got to a point where aggravation exceeded expectation. I should tell you I've written a series of illustrated children's books under a *nom de plume* called "Tiffany Flaxseed's Bugaboo Journals," which have been selling quite well."

"Bugaboo Journals?" Simon said. "My father told me you took hundreds of pictures of bugs with shells and now it begins to come together."

"There are literally trillions of bugs alive at any given moment on this fabulous planet and a huge percentage are blessed with shells," Dr. Trobe said. "They're the real owners of the Earth. Some may be nicer than others. To quote myself:"

> *I wash my hands, I wash my hands,*
> *I wash them six times an hour—*
> *There are bugs in bands*
> *From invisible lands*
> *Who would cut down a man like a flower.*

"Truer words were never spoken," Simon said, making a spider out of his fingers and running it up his cheek.

"Of course, many bugs are our best friends," Dr. Trobe said. "Friend or foe, so far as we know, not one of them is anorexic, bulimic, bipolar or neurotic."

"All the best with your new career," Simon said. "Maybe we'll meet in a bookstore someday."

"It's a brave new world for me. I'm one of the lucky men whose hobby becomes his vocation. There might actually be a God. Like my heroine, Lulu Ladybug, instructs her larvae, 'Don't watch your step, watch *where* you step.'"

"It's a bumper sticker," Simon said. "But let me ask you, what about the turtles. My father told me you were a big turtle fan."

"You reach a point in life when choices must be made," Dr. Trobe said.

"And you went with bugs. Why not? I suppose you feel a pang when you see a turtle on the road. Wondering what might have been."

"Your mockery is a good sign in our relationship," Dr. Trobe said. "It shows I've made some progress getting to you. I hope you'll listen when I say that I want you to stay on your medication. But you should know that Regis Pharmaceuticals has forbidden me, and every other licensed medical practitioner, from writing prescriptions for any of their products for you, and warned every pharmacy, on pain of excommunication, from selling them to you. So, a word to the wise—I'm mailing you a whole prescription pad which, after all, would be the same as if I left it on my desk and you swiped it, as you certainly would, recognizing an opportunity."

That night, Robert J. told Simon that Rowena was pregnant with twins. "It hasn't been easy for her," Robert J. said. "She's been taking fertility drugs. Without the help of modern science those babies wouldn't have been conceived. I know you've had some setbacks arguably traceable to side effects but sometimes the good news cancels out the bad news. And you've got to admit, your peculiar chemistry contributed to your rotten medical history. Who knows why? Maybe if you were a different kind of boy, less angry, more accessible, more content, easy-going, normal, things might have gone differently. It's not as if your mother and I weren't genetically sound and didn't do the best we could to make you happy."

"I wasn't pointing fingers at nature or nurture," Simon said. "I hope the twins are happy, healthy and have the right attitudes."

"We're not blaming you for your supposed side effects," Robert J. said, his face reddening. "But when things don't work the way they're supposed to, it does make you wonder."

52

Dr. Henry Fikel was permitted to see Simon in his cell rather than the visiting area, a professional courtesy extended by Warden Donal. Simon was surprised to see how much the doctor had aged: he walked with the help of a cane, his hair had turned March-sky gray, his skin had the texture of an overripe pumpkin, he spoke with a tremor. "You seem to be holding up nicely," Dr. Fikel said.

"Actually, I feel pretty good," Simon said. "Too good. That could make the dying more difficult. I'm alert as a kitten."

"I expect they'll add some soporific, probably diazepam, to your last meal. That should put you in a pliant frame of mind to meet the reaper."

"You could tell them to add a pinch of saltpeter. I'm incredibly horny."

"Not unusual. Some of the cadavers we dissected in medical school belonged to condemned men and they often arrived with a prodigious bulge in their wrappings. Sex is life's greatest affirmation though these days I have a hard time remembering why."

"I wouldn't mind a conjugal visit or two," Simon said.

"One or two for the road? I don't think our society is ready to offer that solace."

"They won't even give me a pack of cigarettes."

"You still smoke?" Dr. Fikel said. "After all my lectures?"

"I think those lectures started me on the habit."

"I had you pegged as an addictive personality. You were a dedicated finger sucker as I recollect."

"It was hard to find an available nipple in those early days," Simon said. "I used to chew the rubber erasers off pencils in grade school."

"Wasn't that mentioned at your trial?"

"Yes, as an example of pre-adolescent aggression. I thought that was a stretch by the prosecution but it seemed to sway the jury."

"Your attorney should have objected."

"Klipstein was too intimidated to object to anything but his fee. Besides, they promised him a judgeship. He never got it though."

"We go back a long way," Dr. Fikel said. "All the way to *Cripthalizine*. A lot of water under the bridge since then. And I wanted to wish you safe passage."

"Noted," Simon said. "Thanks."

"I've also come to ask a last favor considering all we've been through together. I hear tell you've opted for cremation. That would be a terrible waste. I know you're missing some key organs but many might be salvageable. You could give the gift of life."

"We both know that after they pump me full of poison my organs won't be eligible for transplant. Except maybe in Third World countries."

"Well, yes, that's generally true," Dr. Fikel said. "But even if you won't be the most desirable donor, your body would be invaluable to science. You do have a phenomenal track record, medically speaking. I was hoping you might be willing to sign over . . ."

"Are you here of your own accord? I find it hard to believe you came up from Glenda to scout my body for purely philanthropic reasons."

"Let's not pussyfoot around, Simon. I'm representing Regis Pharmaceuticals. They have a vested interest in you. And they're willing to pay two million dollars in return for—"

"I'm confused," Simon said. "A few hours ago I was told that an urn filled with my hot ashes would give aid and comfort to Regis Van Clay. Now you tell me my cold corpse is—"

"That is so typical of corporate confusion," Dr. Fikel said. "Whoever dared suggest such a thing?"

"Belladonna and Trilby. I was sure those two women were sent by Van Clay. They said the motive for their visit was at least partially altruistic but I never for a moment believed them. It's so touching, to think they were completely sincere."

"Belladonna? Trilby? Did they have credible identification? I smell a rat. Would you want to be scooped up by some German or Japanese conglomerate? Tell me you weren't stupid enough to sign any contract because even if you were we'll match and trump any offer they made you and the most binding agreement can be unbound, Simon. Mr. Van Clay called me personally to ask that I present his offer. The money would be paid in cash to Robert J. and Rowena along with any estate taxes. You know your father dreams of opening a fully digitized portrait studio in West Glenda."

"I didn't sign any contract," Simon said. "But I'm weighing my options."

"I hope your decision won't be influenced by that quack Dr. Trobe your father called in without consulting me? I could have told him *Xanelul* wasn't for you. You'd already shown a proclivity toward *akisthesia* and *agranulocytosis* but did anybody ask for my input? Second opinions. Everybody who isn't cured in time for *The Late Show* wants a second opinion. In my humble opinion, second opinions kill more people than first opinions. I wouldn't put it past a charlatan like Trobe to be involved in industrial espionage."

Dr. Fikel pulled a sheet of paper from his jacket pocket and rattled it at Simon. "You've already demonstrated your patriotism, your willingness to make the ultimate sacrifice. Take the final step. This is your last chance to be an authentic role model, another face on Mt. Rushmore. Sign yourself over to an American company. Regis Pharmaceuticals wants your discards. One way or another they'll get you anyway. Two million in cold cash. Come to your senses, Apple. Don't be an obstinate prick. Sign here."

"It's flattering to know I'm a person of worth," Simon said. "Still, I need to think things over."

"The quickest way to get to heaven is to give the devil his due," Dr. Fikel said. "Don't waste everybody's valuable time."

53

Shortly after Simon's graduation-in-absentia from Celadon College, under pressure from Dr. Trobe, with an assist from Marvin Klipstein, Esq., Regis Pharmaceuticals had agreed to pick up the tab for Simon to retreat to a corner of the world where any recurrence of drug induced nocturnal musicality would go unnoticed. Even with *Solacitrex* such a recurrence was not only possible but likely according to Dr. Trobe's analysis of the latest research statistics from Regis's lab even though Regis's chemists felt 87.4 percent sure that a few months would be time enough for their newest antidote to cure the only documented case of *Xanelul* induced *Atonal Cacophonic Analopathy*. "I don't like the odds. Take the money and run," Dr. Trobe told Simon.

Simon took the money. The very day he deposited Regis's generous check, he was asked, and gladly volunteered, to put in a few hours at Quikpix while Robert J. and Rowena attended a luncheon sponsored by the Glenda Chamber of Commerce. Simon welcomed their absence; he wanted another chance to check out the private album he hadn't browsed in years. When he took the book from its hiding place, what he found were twenty pages of new snapshots. Most of the faces (when faces were visible) and bodies were unfamiliar. Glenda had grown; its population had burgeoned. There was a whole new cast of characters.

Even the pictures were strikingly different: less coy, blatantly sexual, deliberately outrageous. Simon missed the old feeling of peeking under a window shade at some homey intimacy to catch a glimpse of friendly local pussy. The new photos mimicked the style of sleazy tabloids, more prurient and less stimulating. Simon felt a tug of nostalgia for the town's vanished sensibility.

While he was mooning over things past, he was horrified to hear a hyped version of *The Windchime Concerto* playing on Glenda's own KGLN-FM. He slammed his father's album shut when he heard ossified disc jockey Bobby Slaw, older than the maple tree outside City Hall, excitedly announce: "Rumor has it that this haunting refrain was composed and performed by our own Simon Apple, with lyrics written and sung by another Glenda original, Ms. Polly Moon.

There's more! The recording is produced by that Glenda gadabout, Albert Essman! It's rocketing up the charts, folks! We're on our way to the Top Ten! Amen! You heard it here first! *The Windchime Concerto*—it ain't pop, it ain't rock, it ain't swing, it ain't jazz . . . it's a sound like no other from no instrument I ever heard! But what it is is genuine W.O.W! and it's N-O-W on KGLN-FM! Kudos and kisses to Simon, Polly and Albert, wherever you stars hang out!"

Simon heard his music play while Polly Moon's sultry voice half-whispered, half-sang:

> *Do cannibals eat mermaids?*
> *Do mermaids eat sardines?*
> *What random winds determine*
> *Which way a flower leans?*
> *Do questions have answers?*
> *Are the answers truths or lies?*
> *Is the fourth dimension*
> *The dimension of surprise?*
> *Why is it that I need you?*
> *Why can't I do without?*
> *Is it the crinkle of your smile*
> *Or the crackle of your doubt?*
> *What's the lethal magnet*
> *That draws me to your heart?*
> *Is it you shining in the sun*
> *Or naked in the dark?*
> *Is it your whisper's waterfall?*
> *The rainbow of your lips?*
> *Or the soft electric flowing*
> *From your fingertips?*
> *When we lay together*
> *Is there a you and me?*
> *Or do we vanish like a spark*
> *Then drift invisibly?*
> *And if we drift*
> *Where do we go?*
> *To what will we return?*

What makes our shadows dip and dance?
Why does our candle burn?
What draws the lightning from the sky?
What turns the rain to tears?
Why does time evaporate
In a shower of falling years?
And really does it matter
If mermaids eat sardines?
Or cannibals eat mermaids?
Or which way a flower leans?
Or why the angels dance on pins?
Or what your laughter means?

The next morning, after fending off a dozen calls from reporters, agents and record companies, Robert J. drove Simon to the airport, his father insisting that Marvin Klipstein be freed to nail Essman Records, Polly Moon, Celadon College, Gerald Warren and anybody else involved in such an obvious theft of intellectual property. Robert J. correctly felt that Simon had surrendered his rights under duress.

Despite his father's pleas, Simon refused to get involved in any litigation. "I want the whole incident put behind me, no pun intended," Simon said. "Period. The end."

54

Simon sat in his cell writing a thank-you note to a kindergarten class in Glenda that had sent along a bundle of illustrated HAVE A HAPPY DAY messages. Their teacher, Mrs. Althea Murphy, included a note explaining that the school wished to offer some affectionate gesture but that circumstances made it expedient to shield the children from potentially upsetting details of his impending execution.

The moppets were told that Simon Apple had a bad chest cold and were required to express their concern as cheerfully as possible. There were many drawings of happy faces and rainbows done in crayon along with fumbling attempts at script, mostly illegible but surely well intentioned. One kid who knew more than he should have, sent a drawing of a stick figure strapped to a table with lethal fluids flowing into his mouth through curly tubes. Nevertheless, even that drawing was graced with the redeeming virtue of mercy. Near the tubed man, a dog sat weeping a deluge of tears.

Simon was touched by the letters though he had mixed feelings about drafting a proper reply. His first attempt began by correcting the impression that he might recover, listing specific details of his gruesome end. His second draft simply told the children their good wishes were a tonic, that he had generally joyous memories of his days in Glenda. The third draft was edited down to a simple statement of appreciation inside a valentine heart. While he was drawing the heart, a guard told him he had a phone call from his lawyer, Marvin Klipstein.

Simon took the call on a portable phone. The voice at the other end was not Marvin Klipstein's and there was no electronic beep indicating that Klipstein had turned on the timer he used to measure all his calls for billing purposes.

"I'm sorry for the little white lie, Mr. Apple," the voice said, "but it was the only way I could be sure of getting through to you."

"Who is this?"

"My name is Kenny. I'm calling on behalf of www.SecondOptions dot com. We offer discounted prices on any last-minute items you might want and all taxes and delivery charges are included."

"I think you got a wrong number to put it mildly."

"You are *the* Simon Apple? I know I have the right number but please don't ask me how I got it. We have our ways."

"Can you call later? This isn't the best time," Simon said.

"We deal with a select clientele," Kenny said. "We have no other business so you're guaranteed our best efforts. Our company's only purpose is to satisfy the condemned."

"That sounds like a rather iffy enterprise. Maybe you should consider another line of work."

"We do very well, thank you. Our bet is that the folks we contact will win a last-minute reprieve. A final appeal granted, a commutation of sentence by an enlightened governor, best of all, a pardon. All things are possible. You must know about DNA. It's a young science but its use already has had a remarkable impact on law enforcement. Enough to say that a high percentage of inmates teetering at the edge of eternity are being spared these days. More and more men expecting to pass on in the evening are finding themselves still vertical at cockcrow. The condemned are beating the system in increasing numbers. Our business is enjoying exponential growth, especially in election years."

"I'm glad you're doing well, Kenny, but I don't think I'm a prime prospect for either vindication or clemency," Simon said. "I'm out of options. Not even I can say my trial was unfair. It was well rehearsed. And I can't play any race card since I'm a privileged Caucasian. There is no issue of religious prejudice, I'm a pizza pie with a mixed topping—half Christian and half Jewish. So . . ."

"So it ain't over till it's over, to coin a phrase. You still have a few hours left. The point is, I'm ready to offer you a 20 percent discount on anything from clothing to appliances—things you'll certainly need if you're exonerated at the last minute—for a very modest fee, if you'll agree to membership in the Second Options Platinum Club. We accept payment by any major credit card, a certified check or even cash. After the modest initiation fee, you're entitled to cancel your membership at any time."

"Thanks, but I'll pass. No pun intended."

"If you act now, you can even pay in installments. I'm talking pennies a day. Suppose you do find yourself eating breakfast tomorrow instead of dirt. You're going to experience a strong sense of relief. I've seen it happen time and again. You'll have an overwhelming urge to indulge yourself. And you'll deserve some luxury because you earned the right to add a dimension of comfort to your extended life, even if it is life in prison. Don't turn your back on this offer, Simon."

"Please don't call me Simon. I don't know you."

"Mr. Apple, then. I was just being friendly. For a one-time payment of two hundred fifty dollars you can have Second Options dot com in your corner. After that, it's only twenty-five dollars a month. A person your age could expect half a century of continuing benefits. How can you say no?"

"No."

"That is such a defeatist attitude. You understand that our price goes up the closer we get to midnight. I've had people who held back on the two-fifty willing to pay six hundred fifty for the identical privileges I'm offering until eleven P.M. That's a four-hundred-dollar saving. OK, I know resistance when it kicks me in the teeth. You strike a hard bargain and I respect that. For the same fee we'll cover a second family member. Say your spouse hears good news, that the ax won't fall. You'd better believe she'll head downtown for a makeover or grab hold of the nearest Frederick's of Hollywood catalog."

Simon was about to tell Kenny to cut the shit, that for certain men it's over long before it's over but Kenny sounded young, just doing a job of work in a consumer-driven society. Why depress him with such lugubrious information?

Simon still felt benevolent because of those gentle letters from the kids back home so he shut up and slammed down the receiver.

55

Simon's first days in New York City were given over to the joys of disoriented astonishment. He vacillated between ecstasy and pure terror exploring Manhattan, wandering from the Battery to Harlem, swept along by polluted winds from New Jersey, energized by invisible fumes that wafted up from subway grates and garbage pails.

He'd never felt less substantial or more whole in his life. He was swallowed up by the city beast, trapped undigested inside its churning belly, dodging cars, trucks, buses, crowds of people, animals, birds, plants, trees, a whirl of things tumbling down its ravenous gullet on the way to some distant anus. He waited to take that trip himself, eager for the moment he'd be shat out onto some street corner, born again, finally belonging.

In the meanwhile, he used some of his leftover hush money from Regis Pharmaceuticals to rent a room at the Flatiron Hotel on Broadway and Twenty-Fifth Street. He'd read about the Flatiron as home to the future famous, transient zephyrs who went on to become household names.

If the Flatiron had been a rundown but respectable address in the 1920s, by the time Simon Apple checked in fifty years later it was a notch above flophouse, part geriatric home, part welfare holding pen, part catch-all for rootless migrants whose only proof of existence was a set of fingerprints, misplaced dental records and a few thimbles of wine-diluted genetic debris. Then there were resident voyagers like Simon who'd come to test themselves against the *City for Conquest*.

He registered as Sinbad Green, crouching behind the pseudonym after a call to Robert J. informed him that the deluge of interview seekers and fans of *The Windchime Concerto* had reached critical mass when the song was nominated for a Grammy Award as record of the year.

A crazed autograph seeker broke into the Apple residence and was found sleeping in Simon's bed. Rowena's garden had been pillaged by souvenir-seeking marauders transported to the neighborhood by sightseeing vans. Some of those unwanted visitors staged an impromptu dance, stripped down to their underwear, doing what the press called The Thorazine Shuffle, a zombified, Frankensteinian tap dance. They said the dance was divinely inspired by the concerto's "celestial umbilical chords." State troopers had to be called to reinforce Glenda's overwhelmed police force.

Simon Apple was determined to avoid the slightest beam of limelight; Sinbad Green was a blank slate, a man without a history. From his pram, Sinbad aka Simon remembered hearing Victoria Wyzowik and Fritzel Vonderbraun relive the horrors of wandering across Europe without proper papers. Simon's tiny ears could decipher the fear in their voices. He had no idea of what proper papers were. Newspapers? Rolls of toilet paper? The colored paper they gave him to draw on? The pages in books that showed pictures of pink rabbits and smiling pastel children? He suspected Victoria and Fritzel meant some other kind of papers, demonic papers adults whispered about in frightened voices.

Whatever they were, the proper papers the women spoke of made a monstrous impression on little Simon's sponge of a brain. Victoria's quivering voice made it clear that the lack of those papers meant instant death. Now that he knew what proper papers were, nothing less than certifications of the right to survive, Simon was pleased that Sinbad Green had none. Being paperless seemed the ultimate luxury, the perfect passport for a wanderer in a city of the transient transparent.

If Sinbad Green was paperless, Simon Apple kept a few crucial papers like his Social Security card tucked in a secret compartment in his wallet. A file folder back in Glenda protected his birth certificate, records of his baptism, circumcision and proxy Bar Mitzvah. His framed Liberal Arts diploma (Summa Cum Laude) had a place of honor in the Apple home. Simon had plenty of papers, all proper, so Sinbad Green was hitchhiking with money in his pocket, playing a game, a refugee by choice not chance.

Simon felt a little guilty about the deception, but The Invisible Man had been a favorite role model since he'd seen that movie—he spent many hours discussing the virtues of invisibility with Chirp Bennet (especially the ability to sneak into locker-room showers where soap-slick girls glistened, or vaults where jewels could be scooped up by the pound). Chirp gave him Ralph Ellison's novel about a black man suffering metaphorical invisibility in a racist society and Simon could empathize with that man's inflicted anguish. But even if invisibility had its flip side, in his heart of hearts Simon still envied the possibilities implicit in owning a small jar of diabolical potion that would allow him to disappear. As Sinbad Green, he had the formula for vanishing cream along with the serum to solidify at will: the best of both worlds.

There were a few other important papers in Simon's arsenal. When his supply of *Solacitrex* ran low, he scrawled Dr. Trobe's signature on one of the blank prescription pages Simon had liberated. A pharmacy down the block from the Flatiron never questioned the forgeries.

Simon spent his first month in New York catching up on culture at the museums, sampling the zoos in Central Park, Prospect Park and the Bronx, walking over Brooklyn Bridge and the George Washington, riding subways to random destinations, browsing what was left of the Fourth Avenue bookshops, penetrating the inner depths of Macy's and Bloomingdale's, listening to jazz and folk music in Washington Square, moving with rush hour crowds, hanging out in the Forty-Second Street Library, drinking little cups of espresso in Italian coffee houses.

He was fueled by a diet of Sabrett hot dogs, greasy Souvlaki sandwiches, potato knishes, roasted peanuts, and cups of flavored ices, all sold from sidewalk carts that sprouted beach umbrellas for protection against the gangster summer sun or sudden gush of rain. Sometimes he treated himself to a plum, peach or banana displayed on a curbside crate. He indulged himself by going to afternoon movies like *ET*, relishing the guilt he felt knowing it was a workday.

Evenings, Simon liked rattling around Times Square watching faces turned purple, red, orange, yellow, and chalky white, rainbowed by neon light blasting from advertising signs and flickering movie marques. He read news bulletins announcing global alarms and the latest baseball scores parading endlessly along the belt of bulbs circling the Times Building. He played games in the penny arcades, firing electric machine guns and cannons at enemy rocket ships, planes, tanks, ape-faced armies, monsters vomited up from Hell, using up his quarter's worth of ammo, racing against an unforgiving game clock while bells rang up his score of kills.

He mingled with theater goers, bums, tourists, blind men selling pencils, dodged legless beggars (side effects of some war?) lashed to boards, rolling on skate wheels over crowded sidewalks, powered by stubby muscled arms that swept the asphalt like oars.

He pissed against brick walls in alleys and fought the urge to take a crap until he could get back to the Flatiron, because finding a toilet meant he'd have to buy a Coke in some luncheonette as passport to use the facilities reserved for customers only, or pay his way through a subway turnstile to find a filthy stall while watching out for some subterranean pervert peeking over his cubicle's wall. It struck Simon as ironic that in New York he could see genuine dinosaur bones, Rembrandts, Picassos and Egyptian mummies for nothing, but to drop a load required an investment.

Some nights Simon never got back to the hotel. He slept on grass in Central Park near the rowboat lake or waited out the dark hours on a bench near the East River so he could see dawn from a front row seat. He knew about creeps and crazies and probably a few vampires prowling, but the risk was worth the reward; at first light the city glowed silver; Manhattan came awake like a lion, replacing dreams with appetite. So it was that Simon set scent upon New York.

One gray afternoon, his long vacation ended abruptly when he checked his dwindling assets. Simon had to think about getting a job and face the sad reality that he had no salable skills. That became disgustingly evident when he bought a copy of the *Times* and searched the classified ads. Prospective employers with entry level positions to fill made strange demands involving the ability to operate machines ranging from typewriters to things called Wang Data Processors. Simon knew about typewriters though he'd never learned to use one. He had no idea what a Wang Processor was—in Glenda a wang was a dick.

Many ads required a talent for shorthand. Those were obviously meant for females, as were the ones looking for "receptionist, bright, hard worker, eager to learn, opportunity for rapid advancement." Those ads never specified that breasts and vaginas were necessary qualifications, but Simon sensed the truth.

There were many ads for salesmen willing to work on commission, but those insisted on long track records with proof of incredible incomes. No ads mentioned anything like experience in the subtleties of Quikpix operation as the foundation for a career. A degree in Liberal Arts from any college or university was entirely ignored as a virtue.

There was one ad for a "fastidious Oriental houseboy" on a yacht, asking for a list of references and stressing the importance of "people skills and loyalty." Applicants were asked to forward their résumés to the address of a company in the garment center. Simon thought about trying his luck with the yacht owner who might have a shaky knowledge of houseboys and could be convinced to drop the Asian stipulation if it was stressed that on some moonless night off a foreign coast, when the yachtsman wandered his polished teakwood deck with a troubled mind plagued by business or family problems, he might prefer the company of a circumcised, baptized Midwestern college graduate for the comfort of conversation instead of the obsequious presence of an elusive Buddhist, however fastidious; but even if Simon could get that complex idea across there was still the insurmountable obstacle of references.

Filling Dr. Trobe's *Solacitrex* prescriptions, Simon aka Sinbad felt the drain on his finances was well worth the result—the drug kept his bowels as quiet as a Rolex.

56

One morning, while sitting in the raunchy lobby of the Flat-iron, Simon read the latest batch of Want Ads, moving from frustra-tion to despair. Like an echo of his misery, he heard the sound of vio-lent sobbing from a battered armchair hidden behind a snake plant.

Residents of the Flatiron seldom communicated beyond a mandatory nod of acknowledgment, usually on the elevator, but this time Simon's curiosity got the better of him. He folded his newspa-per and walked toward the hotel desk, ostensibly to ask the manager if he had any mail but actually to get a look at the source of audible misery.

The weeper turned out to be a guest Simon had seen many times before: a time warp of a man, slender, gray, meticulously dressed, with the bearing of an aristocrat. He was certainly not the usual Flatiron citizen—slouching, depressed, often disoriented, wearing clothes passed reluctantly between generations of some dys-functional family.

Simon's curiosity and compassion were aroused. He was tempt-ed by the chance to talk to someone, anyone, and grateful to feel a benevolent emotion stir his heart. The only times he'd used his voice in many weeks was to grunt in reply to a comment on the weather by some street vendor, and fend off a carnivorous panhandler or mis-sionary with some petition to sign. Grunting was the staple of Man-hattan's asphalt language; to actually string words into a complete sentence seemed a luxurious prospect. As for benevolent feelings, Simon couldn't remember his last one.

"Are you all right? Is there anything I can do to help?" Simon said.

"Not really," the dapper man said between sobs. "I'm fine. It's funny, I've been mugged three times in five years and shrugged that off as another of the indignities one suffers in exchange for living here, like rent. Today I was crossing Fifth Avenue and coming direct-ly at me was one of those dog walkers with no less than ten dogs strung on a communal leash. Are you a dog person?"

"I once had a cat. It ran away."

"Then this may be difficult for you to understand, son, but one of those dogs was my dog, Excalibur, a King Charles Spaniel, my dog for twelve years. In the divorce settlement, my wife got custody of Excalibur. She never liked him but the bitch knew what losing his companionship would mean to me. I could have predicted that she'd hire a dog walker instead of moving her own fat ass down the street. Do you know what those walkers charge? Why would she care? It's my money. But it wasn't the money that set me off. Excalibur was no farther from me than you are now and he didn't recognize me. For twelve years he could smell me from a block away. When I came home he began barking jumping and panting, his tail going a mile a minute while I was still parking the car. Whenever I left he slobbered and howled, practically begging me to stay. And today Excalibur didn't show the slightest sign of recognition. Nothing. What did that harpy do to make him forget? How could he forget? My own dog and he didn't know who I was. Can you imagine?"

"I'm sorry," Simon said. "Maybe he went blind, deaf, or lost his sense of smell. That might explain it."

"I never thought of that. I doubt the cunt would bother to take him to a vet even if he began foaming and fainting. The poor thing. A victim of infirmity. That never occurred to me. And here I am feeling sorry for myself. What's your name, lad?"

"Sinbad Green."

"I am Wallace Waldo. If the name sounds familiar, you're right. I was the host of *The Wallace Waldo Amateur Hour*, a staple on the Blue Network. That might have been before your time. When radio was king of the airwaves."

"I think my father mentioned *The Wallace Waldo Amateur Hour*," Simon said. "So you're Wallace Waldo! It's an honor to meet you, sir."

"I am what's left of Wallace Waldo. How fast they forget. Why don't I die?"

"From what I see, there's plenty left of Wallace Waldo," Simon said. "You're not dead yet. Where there's life there's hope."

"Thank you for spreading rumors, young man. Without being intrusive, what is it you do, Sinbad? Are you an aspiring actor? I hope not, for your sake."

"Not an actor," Simon said. "I've been taking it easy. I just graduated from Celadon College, Summa Cum Laude, feeling my way around. Now I'm job hunting. But I'm not sure what job I'm hunting for. I was never very inner-directed."

"I sense that you're ambitious to make your way."

"You could say that."

"Sinbad, you volunteered your services to help this fossil. Maybe I can be of help to you."

"Please don't trouble yourself, Mr. Waldo."

"It's no trouble. Actually, I was looking for a bright young chap to fill a vacancy in my company, Wallace Waldo Enterprises. It's a modest position but a foot in the door. With ample opportunity for rapid advancement."

"If there's a Wang involved or dictation, I can't handle it," Simon said.

"Not a problem. Here's my card. Spruce up a bit and be at my office at three o'clock sharp. Ask for Benny Valaris. I'll tell him to expect you. You might just fit in."

"That's fantastic," Simon said.

"A bit of luck," Wallace Waldo said. "New York just tossed you a bone. Speaking of bones, do you know I had a special arrangement with the Madison Avenue Meat Market to deliver a fresh bone for Excalibur to gnaw on every other day? I hope he remembers those delicious treats even if he's forgotten who sent them."

"I'm sure he does. Gestures like that make a lasting impression."

"He must know I would never have abandoned him if it wasn't for the court order."

"He knows," Simon said.

57

Since he'd been confined to Death Row, Simon had received many cards and letters from strangers. Some were *mea culpas*, asking him to forgive the writer for any connection, however remote, to legalized murder, i.e. the death penalty. Others relished his impending execution, reminding Simon that even if his sentence seemed excessive, it wasn't and good riddance.

Many letters asked for souvenirs: an autograph, a lock of hair, a pair of unwashed underwear. There were hundreds of marriage proposals often containing photographs of would-be brides usually taken in a modest kitchen or bedroom not unlike the photos in Robert J.'s album. There were Hallmark cards with messages ranging from GET WELL SOON to JESUS LOVES YOU AND SO DO I.

There were anonymous polemics on a variety of subjects expressing opinions about war, environmental issues, the existence of God, the decline of morals, the high cost of living. There were confessions of crimes big and small, incest to shoplifting. There were requests for money from individuals, faith-based charities, assorted political candidates, the National Rifle Association, the Nature Conservancy, the Public Broadcasting System, *ad infinitum*.

In the first months, Simon made an attempt to answer the most interesting mail but thoughtful replies took too much time and energy so he gave up the correspondence. There was a large pile of unopened envelopes stacked floor to ceiling in a corner of his cell. Simon thought it might be a nice gesture to select one of those letters in his last hours, answer it, and ask one of the nicer guards to post his reply after his demise. That some stranger would receive a posthumous note from Simon Apple's still-warm ghost was an amusing prospect; such a missive, however brief, would certainly have sentimental and very possibly financial value to the lucky recipient. It would be like winning the lottery. There was no shortage of ghouls who'd covet a genuine Apple as a collector's item, something to show the grandchildren.

In the interest of fairness, Simon closed his eyes and selected an envelope from the stack. It was hand-addressed in meticulous script, marked PERSONAL AND CONFIDENTIAL, stamped with pictures of Queen Elizabeth II, canceled in London, but missing a return address. Simon's mail was routinely X-rayed by prison security. Anything remotely suspicious was opened, examined, then Scotch Taped shut and delivered if it passed muster. This letter from an unidentified source, usually reason enough to trigger closer inspection, had managed to slip through the system intact. When he opened the letter, Simon found a page of text in the same pristine penmanship as the envelope's address.

The Simpson Wax Works
23 Portobello Road
London WI I2 ED
England

23 September 2005

My Dear Mr. Simon Apple,

I hope you will pardon the informal nature of this note but you will understand that, since we are a new enterprise, our official letterheads are still in preparation and any delay seemed counterproductive considering this late date.

Let me begin by offering my personal congratulations! You have been unanimously selected as worthy of display in our Pantheon of Privates.

But I am getting ahead of myself. I write with the authority of my position as Director and Curator of the Simpson Alternative Wax Works, a beautiful facility centrally located in prestigious Portobello Road. We have acquired Moorcock Mansion, a landmark structure dating back to the early 19th Century, to house our growing collection.

Make no mistake, this enterprise is in no way associated with Madame Tussaud's Wax Museum with which you are surely familiar. The world has changed significantly since Tussaud's first threw open its doors. Yet that venerable establishment remains mired in what we consider to be an obsolete tradition, i.e. offering the public a predictable selection of figures in an atmosphere reflective of what can be described as "tasteful."

Even rooms reserved for outstanding murderers like yourself, featuring a variety of perpetrators within grotesque dioramas that convey a sense of their diabolical acts, are well-meaning but ultimately tame.

Since World War II and especially The Holocaust, the nature of both celebrity and horror has altered and so has the expectation level of our patrons. By way of example, in this impatient age of the abbreviated attention span, when fractals can communicate powerfully and directly to a modern audience, Tussaud's visitors are unfairly expected to invest excessive amounts of valuable time examining entire scenes of mayhem, whole torsos (or, when decapitation is a major factor, complete body parts, limbs to organs) when artful editing would be a blessing.

Our emphasis at the Simpson is to offer minimalist, sometimes conceptual, post-modern incitement through what we call abridged unification.

We believe that less is more.

Our conviction is that maximum truth is captured by a subject's genitalia—that all else is excessive, unnecessary and euphemistic. A medley of penis, testicle, vagina, clitoris, breast and anus is the door to dimensional epiphany! Thus genitals are what we proudly and exclusively display.

Whereas, like Tussaud's, we work with paraffin, at Simpson's we "wax eloquent" in a manner that allows that respected medium the widest range of expression.

Mr. Apple, we are privileged to offer you the opportunity to have your reproductive organs immortalized in exalted company, on permanent display in one of London's most prestigious neighborhoods.

Our exhibits are eclectic. We juxtapose the genitalia of poets, philosophers, scientists, statesmen, artists of every discipline, industrial giants, saints and serial killers without judgment or distinction beyond the single qualification of celebrity.

Yes, celebrity genitals, beautifully rendered, are the ultimate recognition of fame in our brave new wax world. Be assured that your inclusion in our Pantheon of Privates is well deserved. You have earned the honor. But along with honor comes responsibility.

You must realize that a host of departed greats should be represented in our galleries. Replicating lifelike models dating back to the ancients is hugely expensive. Alas, a daunting problem is that the Simpson is, fiscally speaking, not yet well-endowed. Admission fees (which we will try to keep modest) and grants will defray a portion of our considerable costs. Still, we are forced to ask that you help subsidize our effort to educate and inspire whole generations, especially children who carry the torch of the future.

If you will send us a Polaroid snapshot of your private dimensions (please see exact directions for accurate duplication on the reverse side of this page; note that fractional measurements will be rounded out to the next *highest* whole number) along with your certified check, money order or credit card authorization in the amount of just $2,500 (US) to cover the cost of molding and materials, plus any additional contribution you might wish to make toward the success of our endeavor, we will promptly return an official Certificate of Inclusion along with two tickets to our Gala Opening at a future date to be determined.

> Most Sincerely Yours,
> Espeth Litmus-Plagett, MBE
> Executive Director and Curator

Simon made out a check for ten dollars payable to Ms. Plagett with a note sympathetic to her financial needs and praising her original vision but declining further participation "since I have already negotiated a satisfactory arrangement with the Erectile Project at the Smithsonian Institution in Washington, D.C., and, after all, first and foremost, I am an American."

58

Wallace Waldo Enterprises was located in a three-room suite in an office building on West Fifty-Seventh Street. The ground floor of the building was occupied by the Steinway Piano Company. Before Simon went for his interview, he stared through a large window where the Steinways seemed to graze on a thick carpet like a herd of elephants. That showroom was an oasis of tranquility, a refuge of polished wood and elegance where salesmen and clients appeared to communicate in clefs and quarter notes.

Simon watched for as long as it took to smoke a cigarette, then he entered the lobby and rode an elevator to the eleventh floor while his gut tightened into a Gordian knot. Wallace Waldo Enterprises was, in Mr. Waldo's own words, "a cyst of stress where a smart young man could learn the survival techniques necessary for success in any business, from swabbing floors in a cathouse to the upscale piano biz downstairs."

During the interview, when Simon mentioned the Steinway biosphere and said in passing that it looked like a nice place to work, Benny Valaris, who screened all job applicants, jumped out of his chair and pointed a finger at Simon's nose. "If that's what you want, if you see yourself hustling music boxes to prima donnas for the next twenty years, you're in the wrong place. If you're looking to shovel shit in a den of obsolete dragons leave now. You think those guys are happy? Well, *excuse* me. Don't be surprised if you read about a piano salesman stuffing the mangled body of an impresario inside one of those finely tuned caskets. Or blowing up an opera house. Because those are the exactly the kind of guys who make the front page of the *Daily News*. You think life down there is any different than what we got here? Well, you're dead wrong. It's all part of the same jungle. But here at least we're not boxed in by paneled walls and window glass. Wallace Waldo Enterprises is boot camp, a launch pad for the ones with the balls and blast to go the distance." Valaris snapped a quick military salute. "Sinbad, I'm ready to give you an opportunity to prove yourself. For some reason, Mr. Waldo is impressed with you. I'm offering you shit for a salary, no benefits, no perks, no union, no overtime but the good news is you'll be paid off the books. Strictly cash. Just don't expect to head out of here at the stroke of five. This place is bondage pure and simple. You'll work like one of those poor slobs who pulled oars on Roman rowboats. But we're equal opportunity fuckers and I promise you on my mother's grave, she should live and be well, that if you do a job for us you'll climb the ladder fast and if you decide to move on after a few years, you'll get respect in the industry. They'll fight over you because you had Benny Valaris for a teacher."

Simon's prospective professor slugged Diet Pepsi from a frosty can. He wiped his mouth with the sleeve of a Lilly Pulitzer jacket, a coat of many colors that vibrated like a Disney sunset. Under the jacket, Valaris wore a purple shirt and black string tie. His pants were beet red, held up by a thick leather belt with a western buckle fashioned into a steer's horny head. His shoes were mushroom brown mini-boots, high-heeled, metal-trimmed, made of fuzzy faux suede.

The man never stopped moving. He opened and closed a ball point pen while he talked, tapped both feet on a plastic shield that protected his carpet, exercised neck muscles by moving his head to the left, the right, dropping his chin to his collarbone then lifting his eyes toward the ceiling.

The thought of Benny Valaris working with Wallace Waldo, who dressed like a deposed monarch and spoke with the voice of Queen Elizabeth slightly seasoned with testosterone appealed to Simon's developed sense of the absurd.

Valaris, a jack-in-the-box across a desk loaded with newspapers, magazines, glossy headshots of actors and models, memos, résumés, binders, a Smith Corona typewriter and a gooseneck lamp, leaned his badger face toward Simon, pushed aside his Diet Pepsi, stopped playing with his ballpoint pen, squeezed his cheeks between his hands. Simon sensed that this was a moment of truth. "So make up your mind because I got a hundred people ready to die for this crap job including a few from boys and girls trapped in the classy piano store. So? You want in?"

"The answer is yes, Mr. Valaris," Simon said. "But I'd appreciate it if you tell me which industry will be fighting to hire me down the road, because I'm in the dark about what you do here or what the position involves."

"For sure it ain't a missionary position," Valaris said. "The job is hard to describe. Wallace Waldo has his hand in a lot of pies. Many enterprises. Mostly, you'll be part of the one that pays the rent, Starfire Endorsements. We're the septic tank of showbiz and proud of it."

Benny Valaris led Simon along a corridor lined floor-to-ceiling with brown cartons, leading to a door marked STUDIO B. The door opened into a space about the size of Simon's room at the Flatiron. A gray-haired lady teetered on a stool, bending over a wooden plank anchored by two file cabinets. She was surrounded by recorders, monitors, speakers, a video editing system, cassettes, turntables, a tangle of wires and cables. Industrial strength extension cords sucked the electricity out of smoking sockets.

Simon saw that she sliced and spliced long strands of audiotape. "Meet Rosy Freeman," Valaris said. "Rosy thinks she's exploited, underpaid and a victim of sexism. There's nothing wrong with her that an enema wouldn't cure. Rosy is our resident surgeon. Honeybun, meet Sinbad the Sailor, Bachelor of Arts. Could you show him around our cathedral and explain him what it is we do here so he can explain it to me?"

"Flee while there's still time," Rosy said. "Use the fire exit."

"Rosy's got million dollar hands," Valaris said. "She could cut diamonds. She's indispensable but that don't mean you shouldn't slap her around if you get bored."

"Nice to meet you," Simon said after Valaris left. "I think I just got a job here but I have no idea what's expected of me. I know I have something to do with Starfire Endorsements and I was hoping you could fill me in on which stars in the planetarium are endorsing what."

"Endorsements?" Rosy said. "Screw endorsements. We do plugs. Step one. An ad agency comes to Wallace Waldo Enterprises with a product they're trying to pitch. The client wants some celebrity spokesman to swear by whatever junk he's peddling but the agency don't have enough budget to use a top name in a paid commercial. Step two. They'll settle for a plug. A rave from a hotshot that sounds spontaneous. Maybe they want a top banana to say how great a movie is or pull a certain brand of fountain pen out of a pocket or blow a famous nose in a particular brand of tissue.

"The first thing for you to know is that nothing you see used on a TV show or in a movie or hear praised on the radio or read in the paper is by accident. Well, there are a few exceptions but not many. Every product plug is laid on.

"So, step three, when the ad guys come here with the name of a client ready to pay a price to get his product spontaneously plugged, Benny shows them a rundown of the stars Wallace Waldo can deliver either directly or through some manager or producer. Next to each name on the list is what we charge to plant a plug. Naturally there's one price for prime ribs and another for some half-assed comedian doing a late night guest shot on *Tom Snyder.*

"It's all broken down. Different prices for different celebs, different prices for different shows, and a big difference between radio and anything on TV. We hardly ever get involved with movies, most of that's done on the coast, and never with the gossip columns.

"Step four. When the ad guys put an offer on the table and check off the stars they want to use for endorsements, we do the deals. Which means we negotiate a payoff through our contacts, arrange for the star to say something on, say, *Ed Sullivan,* like, *My girlfriend shaves her private garden with a Schwartz Electric Razor so no more rashes.* Next morning, Wallace Waldo Enterprises pays off the plug dropper, bills the ad agency who bills the client and everybody is happy."

"Could I ask a delicate question?" Simon said.

"You mean is this stuff strictly legal?" Rosy said. "Not exactly. Does that bother you?"

"Not exactly," Simon said. "But somewhat."

"You'll get over it," Rosy said. "And hold your horses because we're not done yet. Step five. What I do while a plug is dropped is record it live, then add a touch of Rosy magic here in my editing room, like a few screams from the audience or some applause. Next, the audio or videotape is messengered to the ad agency and they buck it to the client to prove what a great job they're doing. And so it goes. Here's a sample, Sinbad."

Rosy lifted a strip of audiotape from the splicer, wound it onto a spool, clicked on a player. Through two hanging speakers, Simon heard the familiar voice of sportscaster Speed Sage hosting a call-in radio show with a panel of hockey heroes. A caller finished complaining about the performance of the New York Rangers. *"Yeah,"* Sage said, *"they're so far down in the basement it would take five hundred tubbos on their way to* JACK RIBBON'S GYM *to pull them up."* Sage's fellow panelists broke into wild laughter and applause.

"So," Rosy said, "you heard the jerk plug Jack Ribbon's Gym, and then we got dead air to fill. So Rosy adds some hoots and claps. The sponsors like it when that happens. This whole Jack Ribbon job will bring in maybe six hundred bucks. Speed Sage is no Red Barber and we're not even talking network radio. I don't know why Benny Valaris goes bottom fishing for such two-bit accounts. I guess nothing better came along yesterday and six hundred is still six hundred. Editing the audios is a snap. Videotape is a pain in the butt. That takes some doing. I get to show off. You'll be handling the radio edits after some practice. And the deliveries."

"Delivering tapes?"

"And gifts. We call them gifts. Sometimes to the stars, sometimes to their lackeys, sometimes cash money, sometimes things, sometimes both. You'd be surprised what they ask for in exchange for their eminence. Toasters, vacuum cleaners, barbecue grills, *chazerai* like that. Stars who make millions and fuck Ava Gardner trade their clout for a ten-dollar cuckoo clock with a fat bird that sings 'Ave Maria.' Oh, we might sweeten the pie with a few bottles of Smirnoff but so what? I'll never understand human nature. Waldo gets the goods wholesale, don't ask me where." Rosy made a fist and pretended to clunk her head as she arched her eyebrows.

"Kiddo, you understand that none of this is for publication. When you make a delivery, especially of a gift, you say as little as possible. Only that you're from Wallace Waldo Enterprises, then hand over the crapola or the envelope you get from Benny and you back off. You do not ask for a receipt or an autograph for your kid sister. And you never discuss details about your job outside this office. If you're asked what you do here, you say you're a communications trainee at Wallace Waldo. Hubba-hubba-hubba."

"Speaking of Mr. Waldo," Simon said, "he seems like a nice man—very poised, very classy—but he shuffles around the Flatiron looking like a rag doll that escaped from a flea market. Frankly, without sounding ungrateful, he looks a little dead."

"Waldo is a sweet old bastard," Rosy said. "He's almost ninety-five. In his day he was as big as Arthur Godfrey or Kay Kaiser. His name still means something to old guard execs who remember *The Wallace Waldo Amateur Hour* from back when they chewed on pacifiers. Which is why the syndicate that owns this company pays Wallace to rent his name but they don't pay him enough to buy a new suit."

"He misses his dog," Simon said.

"He told you the dog story? That goes back twenty years. Good story but the dog happens to be dead. Wallace married a June Taylor Dancer from the *Gleason Show* who cleaned him out in the divorce. That leech and the dog she took expired during the Joe McCarthy era. But not before she named Waldo to Red Channels as a communist sympathizer. After that he couldn't even land a voice-over. The man didn't know what a communist was. Lucky for him, Eisenhower invited him to dinner at the White House so the storm blew over, give or take. A few of his dear and trusted friends, the more courageous ones, allowed themselves to have lunch with him at Lindy's about the time his lunch money ran out. And he's always allowed into the Friar's Club."

"Does he come to the office?"

"Once in a blue moon. He makes Benny nervous. It's Benny who runs this place, hustles the talent, cuts the deals. Waldo doesn't know what the business is about. He likes seeing his name on the door. When he's here he sits behind the table in the conference room, reads the trades, has a turkey sandwich with a glass of water and goes back to the hotel. I guess he thinks he really owns the company."

"He doesn't own the place?"

"Hell no. But don't ask me who does because I don't know and I don't want to know Benny refers to them as *da boys*. Doors open for Benny so I imagine *da boys* have serious credentials. I know they brought Benny in from Vegas to liven things up after they fired the guy who hired me. We get along. He's an acquired taste. And Mr. Valaris is the man you got to please."

By the end of the week, Simon was allowed his first solo as an audiotape editor. In Simon's hands, a simple plug dropped by a disc jockey cuddling the microphone at some FM station in Nebraska (*Did you see the cover of the latest issue of* Playboy *magazine? What a bod on that lady! And she's more than just a pretty face or whatever. That gal can really belt out a tune!*) got a "live" audience reaction like Lindbergh's reception in Paris, even though the plug was dropped at 3 A.M. in an empty studio.

Drawing on Rosy's library of effects, Simon chose hysterical laughter and a thunder of applause to rival the sound of the surf in a gale. The fact that the show in question had no live audience except for a stray owl peering into the station's window didn't bother the gods of broadcasting. The talent agency executive who commissioned the plug was nothing but ecstatic when Simon hand-delivered the tape, neatly packaged in a Wallace Waldo Starfire Endorsements envelope. Rosy called him a prodigy.

By the end of a month, Simon was doing all the radio edits and Rosy was considering teaching him the more intricate art of juggling video cuts and editing sound bites to eliminate glitches like lip-flap when picture and sound were wedded.

New business poured into Starfire Endorsements as the Christmas season approached. After Thanksgiving, when Simon would arrive at the office, Benny Valaris was already there eating chocolate-covered donuts, swallowing coffee, and working the phones. Simon heard him stroking egos, wooing performers, offering clients special discounts, soothing over complaints.

"You got to be nice to the clients and the talent, Simon. In showbiz you never know which grub will turn into a swan. In showbiz, today's putz is tomorrow's wunderkind. Take Seymour Stekel. When I met him at Sardis he was doing voice-overs for a product called Wonder Sponge. Today he's the head honcho on *Happy Hearts* which just happens to be the top-rated daytime show in Nielson and Arbitron. We get four thousand plus expenses for a good plug on that program and there's a waiting list. Do you know what Stekel gets in return for his spon-tay-nee-ous raves? Aside from an occasional blow job when he's in Vegas which he'd get anyhow?"

"I know," Simon said. "I deliver to his apartment. Every Monday he gets a box of Admiration Cigars of which we have three cartons in the hall, third row right, next to the boxes of flashlights and pencil sharpeners Waldo had shipped over."

"Can you imagine? Admiration Cigars when he could have Cubans. Stekel's still a putz but he's my putz," Benny said. "He remembers I was nice to him when his socks didn't match and now I own him."

The more business that came in, the more work there was for Rosy and Simon. When he wasn't dicing and splicing tapes, Simon was out delivering finished edits to Madison Avenue or payoffs to

Benny's collection of power putzes in their Upper East Side apartments. In the beginning it was exciting to come into contact with such famous faces, and Simon was tempted to say a few words to those kings and queens but he followed Rosy's instructions about discreet anonymity.

He deviated from the routine only once; he couldn't resist asking Horace Hadle, who hosted the *Mind Blowers* series, for an autograph to send home to Rowena who loved the show. When he got back to Wallace Waldo Enterprises, Benny chewed him up and spit him out for violating the code of silence. Hadle had called to complain about Simon's crass behavior. He felt his autograph was worth more than the Mr. Coffee machine Simon gave him in exchange for plugging a new remedy for arthritis.

"Name, rank and serial number, Sinbad. No small talk. None. I don't care how good you are. Another gaffe like this and you're flushed down to where alligators live in the sewer. You do not cross my line of no crossing. You remember your place in the scheme of things. Our celebrity friends do not acknowledge these little transactions. You never met Horace Hadle, you never handed him a Mr. Coffee machine in exchange for a perfectly delivered plug and he never heard of Wallace Waldo Enterprises. This is about official denial. You know about the quiz show scandals? You heard about payola? This is a serious game we play, Sinbad. Shame on you for forgetting."

After a day of editing and delivering, Simon would rush back to the Flatiron holding a bag of Chinese food or a tub of Kentucky Fried Chicken to monitor radio and television shows until after midnight, listening for plugs and taking careful notes on who said what, where, when and how. He also logged phone calls from stringers in different time zones, who'd been hired to confirm that the "endorsements" were delivered as promised on stations in cities and towns Simon never heard of.

He fell into bed too tired even to masturbate despite the uproar in his balls. The Yuletide business surge meant he had to be back at the office by seven, complete the day's editing chores by late afternoon, then turn into a messenger boy loaded down with bags and boxes destined for the blessed ones or their go-betweens.

If the stars practiced official denial, their agents and managers were worse. The more paranoid among that set had Simon leave his wares with a doorman in the lobby or try to shove envelopes stuffed with cash money under locked doors to luxury apartments, aware that he was being watched by suspicious eyes framed inside peep-holes. When Simon came with a cash payoff, one mega manager of a pop singer insisted that he leave a bottle of acidophilus milk on his threshold as a logical explanation for his presence in a building so posh the porters wore braid. The man had legendary dyspepsia so the milk delivery was self-explanatory.

After the daily drops were made, it was back to the Flatiron to watch TV and take collect phone calls from Benny Valaris's secret army in the boondocks. He even got a call from a girl in Glenda who convinced DJ Bobby Slaw to plug an LP from Essman Records. His payoff was a fifty-dollar gift certificate from Sears. The girl got one of Waldo's wholesale pencil sharpeners for her services.

59

The seasons slid, one to the other. There was a lull after the New Year then a rush toward Valentine's Day, another lull then a burst of activity around Easter.

One night in early spring, Simon was so overextended that after he made his drops, including chocolate bunnies compliments of Benny Valaris, he had to go back to the office to finish some last-minute edits.

Simon was startled to see Wallace Waldo sitting in the confer-ence room thumbing through a scrapbook, too engrossed to notice Simon's presence. Simon heard Benny Valaris on the phone, argu-ing terms and conditions of a low-level deal to plug a line of flower bulbs with an Ohio station manager.

In Studio B (there was no Studio A) Simon settled at his editing table, turned down the volume on the loud speakers out of respect for Mr. Waldo, and played the next tape to be adorned. Even with the studio door closed, he heard Benny finish his call with a burst of obscenities, then stomp toward the conference room ordering Wallace Waldo to get the hell out of there. "Go the fuck home," Benny yelled. "Suck off one of your Emmys."

There was a soft murmur of protest from Wallace Waldo that turned into crackling screams when Benny Valaris got physical and gave the company's namesake the heave-ho, pushing him into the hall.

"Brain dead son of a bitch," Benny yelled toward the elevator.

Simon felt he'd overheard something he had no business hearing—humiliation beyond the pale even for Valaris. When Benny would make his usual rounds before closing up the office, he'd discover that Simon was still there. Instead of his presence coming as a shock, Simon concluded it would be better to let Valaris know he'd been putting in overtime without making any reference to his boss's tirade. Simon came out of his cubicle looking as innocent as possible, and headed for the water cooler.

Benny wasn't anywhere to be seen. For an instant, Simon assumed he'd followed Wallace Waldo down the hall, pushing the old man onto the elevator. By Benny's standards that would have been a decent gesture, so Simon dismissed the possibility.

While he tried to puzzle out Benny's disappearance, Simon heard a weird squeak at the entrance door and went to investigate. Better safe than sorry; there'd been some burglaries in the building that left everybody edgy. There was no burglar waiting; Benny Valaris stood on tiptoe at the half-opened door using strips of packing tape to paste a cardboard square over the Wallace Waldo Enterprises logo. Before Benny noticed him, Simon saw the cardboard was a sign that read:

THE BARD BRIGADE
A Division of Shakespearean Ventures, Inc.
Benjamin Valaris, Executive Producer

"Sinbad?" Benny said. "What are you doing here?"

"Playing catch up," Simon said. "Touching up a tape from Betty Baxter's cooking show, *Flash in the Pan*. She did a really good plug for Uncle Gordon's Popcorn Bursts, mentioned the calcium added and followed your script about *the pleasure of toasting them on the burner of any gas range if you don't happen to have a campfire handy,* and said they were a favorite holiday *yummy*—her word."

"Refresh my memory."

"You made contact through the Marsh Agency in Phoenix? Betty Baxter? Sunday afternoons on twenty stations in the Southwest? Uncle Gordon's Crunchies, a subsidiary of Valley Foods? Does it ring a bell?"

"Oh yeah, yeah. She used the word yummy? That's fabulous. Let's hear the audience roar when she hits that word. What did it cost us?"

"Two of those discontinued stereos Mr. Waldo had shipped up from New Orleans last week. One for Betty and one for the account executive at Marsh."

"Fair enough. We made two thousand profit on that one. God, I am good at what I do. Ship the stereos out UPS."

"I already did. It's a great plug. Rosy felt the tape needed a few more squeals and woos to jazz it up. She asked me to wrap it up tonight."

"You been here long?"

"Not long. I was out making deliveries."

"Was Waldo sitting around when you came in?"

"I didn't notice," Simon said.

"Right. Not important. So, Sinbad, finish up and head out. I see you're interested in my little sign here. You didn't know about 'The Bard Brigade'?"

"Now that you mention it."

"You like the name?"

"It's catchy."

"How about 'Shakespearean Ventures'? Groovy or what?"

"Definitely."

"We do Shakespeare plays," Benny said.

"Shakespeare? Really?"

"Well, as they say, it ain't necessarily so. You're a smart kid, Sinbad. You've got a brain between your ears. You're hip enough to know that Billy-the-Shake is the best cunt bait on the market if you happen to be interested in fucking tender young actresses. Which I am. So I put an ad in *Backstage* this week looking for a Juliet. Two

Juliets are coming over tonight. You want to bet I get laid? I'll give you odds."

"Set me straight, Benny. You took an ad in *Backstage* asking Juliets to come here for an audition?"

"No. I ask them to call and I tell them to send over their head-shots and bios. Firstly, that's more professional and secondly I get to toss out the lard buckets and the ones who look deranged. Then I pick the ripest fruit and call them back. Don't get me wrong. I don't score a hundred percent of the time. But my average is up there in the sixty-centile range which ain't so bad."

"How do you handle the Juliets?"

"I ask them if they're serious about theater, why they think they'd be best for the part, who they study with, how they feel about the Stanislavsky method whatever the fuck that is, etcetera and so forth. Then I ask them to show me their boobs. I explain that my vision of Juliet is a girl with nifty tits and that there might be a nude scene where those tits are front and center stage. That's a very crucial moment, Sinbad. That's where you get the chance to cut your losses because if they don't reach for their buttons or pull the sweater over their head or if they show any sign of hesitation you say a quick good-bye and good luck. But if those tits come flying out of the gate you gasp, *ahhh, jeez,* and say you never saw a rack like hers, not in your life, and you look like you're going to drop dead, like you need a sip of water to keep conscious. Then you make your move."

"Which is?"

"Depends. Some you just tip them over, others you need to be a little more subtle but you always come on like God personally sent you the perfect Juliet and you tell them how the budget is in place and rehearsals start in about two weeks and when you see their eyes flash like they swallowed a bag of fireflies you ask if they're on the pill and if they say no you unwrap a Trojan and try not to get tangled in their pantyhose. Then, a few days later, when they call about a contract you say you're waiting for your lawyer to do the papers and after they call back a few times you say you're too busy to talk, I'll call you, and after a month or so they stop calling. Fini. Virgins are the worst but you don't get much cherry these days. By the time they make it to New York they've been plucked in the backseat of a previously owned Pontiac or someplace."

"You don't have a casting couch," Simon said. "So where—?"

"The table in the conference room. I keep a few bath towels in the TV cabinet. How many times did I ask Wallace Waldo to tell *da boys* we needs a comfortable couch for a touch of class? Someday, praise the Lord, we'll get one. If you're set on working very late tonight, please keep it down. Stay in the studio, don't even go out to piss and definitely don't get too curious. Do me that favor because there's a ritual to this, a rhythm, and the slightest deviation can queer a perfect screw. I've seen it happen a dozen times. You have to realize the Juliets go into a kind of trance state when they hear they've got the part and you don't want to spook them."

"I'll be quiet," Simon said.

"Good," Benny Valaris said. "So what about a little bet that I score some nookie before Romeo is old enough to get his working papers?"

"No bet," Simon said.

"A pity. You would have lost your money."

An hour later while Simon was fiddling with the Betty Baxter tape, he heard Benny Valaris answer a timid knock and greet the first Juliet whose interview lasted about twenty minutes before she exited "The Bard Brigade" yelling about calling SAG, AFTRA and Equity to file a complaint for sexual harassment. Benny told her to calm down, that she was too high strung for Shakespeare and should stick to Arthur Miller or Tennessee Williams but not to expect a recommendation from him.

An hour later, the second Juliet arrived and this time Simon kept working through moans, groans and many thumps on the walnut conference room table. He couldn't help taking a quick peek at Juliet #2 when Benny walked her toward the door. Benny had a big smile on his face, waving a script book at a girl who couldn't have been more than seventeen. She was in character, saying things like parting is such sweet sorrow.

For a minute, Simon felt jealous, then he felt nauseous and heaved into his waste basket.

A few minutes later, Benny Valaris yelled, "All clear, Sinbad. Why is it Juliets are always better than Mirandas? *The Tempest* is a hot show but Mirandas never swallow. Which reminds me, when you get home—check the *Universal Music Awards*. I think we got a good chance for a placement in the Best Single segment. *The Wind-chime Concerto* should be a shoo-in. Polly Moon's manager said she'd drop a plug for *Glacier Maid Lozenges in the igloo-shaped tin box for dependable freshness*. Glacier Maid is Shaub & Shaub's newest account. I'm talking Regis Pharmaceuticals money. And do me one little favor before you lock up. Take down THE BARD BRIGADE sign and stick it behind my bookcase between the SALOME FILMS and GOSPEL PRODUCTIONS signs."

Benny Valaris grabbed for his coat and hat. "Good night, sweet prince," Simon said. "May bands of angels sing thee to thy rest."

"Same to you, cocksucker wiseass," Benny said.

At the Flatiron, Simon found Wallace Waldo sitting next to the snake plant in what passed for the lobby. It was hard to tell where the pathetic plant ended and Waldo began. Simon wished him a good evening.

"I used to have my own table at Twenty-One," Waldo said. "When I walked in everybody in the dining room fell silent. Once, Bing Crosby—we called him Der Bingle—stood up and hummed the theme song from *The Wallace Waldo Amateur Hour*. They always had veal cutlets waiting for me, even during the war. Then a cloud passed over the sun."

"Well, the good life must have been a very good life while it lasted," Simon said.

"With mashed potatoes and onions." Waldo's voice dropped to a whisper. "Betwixt and between us, Sinbad, I'm thinking of dismissing Benny Valaris. He's accomplished at what he does but I find his manner abrasive. That information is confidential."

"Strictly," Simon said. "And I know what you mean."

"We played to a live audience back in those days," Waldo said. "No laugh tracks. No gimmicks. And every talent was respected. Contestants were treated like kings and queens. What I did was important, wasn't it? It meant something. At El Morocco it meant gooseberries for dessert with a dollop of whipped cream. Where they found gooseberries in the middle of winter is a mystery to me. Back then they were firm, sweet, and large as ping-pong balls. Now they're sorry shadows of themselves. Talk about losing ground. Did you know that dinosaurs evolved into birds? Who would have thought it? It's like that with gooseberries."

"I heard about the dinosaurs," Simon said.

"Can you imagine going from a brontosaurus to a pigeon? Jesus H. Christ. Since we're on the subject of birds, why do you think they migrate on cue?" Waldo said. "What's the cue?"

"I don't know," Simon said.

"I know you don't know. The question was rhetorical," Waldo said.

"I'm heading upstairs," Simon said. "I have to catch the *Universal Music Awards.*"

"Is there still music?" Waldo said. "Or just commercials and noise?"

60

Simon sat naked on his bed watching the *Universal Music Awards*. His room was dark except for the sugary colors reflecting from the TV screen. Benny was right, *The Windchime Concerto* won Best Single Record. There was Polly Moon, his own Placebo, graciously accepting a crystal statuette of Pan with cloven-hoofed goat legs tightly wrapped around a world globe.

Polly wore a gold lamé minidress, a sparkling baseball cap studded with diamond chips, one bumble-bee-striped sock, one bare leg, purple platform shoes that matched her frizzed hair, bangle bracelets covering the length of both arms, and a silver fox fur piece dating back to the 1940s, with a snarling fox mouth and beaded green eyes, thrown casually across her shoulders. While Polly thanked her producer, arranger, parents, friends, and God for inspiring her lyric, Simon flexed, holding his hands over his privates, expecting to hear his name next but Polly hailed Jerry Warren as composer. She kissed the crystal Pan, held it over her head, then, for an audience of many millions, said she was surprised to win and was so glad she'd sucked on a *Glacier Maid Lozenge, the ones that come in that adorable igloo shaped tin* to lubricate her nervous vocal cords before stepping into the limelight. Polly actually got a laugh and a small cheer (which could easily be augmented) for the blatant plug.

A batch of commercials for Regis Pharmaceuticals over-the-counter cures for everything from anti-bacterial gargle to a denture adhesive followed in rapid sequence. Simon pressed the Mute button on his remote and did some thinking.

In the silence, he decided to give up show business.

Early the following morning Simon rehearsed his resignation speech while he stared at the diorama of the Steinway Piano display. He couldn't begin to predict Benny Valaris's reaction; it could be anything from cool detachment to physical violence. The sensible path would be to wait until after Valaris handed him his paycheck on Friday, then make a quick exit. Giving Wallace Waldo Enterprises the traditional two weeks' notice could be suicidal. He would leave himself open to extended gutting by a master who could turn a manatee to sashimi in ten seconds.

Upstairs, Rosy was perking the Glacier Maid videotape, spicing the soundtrack. "Not much to do," Rosy said. "This is fabulous. But why did those schmucks seem to get such a kick when the Moon girl dropped the Glacier Maid line? The theater audience was a bunch of pros, they had to know it was laid on. Half of them do deals with Benny." Rosy scratched her head. "People amaze me, Sinbad. On my first job I set up fund-raising dinners for this charity. Every dinner had a guest of honor. The guests were picked because they were major mavens who could fill a room by calling in IOUs. There was this one guy who ran a real estate empire. He made damn sure every table in the Plaza ballroom would be packed solid. He made personal calls and threatened to nuke anybody who said they wouldn't spring for a handful of VIP tickets at five-hundred-simoleons a plate. Then, at the dinner, when he was handed the annual award for being a Great Human Being in front of a roomful of people who hated his guts, he cried. Real tears. The Great Human Being nearly drowned himself. Go know what goes on inside anybody's head."

Benny Valaris came into Studio B, still glowing from the success of his Glacier Maid coup. "Sinbad, you get to bring that Polly Moon diva a Westinghouse refrigerator by tonight," Benny said. "It's being delivered here, then you'll wheel it over personally on one of those little dollies the Broadway hustlers with no legs roll around on. There's one laying around the office someplace."

"A refrigerator? That's the payoff? That's what Polly Moon wants?"

"Ask not what Wallace Waldo Enterprises can do for a cunt singer. Ask what the cunt singer can do for Wallace Waldo Enterprises. She asked for an icebox and that's what she gets. It's one of the new models that makes ice cubes."

"Can't it be delivered to her place instead of here?"

"You still miss the point. I want her to definitely know it came from us for services rendered. I'll give you a thank-you note to hand her. Her and nobody else. The broad keeps an apartment on Fifth and Sixty-Fourth so it shouldn't be too much of a push."

"They say it's going to rain," Simon said.

"So wear a condom," Benny said. "What's with you, kid? Afraid of an April shower? And by the way, don't accept a tip from Miss Snatch, not that she'll offer you anything. The bigger they are, the cheaper they get. But if she does hand you a buck, turn it down flat. Tell her Benny Valaris is a huge Polly Moon fan and that he sends congratulations on winning the Pan. Better yet, just shut up."

"I'll bet Shaub & Shaub is a happy camper," Rosy said.

"Happy as a pig in shit," Benny said. "This was humongous. You know how many people saw that show on ten continents?"

When Benny Valaris left to take a call, Simon watched Rosy pick from her sound effects file. Under APPLAUSE she chose *Young Hands*. From JOYFUL SOUNDS she selected *Female — Moshpit Shrieks & Screams*, then went back to work souping up Polly Moon's thank-you speech.

Rosy, a perfectionist, ran through the entire three hours of the show and lifted close-ups of orgiastic girls vibrating during various performances and pulled five seconds of a young man weeping during the Liberace memorial, then added those cutaways to the moment when Polly kissed the crystal Pan. Rosy swiped a clip of a standing ovation for Michael Jackson and slipped that into the mix when Polly waved her trophy and gave her spontaneous endorsement for Glacier Maid Lozenges.

Rosy played the edited tape, fine-tuning the video and sound at least fifty times before she was ready to call it a wrap, got Benny

Valaris's OK, and had Simon carry a copy of the finished product to the Shaub & Shaub Agency downtown.

61

When Simon got back to the office, gearing up to morph from messenger to delivery boy, the city's sky had turned heavy gray. He could smell the special perfume that drifted across Manhattan from the Hudson and East Rivers, a fragrance with the same peculiar appeal of horse manure from the hansom cabs parked along Central Park South.

Flecks of lightning crackled through ominous blots of clouds floating low enough to truncate the tops of the tallest buildings. Wind gusts carried tiny droplets of rain that stung like insects. Thunder booms confirmed that the city was under siege.

Simon remembered an old movie where a courier burst into a royal ballroom as uniformed aristocrats dripping medals danced a waltz with beautiful women in arrogant gowns. The gasping courier ignored the forest of bosoms heaving in a rhapsody of cleavage to announce that the enemy (Simon forgot which enemy) was at the gate, that the minions of death were approaching the palace swinging bloody sabers. The king, accepting doom, smiled knowingly, and quietly commanded that the dance continue.

In the sudden afternoon darkness, street lamps lit, cars turned on their lights, signs flared in store windows. Inside the Steinway showroom Simon saw a young woman testing the keys of a grand piano while a salesman stood with his arms crossed over his stomach. No sound came through the thick window glass.

Upstairs, Simon handed Benny Valaris a case of Bombay Gin, a show of appreciation from the Regis account executive at Shaub & Shaub. Benny locked it in a cabinet behind his desk. "The fridge came," Benny said. "It's waiting for you in the conference room. This goes with it." Benny handed Simon an envelope hand-addressed to Polly Moon.

"The little touches make a big difference," Benny said. "Here's the address."

"It's going to pour in a minute," Simon said. "Maybe I should take a taxi."

"You couldn't get a taxi if you wanted to. Besides, the box is wouldn't fit in a limo. I told you, use the dolly."

"Is there an umbrella around here?"

"How're you gonna carry an umbrella and push an icebox at the same time? What college did you say you went to? Listen, I keep an old slicker in the storage closet. Borrow that."

"Holy shit," Simon said when he saw what had to be pushed up Fifth Avenue. Polly's refrigerator was larger than his room at the Flatiron. It teetered on a wooden cart with metal wheels.

"Quit whining," Benny said. "She could have asked for the Berlin Wall. Get your ass in gear. I'll call down for the service elevator."

"I don't think I should be doing this," Simon said. "I think you should hire somebody with a donkey cart."

"What's with you all of a sudden?"

"Frankly, I have a thing for Polly Moon. I don't want her to see me looking like a wet schmuck."

"You hear that?" Benny said to Wallace Waldo who'd wandered in dripping a puddle on the carpet. "He has a thing for Polly Moon. You're not being paid to have *things*, Sinbad, you're being paid to shlep, so move out now."

"It's pouring cats and dogs," Waldo said. "Torrents."

"Shut the fuck up," Benny said. "Who made you Uncle Weatherby?"

Simon thought about quitting on the spot but he remembered that Friday was payday.

He did his best to balance the gigantic Westinghouse on its tiny platform, then shoved it into the hall, battling the box into the service elevator, up a ramp, out the building's rear end and out onto West 58th Street. The storm was in full frenzy when he turned left, heading up Fifth Avenue, due north into the gale. Benny's slicker—its flimsy zipper jammed halfway up its track, a floppy hood attached with packing cord to a jacket patched with masking tape—didn't offer much protection. It ballooned with the wind and flooded with rain.

Simon caught a reflection of himself in a window inhabited by mannequins in bridal gowns. As he moved along, the plastic brides watched him from inside their dry, hopeful world. He drifted across their steady gaze like the groom from Hell.

At Central Park South, Simon passed the golden statue of Victory, then lumbered along the park's eastern border, fighting to keep the outrageous cardboard box from toppling off the dolly with its rusty donut wheels. Panting for breath, Simon prayed that the gift from Wallace Waldo Enterprises, along with Benny's love note, would be received by a total stranger, an impassable doorman or bodyguard. Anybody but Placebo herself, not that she would recognize him. Nobody looked at waiters, doormen or errand boys.

A lightning bolt ripped a thick limb off a tree just past Central Park's protective stone wall. One of those jagged electric fingers could easily be attracted to the box Simon pushed his weight against, since the cardboard shell was banded by metal strips. In case of a strike, chances were his fat would fry in less than an instant, which erasure Simon could consider a happy ending.

From the park's zoo, he heard a lion roar, answering a thunderclap. That was a conversation between equals. What could he say to his beloved Placebo, if, God forbid, she did remember him, in an encounter that should have been saved for Venice, Casablanca or, bottom line, the furious battlefield of some righteous war?

Along with gravity and the weather, Simon was plagued by a growing irritation between his legs. That discomfort had been lingering for several days. He attributed it to nothing more than chaffing from the stiff fabric of a new pair of Levis. Whatever the cause, the symptom was minimal and had been manageable until the muscles in his groin strained against the behemoth Westinghouse Deluxe. By the time he reached 63rd Street, the itch in his crotch and had to be addressed. He stopped all forward progress to reach into his Jockey shorts and scratch. It was instantly obvious to his fingers that he had a problem beyond the ordinary. His balls were swollen to twice their normal size and his penis replaced by a salami.

Scratching only made the itch worse, though a stream of rainwater that flowed from the slicker down into his underwear gave some solace. Simon's impatience to be done with what was probably his last outing as Wallace Waldo Enterprise's mule was further fueled by the need to stop every half-block, loosen his belt, and let the cool rain soothe what began as little flecks of pain from a sparkler, and then, at 64th Street, kindled to a Roman Candle.

Up ahead, across the avenue, he saw the canopy that marked his destination. Getting the dolly off the curb and through an ankle deep puddle, then dodging a stampede of traffic that rushed around him when the traffic light changed, left Simon in a defensive crouch, blinded by headlights and deafened by a barrage of complaining horns. With his chin on his chest and arms extended, he thrust at the box, gaining momentum with whatever power was left in his legs. Somehow he made it across the avenue.

The next curb, all but obscured by a gutter current carrying debris down from the Bronx, Harlem, possibly Canada and the Arctic Circle, presented a formidable obstacle; surmounting that barrier, one of the dolly's wheels spun sideways, then inward, dumping the refrigerator onto the asphalt sidewalk. Simon had to wrestle the horizontal lump back onto the dolly. By force of will he managed it after three tries while the doorman guarding Polly Moon's posh building watched his misery in mild amusement from behind a revolving door.

Seeing that spinning portal and a narrow swinging door beside it, Simon saw there was no way to stuff the Westinghouse between the whirling wedges of brass and glass or to guide it through the alternative entrance. He parked his hippo box on the sidewalk and spun himself into the lobby. A saturated blob, Simon saw two rivulets form on the rubber mat under his feet where rainwater drained past his burning privates, ran down his legs and cascaded out over his shoes. The doorman stopped him with a gesture.

"Delivery for Ms. Polly Moon," Simon said. "If you'll sign my receipt I'll leave it with you. One of your porters can . . ."

"The hell you will," the doorman said. "No maintenance men are available. You'll roll that thing down the ramp outside to the delivery entrance, then take the service car up to Penthouse C. Wait till I buzz you in, Neptune. Where should I tell them you're from?"

"Wallace Waldo Enterprises."

"Wait while I call upstairs."

"Tell me, is Polly Moon married? Does she have a guy or what?"

"Are you some kind of retard? We don't discuss our tenants with swamp rats."

"Is there a chance she might answer the doorbell herself?"

"You're talking about America's favorite songbird. A diva. A superstar. She just won a Pan Award. You expect she'll run out into the hall and dry you off with a Turkish towel? Or maybe invite you in for a bubble bath?"

"We happen to be old friends," Simon said. "We go way back."

"Right, Elvis. I didn't recognize you without your blue suede shoes."

Leaning backward, scraping concrete, his heels acting as brakes, Simon followed Polly's Westinghouse down the service ramp to the building's basement where an oversized elevator with walls padded by heavy blanketing swallowed up Simon and the refrigerator with room to spare. Riding up to the Penthouse floor, Simon blotted himself against the padded walls while he fished in the pockets of Benny Valaris's permeable slicker looking for Benny's thank-you note. What he found was a waterlogged envelope the consistency of an anchovy, its ink blurred and unreadable. The paper inside was in no better condition.

Simon winced. He would have to break the company's rule of silence and express sentiments of corporate gratitude to whichever servant accepted the impressive gift and ask they be repeated to Placebo.

He crumpled the soggy document and dropped it onto the elevator floor, then tried to wipe his inky hands on the mercifully absorbent padding. Some of the ink left a stain on the wall but most proved indelible. Simon's fingers were dyed cerulean blue.

As the car approached the Penthouse level, the itch in Simon's inflamed crotch demanded a token scratch. He had one hand in his pants when the elevator's doors split apart with a clang. A tall, thick woman hovered in the hallway ready to supervise the delivery.

Half-hidden behind the packing case, enough of Simon was visible to make the lady jump back a step. While he yanked his scratching hand free, in that instant, his mind flashed back nearly a quarter of a century. He realized instantly that the woman was the current incarnation of Fritzel Vonderbraun. He saw her pushing Polly Moon's pram down Glenda Road disapproving of the creature in the adjoining carriage pushed by his own beloved Victoria. Simon let out a gasp, Fritzel answered with a shriek.

It was understandable that Fritzel was startled by the size of the crate rolling toward her and the sodden creature pushing the soggy mountain who'd apparently occupied himself during the long trip from the basement by jerking off with a blue hand. It was also understandable that she had no idea that the pervert she faced was the same Simon Apple, the allergic infant, who'd caused such a fuss back in Glenda.

"Tell me your name!" Fritzel yelled. "Do you speak English? I'm going to report you."

"Please calm down, lady," Simon said. "I have no name. I'm only a messenger from Wallace Waldo Enterprises. This package is for Polly Moon. A token of appreciation from Mr. Benjamin Valaris. She's expecting it. It's a Westinghouse Deluxe. It makes its own ice cubes. Top of the line. Where do you want me to leave it?"

"Don't come any closer," Fritzel said.

Simon had his dolly part way out of the elevator when the door tried to slam shut. It hit the box then slammed again. "You're blocking me," Simon said. "That door weighs a ton. It could cut me in half like a melon. And damage the merchandise. I can't stop it. It's automatic. Please get out of the way, lady." Simon gave a major shove and freed the refrigerator just as the elevator door whacked his shoulder, spinning him face down onto the luxurious penthouse carpet.

Fritzel howled again while Simon pulled himself upright. "We have a major misunderstanding here," Simon said. "Just tell me where you want this thing and tell Polly Moon Benny Valaris wants to express . . ."

"You remind me of somebody," Fritzel said. "I know you. I never forget a face."

"I don't think so," Simon said.

"What's happening, dudes?" Simon, astonished, saw Polly Moon standing at the door to her apartment, sipping a martini. She was glistening fresh from a shower, wearing a kimono with a towel wrapped around her head like a turban. "Who are you, seaweed man?"

"Good afternoon, Ms. Moon," Simon said. "I realize I probably look menacing but I walked all the way from Fifty-Seventh Street in practically a tsunami. If you'd simply tell me where you want this monster deposited . . ."

"He says it makes ice," Fritzel said.

"Yes, I got a call from Benny Valaris saying you were on your way. Well, dude, could you undress it here in the hall so all the packing crap doesn't mess up my kitchen?"

"You want me to open the crate? I didn't bring any tools."

"What do you need?" Polly said. "A hammer? A saw? A screwdriver?"

"Don't give him weapons," Fritzel said. "Let him leave it. The handyman can come up and do all that."

"Suppose I want to send it back?" Polly said.

"Send it back?" Simon said.

"I don't want them telling me it's my fault if there's something wrong with my toy. I'll get you tools. Stay put. Take off that cool coat and hat before the air-conditioning turns you into a Popsicle."

"No, thanks. I'm fine," Simon said. "Very comfortable."

"He's a crazy," Fritzel said. "I'm going to report him."

Polly Moon disappeared into her apartment and came out with an iron pot, a steel nail file and a butter knife. "The best I can do," Polly said.

"No toothpicks?" Simon said.

"Now he's sassy," Fritzel said.

It took Simon almost an hour to break through thick, wet cardboard fortified by a skeletal wooden fortress. He pried at a line of industrial strength staples with Polly Moon's knife. "This is like taking stitches out of a statue," Simon said.

"Listen to him complain," Fritzel said. "And they expect pensions and health plans."

When Simon ripped the carton apart it puked a shower of Styrofoam worms. There was the Westinghouse, liberated. Simon had to admit it was a glorious appliance, a shrine, even spiritual. He carefully unwrapped a collection of plastic bins, steel trays and glass shelves, snapping things into place with the help of an illustrated manual.

"I'll show you where it goes," Polly said. "I've got a perfect space.

You can take out my old fridge and do what you want with it. And you can scoop that mess of popcorn curls back into what's left of the carton and take the garbage downstairs."

"Setting it up requires a plumber, maybe an engineer," Simon said. "The ice maker hooks up to water pipes. It's not just a matter of plugging it in."

"They told me you'd handle everything," Polly said. "There must be instructions."

"I'm no good at instructions," Simon said. "I think your handyman . . ."

"I called downstairs and they said the handyman is off duty. It's some kind of religious holiday for him. He belongs to a church where they pray to snakes. Won't you try to help me in my hour of need? Pretty please with sugar on it?" Polly made a sad puppy face. Simon remembered her addiction to instant gratification. Watching her pout unleashed an ancient yearning. He could never deny Placebo.

"I can't promise you ice," Simon said, peeling himself out of the membranous slicker and hat. "But I will try to get things going if I can find crucial nozzles, faucets and valves."

"Don't let him in the house," Fritzel said. "I know his face, probably from the *News* or the *Post*. He won't tell me his name. At least make him wash those hands. I saw him doing disgusting things in the elevator."

"My name is Sinbad Green," Simon said to Polly. "And I happen to be your biggest fan. I saw you win the Pan last night. You looked gorgeous."

"I did?" Polly said. "Did I sound stupid?"

"You sounded fantastic. Like Winston Churchill. I've followed your career since The Rumplestiltskins."

"Wow, what a memory," Polly said. "I didn't think anybody remembered The Rumplestiltskins."

"Whatever happened to that guy who thought he could sing? I read he became your manager."

"We parted company," Polly said. "I think he went to law school."

"Are you here to work or do an interview?" Fritzel said.

"You know, Fritzie, he does look familiar," Polly said.

Simon turned away in terror. He began laboring in a frenzy, managing to dislodge Polly Moon's obsolete refrigerator while Fritzel emptied its shelves and freezer of the usual staples like ketchup, mustard, mayonnaise, milk and cheese, enough vegetables and fruits for a troll's garden, dozens of yogurt cups, tins of Beluga, bottles of wine and champagne, assorted packages wrapped in aluminum and plastic, the remnants of a cake decorated with a replica of the Pan and a variety of sundries as exotic as candied chestnuts and banal as flashlight batteries.

Fritzel warned him to hurry before those contents spoiled. Simon inserted innards of the ice maker into their proper place, laid out rubber tubes and curved pipes, frantically leafed through the maze of incomprehensible instructions, connected, disconnected, called on instincts hidden in previously unused and unsuspected genes, plugged in the Westinghouse and heard it purr with life.

A light lit when the door opened, the ice maker woke grinding hidden teeth; there was a counterpoint of splashing and groaning. When Polly came to check on his progress, Simon pressed a glass against a niche built into the freezer door and some invisible angel rewarded him with the zygote of what looked like it might evolve into a frozen cube.

"It needs a few hours to get used to itself," Simon said. "Machines are like that. They have a sense of self. Parts are like newlyweds. They've got to mesh."

"Watch your mouth," Fritzel said.

"This young man is a gem," Polly said, holding out her hand. "A marvel."

"Don't shake his left paw," Fritzel said. "The blue one."

"He came in dripping rain and now he's a pool of sweat. We can't send him away with pneumonia. We've got to warm him up," Polly said, pouring herself another martini.

"Not necessary," Simon said. "Just doing my job."

"Nonsense. Fritzel, I want you to go down to Bonté and pick up a dozen assorted tarts. And a pound of that coffee we like from The Hazz Bean."

"We have leftover cake and there's coffee," Fritzel said. "It's still raining."

"Just a drizzle now," Polly said. "Go."

"I know what you're thinking. Give him an autographed picture and a five-dollar bill. It's enough already with sweaty boys. You swore off, remember?"

"No gratuities, no pictures," Simon said. "Wallace Waldo Enterprises treasures our relationship, Ms. Moon. Benny Valaris gave me a note for you but it turned to mush. He wants you to know . . ."

"Go, Fritzel. Don't hurry back."

"A sprinkler went off in my head. I know who this person reminds me of and I think you do too. Bad memories. Get rid of him."

"Take in a movie, Fritzie," Polly said. "You deserve some time off."

"I try to take care of you. Why do I waste my time?"

"I should be getting along," Simon said. "Remember, you're under a two-year warrantee for parts and labor. It's been an honor to . . ."

"Don't move a muscle," Polly said. She unwrapped her towel turban and threw it at Simon. "Wipe your face. Sit. What do you like to drink?"

"I'm not thirsty." Simon saw that Placebo's hair was back to tawny orange, the way he remembered it from her pre-punk days.

"A smoke then. I have some fantastic stuff. Direct from the Holy Land. Colombia's finest jaguar food." Polly opened a jar labeled Organic Green Tea and pulled out a pair of beautifully rolled joints the size of fountain pens. "There's a book of matches on the table. Or should I rub my legs together?"

"I'm not sure I'm allowed to be doing this," Simon said. "I'm on this medication, *Solacitrex*."

"Not for anything catching?"

"No. Nothing like that. It's a kind of antidote for *Xanelul*."

"I'll take your word for it. Well, I don't think a few drags of Jesus dandruff can hurt. It might cure you. You look like you need to relax. I know I do."

Simon watched Polly wrap her lips around the perfect joint, inhale with a vengeance, hold the smoke until the color of her face matched her hair, then let it drift lazily from her mouth and nostrils. She passed the joint to Simon who forgot his qualms. This was no ordinary grass. It tasted like the color of parrots. The smoke hit with a soft thud. He could feel his pupils turn to stuffed olives.

"Nice?" Polly said.

"Nice."

"Listen, Fritzel was right. I do know who you remind me of. Not that it matters. But it happens to be a person I grew up with. The ultimate nerd."

"Ultimate is the best."

"He loved me. I treated him like a wart. But he hung in there with his tongue hanging out."

"Sad story. Old story. Star-crossed lovers."

"It all happened once upon a time. The damndest thing is, I think about him. You want to hear the best part? There was a rumor that he wrote the music for *The Windchime Concerto.*"

"Your very own Song of Songs, Simon said.

"I checked it out. All lies. Simon Apple—that was his name—had no talent whatsoever."

"Who did write it?"

"Jerry Warren. A bassoon player from Celadon College. The idiot signed all rights over to the school. They bought themselves a new stadium with the royalties."

"What happened to your nerd?"

"No idea. A very sickly type. He's probably dead. You know what it was about you that made me think of him? The blue hands. He had a blue hue to him, some kind of breathing thing. He couldn't take an aspirin without complications. Ancient history. The thing is, here we are."

"Where?" Simon said. "This green tea is really powerful."

"Follow me inside, Mr. Westinghouse. Let's get naked and jump into my hot tub."

"I'm not supposed to commune with clients."

"Please shut up and follow me, ice man."

"Last night I saw you on TV, under glass like a pie in a diner and look at us now."

"One thing about New York," Polly said. "Whatever happens here never happened. Not that I personally care if you tell *The National Enquirer* you got a peek at my Mound of Venus but I do have a reputation to protect."

"So do I," Simon said. "Don't worry about me, Ms. Moon. I'm very discreet. Besides, you're not the first Pan winner to share her hot tub with me. It happens all the time."

"And I hope you don't mind that while what might happen happens, I'll be thinking about somebody else. It's no skin off your ass because you'll be getting yours no matter whose ghost is in the hot tub with us. It's just that I owe a certain person about a thousand bitch credits and I'd like to get him over with. Am I making any sense?"

"The nerd?" Simon said. He followed Polly Moon into a bathroom larger than the Apple's house in Glenda. She dropped her kimono and climbed into a steaming circle of jade-green water. Simon stripped off his drenched clothes while she made waves with her arms. Polly looked up at him. "You're not anything like my nerd," Polly said. "Compared to you, he was hung like a peanut. You're hung like a gift horse. And that set of basketballs is bluer than your hands. How long has it been since you emptied that reservoir?"

Simon got a glimpse of his reflection in a wall mirror. He saw why he was feeling pain on the way up Fifth Avenue. His genitals were five times their former size. "I have something to tell you. A confession," Simon said.

"Say a Hail Mary. I'm the one atoning here. Don't try to steal my thunder."

"My name is—"

"No passport required," Polly said. "Just climb aboard."

Simon left Polly Moon asleep in a bed the size of a runway. He kissed her forehead, then, on his way out, stopped to check the ice machine and got two well-formed cubes. In the hall, he scooped up Benny's rain gear and headed down Fifth Avenue pulling the company dolly behind him.

The storm had passed, the air was clear, the sky opalescent as the inside of a shell. Simon heard sheep bleat from the Central Park children's zoo. A disoriented rooster crowed at the rising moon. Taxis showered fountains in the flooded gutter. Droplets flew from city trees, reflecting the day's last light like shimmering pearls. Simon tongued a few of those drops. They tasted like Placebo's honey.

He made way for a jogger and began to run himself, moving

toward new horizons. At 57th Street, Simon nodded to the stoical Steinways grazing in their abandoned showroom. One or two of the complacent pianos acknowledged his greeting by raising their lids.

He floated up toward Wallace Waldo Enterprises breathing Placebo's perfume, riding the high from her magical leaves. In the hallway, Simon headed for the office door, lying belly down on the dolly, using his hands for oars. When he got there and managed to assume a vertical posture, he saw a hand-lettered sign that read:

THE STANISLAVSKY ALLIANCE
Emile Valaris, Dramaturge

Simon found his key and entered as quietly as possible. He heard murmurs from the conference room where Emile the Dramaturge was presumably auditioning some pubescent child of The Method on the long walnut table where Wallace Waldo often sat reveling in a blizzard of vanished rating points.

Simon hung up Benny's porous slicker, stashed away his hat, put the dolly back where it belonged, and was about to tiptoe back out the door when he realized that if he postponed announcing his decision to quit he might never again muster the guts to give up the solace of a weekly paycheck. It wasn't just the money. In New York, you are where you work and who you eat. Besides, the thought of barging in on Benny's latest tryst had a certain perverse appeal.

Hadn't Simon Apple, aka Sinbad Green, spent the shank of a long afternoon, his limbs entwined with the luminous object of his desire? Even though, in Placebo's peculiar mind, he'd served as a surrogate for himself. Empowered by all that delectation, Simon, usually shy, exuded confidence; he was a walking aphrodisiac, the embodiment of the little horned Pan Award, his Steuben crystal legs locked around a verdant world.

Simon was certain his very presence was orgasmic. Even the Steinways downstairs had opened to him. The sudden appearance of such a lubricious incarnation of sensuality could only be welcomed by a clod like the ersatz Emile and certainly by his latest cohort recently freed from her training bra.

Simon took a deep breath and burst into the conference room

ready to proclaim his resignation from the company "due to unexpected developments, prior commitments, new aspirations and utter
disgust." He couldn't say anything. There, on Wallace Waldo's
totemic table, a young man lay prone while Benny Valaris fumbled
with a tube of KY Jelly. When Simon appeared, Benny yelled, "He
left a message saying his name was Francis. How the hell was I supposed to know?"

Simon shrugged and began backing out of the auditioning
room. "Besides, you're fired, you bastard," Benny screamed. "A certain woman who works for a certain woman called to tell me how
you dared fraternize with a certain celebrity. You hurt me, Sinbad.
You hurt us all. I was proud of you. Rosy had high hopes for you.
Waldo told me you were like the son he always wanted. And here you
spit in our faces. You broke our heart. So get the fuck out of here and
don't expect a reference. You're dead in this business."

"Good luck with the *Beowulf* project," Simon said. "It'll make a
great musical."

"Is that your next production?" the young man said. "I'd be so
right for *Beowulf.*"

Simon arrived at the Flatiron holding a few personal possessions
salvaged from the office and a box of paper clips he'd pilfered in lieu
of severance pay. His spirit was buoyed by the same updraft of optimism he'd experienced when he first shucked off his old skin and
became Sinbad Green, Professional Voyager.

Placebo's delicious aura, sweet as the crust of a toasted muffin,
still circled his soul like a hula-hoop protecting him from negative
ions. But he felt the pot high ebbing away, dissipating like the smoke
from that elfish uptown weed. He sensed that his motor was sputtering; he was losing altitude fast.

The events of his afternoon in Eden began to seem less real, as
if lying with Polly Moon was only a mirage, a quick trip through the
parallel universe he and Chirp used to talk about during teasing
teenage sunsets. Who'd believe that the brat in a pink carriage,
expert at precision projectile vomiting, now an American idol, in the
money and on the charts, had invited a nobody like himself to enter
her innermost sanctum?

Simon doubted his own memory, much like Wallace Waldo

who'd once surfed a curl of radio waves with the grace of an angel. At least Waldo had proof of glory—a book of clippings to console him in his time of static.

Ms. Polly Moon had an endless supply of ice cubes. Simon Apple had no momento of bliss beyond a scratch across his belly, a throbbing dick, an aching set of ink-stained balls and no job, not even a letter of reference. He had no certifiable identity; it was back to square one.

In the Flatiron Hotel's molding lobby, the clutch of gravity dragged Simon from the stratosphere and crushed him like a pigeon under the wheels of a sightseeing bus. Crashing, he heard his own splat and let out a desperate moan. "What's wrong?" Wallace Waldo said from behind the obituary page of the *New York Times*.

"Mr. Waldo? I didn't see you there. Nothing's wrong," Simon said. "Long day's journey. Hard day's work."

"Ah."

"I want you to know, I'm leaving the company."

"Which company is that?"

"It doesn't matter."

"You shouldn't be discouraged, Sinbad. Regard rejection as a valuable lesson. Not every contestant on *The Wallace Waldo Show* can be a first-time winner. Many of my boys and girls have gone on to illustrious careers. I'm talking about the losers. And several of our winners have experienced nothing but future failure. It's the way of the world."

"I feel better already," Simon said.

"Consider the case of a small shelled creature tossed up on a beach. Suddenly a gull swoops down and grabs it. The gull flies high into clouds then drops the shell onto rock. When the creature splits open, the gull's beak rips at its exposed salty flesh. Now tell me, Sinbad, would you rather be the creature lifted from a lugubrious existence nearly to heaven if only for a moment? Or the gull for whom the experience was nothing, all in a day's work and not a meal worthy of boasting about?"

"I'll have to think it over."

"What was it you did on my stage? Sing? Tap dance? Were you the ventriloquist? My point is, thousands of people out there heard your name tonight. It flew through the air.

Priceless exposure. Some will remember you."

"You're right," Simon said. "Good luck to both of us."

"Luck is another name for God," Waldo said, beaming. Simon nodded and aimed for the elevator.

Before the door closed, Simon saw Wallace Waldo lift half out of his chair and heard him stage whisper to the lobby rubber plant, "Wait. Script change. Delete God. Insert bitch." Then he went back to reading about the departed illustrious.

62

"We located him," Bryan Beem said.

"Where?" Regis Van Clay said, trying to steady the receiver. He was hanging upside down, his ankles manacled together, swinging like a pendulum over a simmering kettle filled with some foul brew Belladonna had imported from San Francisco. He'd just been flailed with cactus fronds and felt invigorated.

"He's been in New York City using an alias. Sinbad Green."

"Under our noses," Regis said. "Why an alias? He couldn't possibly know about Operation RX. Or could he?"

"I can't answer that," Beem said. "He hasn't been in touch with anyone until this morning. He placed a call to that Doctor Henry Fikel in Glenda and got hold of his wife, Honey. Simon said he wanted to talk about some symptom but she told him her husband was on the sick list himself, recuperating in a rest home. The good doctor flaked out—you're going to get a kick out of this, Regis—one of his patients saw a television ad for AK-48—that's one of your brands, isn't it? *Soothe Those Painful Hemorrhoids. It's Better Than Having a Shrink in the Family. AK-48. The Dream Cream for Rapid-Fire Relief.* Nice copy."

"I know what the ad says. Please get to the point."

"At the end of the ad when it shows the guy with the shrunken piles kissing his wife, after you hear about possible side effects, the announcer says: *Wouldn't you'd rather be sitting pretty? Ask your doctor if AK-48 is right for you.*"

"I know what the announcer says."

"How do you guys come up with that stuff? Well, one of Fikel's patients called him to ask if the Dream Cream was right for her. It was the fifth call he got that evening because of your ad. He'd spent the whole day seeing patients, then yelling at Honey for screwing up Medicare, Medicaid and insurance forms. When that woman called to say she saw the commercial and wanted to know if she was a candidate for AK-48 Rapid-Fire Relief, Fikel lost it. He totally lost it, practically wrecked his office and ran outside yelling for his sainted mother. A complete nervous collapse. They carted him away. That 'ask your doctor' message is an inspiration, marketing-wise. Unless you happen to be a doctor.

"Anyhow, Honey Fikel told the Apple kid her husband wasn't available to answer questions at the moment but he'd want to know how Simon was doing, that he was interested in the state of his health, etcetera, etcetera and, sure enough, Apple described his problem."

"What problem?" Regis said.

"We had some trouble with interference on the line but the way it sounded was that his tool had swelled up about three times its normal size and his scrotum looks like a pair of party balloons. And getting bigger. Apple said he couldn't ambulate without the help of a special walker they'd rigged up for him at Bellevue Hospital Emergency with these sling and bag attachments. The medics suspected the cause of enlargement might be a previously unknown sexually transmitted disease but one Indian intern said it might have something to do with Apple's medication. Which, as you must know, is *Solacitrex*."

"*Solacitrex*? How the hell could Simon Apple get on *Solacitrex*? It's impossible. . . . Every pharmacist in the country knows that anything manufactured by Regis Pharmaceuticals is absolutely off limits for Simon Apple. He couldn't buy a tube of our toothpaste if he was dying of gingivitis, not a deodorant if he smelled like Love Canal, not *Nick-O-Time, the smoking patch that looks like a tattoo,* not a vitamin pill, nothing, no exceptions. Who the fuck would dare sell him *Solacitrex*?"

"I told you, he changed his name to Sinbad Green. He got his hands on blank prescription pad. That young man is certainly enterprising."

"*Solacitrex* aka *Silentush* is the centerfold of our annual report. It's the industry success story. *Fight Flatulence the Modern Way!* We eliminated chronic farting and there's never been a single documented side effect. A few sudden deaths in Uganda, during the early beta phase but no direct link. You have got to sit down with that Indian intern. Say we'll build him a clinic across from the Taj Mahal . . . whatever it takes to keep his mouth shut."

"He already sent a report to the Centers for Disease Control."

"Condition red. Get in touch with Congressman Eff."

"I'm a step ahead. I spoke with Congressman Eff. You know he's running for the Senate. He said he already did enough for you, got you what you asked for, set the wheels in motion, put himself on-the-line, said any further action on his part could jeopardize—"

"All right, all right. Fuck Eff. It's your move, Beem. Pick up the Apple kid. Make him disappear before we have to plaster warning labels on our golden goose."

"Not so easy. Simon told Fikel's wife he'd lost his job but didn't say where he worked or where he lived. He made that phone call from a pay booth in Grand Central Station. He gave Bellevue that phony Sinbad Green name and an ersatz address. But he is due back at the hospital in a week."

"You can't find a man pushing his testicles through Grand Central on a cart? New York isn't *that* big."

"Be calm, Regis. I'm on the case, as they say in the movies."

"I was hanging loose and very calm until you called. I was blissful." Regis dropped the phone into Belladonna's cauldron and watched it dissolve.

"Why are you giving out my number?" Belladonna said when she came back into the room holding a vice. "You're not here to take business calls. You're here to slow down so you won't get a coronary."

While she tightened the vise around a big toe, Regis's agile mind did a turnabout. He was thinking that, worst case scenario, even if *Solacitrex* had a tragic flaw, how tragic would it be to list a side effect like Simon Apple's? With a little molecular modification, some creative rethinking of the formula and dosage, he might have a King Kong product on his hands, bigger than the Washington Monument.

While Belladonna used forceps to tug at a nail, Regis realized his instructions to Brian Beem were way off base. This wasn't the moment to pounce on Apple. That could wait. This was the time to pray that the Bellevue intern was exactly right, that *Solacitrex* was directly responsible for enlarging a set of crown jewels.

But it would be a definite minus if Simon Apple expired from excessive edema. The full resources of Regis Pharmaceuticals had to be turned away from distractions like cancer and AIDS to make sure Simon Apple survived his latest affliction. Then news of Simon's symptoms, along with a public admission of liability, could be published in the *New England Journal of Medicine* along with a warning that *Solacitrex* might cause serious *erectotesticular phalusial goliathism.* "*Ask your doctor if you experience . . .*" That warning would be black boxed on the front label of every *Solacitrex* dispenser. The rest would take care of itself.

"I have to terminate this session," Regis said."

"You're getting tired of me," Belladonna said. "Go home to your wife. Eat sunflower seeds from her pernicious pudenda."

"Pernicious pudenda?"

"I signed up for a vocabulary course, Verbal Flagellation: Erotic Expression for a New Age, Belladonna said. "On six cassettes. They teach you power words. More of my clients are asking for phone sex. The telephone certainly offers convenient conjugation."

"Phone sex is like listening to your grandmother read a recipe," Regis said. "Where is it written that conjugation should be convenient?"

63

Before Simon showed up for his next appointment at Bellevue Hospital, he called Wallace Waldo Enterprises hoping that Rosy would answer the phone. He felt bad about leaving without having said a proper goodbye to her and he wanted Polly Moon's unlisted number. If he wrote Polly so much as a postcard it would never get past Fritzel's dragon eye and he didn't want to show up at Polly's apartment pushing his groin on a dolly instead of a Westinghouse.

Rosy wished him the best but she fudged about giving out a

celebrity's phone number. Simon tried to explain that he knew it was borderline ridiculous and less than gallant for Sinbad Green to suggest any future encounter with Ms. Moon but he'd noticed in the latest issues of *Billboard* and *Variety* that *The Windchime Concerto* was off the charts and Polly's name was nowhere on the Top Ten list; he told Rosy he felt a strong urge to console the singer while she coped with the looming terror of invisibility. Rosy was adamant. She wouldn't risk Benny Valaris's wrath and lectured Simon about the dangers of turning into a star-fucker, maybe a stalker, maybe worse. Rosy reminded Simon there was always the chance of making a comeback even for obsolete overnight sensations.

Worrying about Placebo's anguish helped lessen Simon's own building anxiety. He hadn't left his bed in days. Food was sent up to him from Gussie's Luncheonette around the corner from the Flatiron or from Charlie Woo's Jade Palace down the block.

His room was filling with empty coffee containers and flapped white boxes that still held remnants of sesame noodles, stir-fried vegetables, slivers of pork and half-eaten egg rolls growing strange fur like Chia Pets. He posted a DO NOT DISTURB sign on his doorknob to keep the floor maid at bay. Blockade seemed the sensible solution for dealing with his embarrassing scourge. His penis was longer than his foot, his testes nearly the size of his head. To replace the sling provided by Bellevue which was already too tight for easy mobility, he used a scratchy burlap sack that once held Jamaican coffee beans.

Simon remembered a joke Chirp Bennet once told him about Adam saying to Eve, "Watch out, honeybunch, I don't know how big this thing gets" but he couldn't remember why it once seemed funny. He took regular doses of *Drainamerol*, a strong diuretic from Regis Pharmaceuticals prescribed by his doctor, to flush away excess fluids, but while that drug didn't do much to reverse enlargement, it forced Simon to urinate twice an hour. He learned to relieve himself without the anguish of getting up—he lay back, aimed and fired a stream of piss across the room, through the open bathroom door, directly into his toilet. Pulling at a chain fashioned from the paper clips he'd expropriated from Wallace Waldo Enterprises accomplished the flush. Pissing and TV were his only diversions.

When Simon got to Bellevue with the help of a Flatiron desk

clerk, two formidable men met him at the reception desk wearing scrub suits and surgical masks. They lifted him into a wheelchair and rolled him to the Isolation Ward, explaining that his condition might be contagious, that he could be a virulent carrier like the legendary Typhoid Mary.

While he was undressed and wrapped in a hospital gown, Simon demanded to see the intern familiar with his case. "He knows me. I like him. He's caring and compassionate. He has my test results. I feel comfortable with—"

"Don't complain," one of the attendants said. "You're trading up. The intern is out of the picture. The good news is Dr. Mercy Merriweather is taking you over. She's the one I'd want to see if I was in your underwear. *New York Magazine* listed her as New York's most brilliant surgeon."

"Surgeon? I'm leaving right now," Simon said. "Get me my walker."

"You're not going anyplace, Mr. Green. Relax and settle in."

Simon was hooked up to a bank of monitors. Wires and tubes wrapped around him like vines. They trailed tendrils linked to ominous machines, each with its own high frequency hum and erratic beep. His every breath and movement caused a cascade of tiny lights to blink like insect eyes.

Heavily sedated, Simon fell into, and climbed groggily out of, chemical euphoria He was considering the possibility that he'd changed from a person to a tropical plant in an unknown forest. When Dr. Merriweather came to examine him he felt as if she was probing his branches for fruit.

"How are we feeling today, Mr. Apple?"

"Cross pollinated," Simon said.

"I am Dr. Mercy Merriweather, your attending physician." Simon's glossy eyes focused on a short, slender woman wearing a white coat, white shoes and white rubber gloves. She had a square white face half covered by a white mask under a tight crown of white hair. She reminded him of a blank notepad. "I've been reading your medical history. It's quite fascinating. Reads like a Gothic novel."

"You called me Mr. Apple. My name is Sinbad Green."

"We can drop the alias," Dr. Merriweather said. "I know exactly who you are. And by the way, I dislike *The Windchime Concerto.* The idea of cannibals eating mermaids is reprehensible."

"I can't take credit for the lyrics. Or the music. I was more conduit than composer. Just following orders."

"I dismiss that defense," Dr. Merriweather said.

"But how do you know about—?"

"I could say you talk in your sleep and I could say several people have shown an unusual interest in your progress or lack thereof."

"Is it true that I'm a carrier of some deadly disease?"

"Not in the usual sense. I don't think your condition is directly transmissible to other humans. But economically speaking, I'm told on excellent authority that you are a host for a disastrous pharmaceutical virus. I see on your chart that you've been responsible for inhibiting the distribution of *Cripthalizine, Nonacripthae, Viloxidril, Aquathaline, Expeloton, Xanelul* and now what? Your test results show a distinct possibility that your genital enlargement is connected to the use of *Solacitrex.*

"Mr. Apple, you've personally cost the health care profession, most directly Regis Pharmaceuticals, billions of dollars in lost revenue. It might interest you to know that Regis Van Clay, whose wife happens to be my sister, has been forced to print warning notices of potentially horrendous side effect on every package of wonderful drugs which gave few, if any, previous hints of causing any life-threatening symptoms beyond mild attacks of dementia in non-smokers. How do you feel about that?"

"I feel sorry," Simon said, "for myself."

"Typical of your solipsistic generation. Uninvolved and uncaring. Don't you comprehend that this kind of fiasco has a humongous price tag and that those costs are ultimately passed on to the people who can least afford to pay? Widows, orphans and insurance companies? Doesn't it bother you that you don't seem to be a signatory to the social contract?"

"I resent that," Simon said. "Those warnings could save lives."

"Which affects another vital industry. Undertakers, cemeteries, clerics—the list goes on and on. The ripple effect is virtually endless. Mr. Apple, even before I examined you, my recommendation was for immediate amputation."

"The A word? Did I hear right?" Simon said.

"I could have you home in a week practically as good as new. Would it be such a tragedy if you couldn't reproduce? I think not. It's the efficient way to go and that course of action is still very much on the operating table. The only one urging me to sheath my scalpel is, ironically, Regis Van Clay. His gnomes are searching for a miracle cure. My educated guess is that no panacea will be found. You've had more than your share of miracles, Mr. Apple. When all is said and done, you'll tie up valuable hospital space and squander precious attention while we wait for the impossible. I like to ask my patients, humorously of course, wouldn't it be better to—no levity intended—cut your losses? Frankly, your prognosis is miserable. Why subject yourself to needless suffering and the risk of an agonizing death? If I were you, I'd refuse further delay and give me the green light to proceed. Did you know that not once but twice geldings won the Kentucky Derby?"

"I'm not entered in this year's Kentucky Derby."

"Selfish, self-centered, self-destructive," Dr. Merriweather said. "True to form."

"Could I get a telephone in here?" Simon said.

"No. No distractions."

"Then could you make a call for me? I would like my family to know where—"

"In due time," Dr. Merriweather said. "You wouldn't want your nearest and dearest to see you looking like a satyr.'"

"You have a wonderful bedside manner," Simon said.

64

Amos Blum, a Customer Relations man at one of the Regis Pharmaceuticals subsidiary companies in Canada—Eucalyptus Shamanics—owned a world-class collection of shrunken heads. When one of his colleagues was given a retirement party, Blum brought one of his heads, a grizzly skull the size of a Bartlett Pear.

His intention was to use it as a prop, a visual aid to illustrate a short farewell speech he'd written about the importance of keeping an active mind through one's golden years by doing things like crossword puzzles, taking adult education courses and embracing a hobby to stimulate the brain cells.

After the party, Marvin Latch, a research technician, aware of the mother company's sudden interest in shrinkage, expropriated the head on a wispy hunch. Alexander Fleming had discovered penicillin by paying serious attention to a piece of moldy bread. That mythic story had motivated every scientist since; nothing was too innocuous for study, anything might yield a secret worthy of the Nobel Prize. Latch promised Amos Blum the diminutive head would be returned fully intact.

The technician had been led to believe his employer was interested in finding a substance for use by the textile industry. Following that assumption, Latch spent weeks treating natural and synthetic fabrics with hormonal extractions laboriously culled from the head without any significant result. Amos Blum was demanding the head's return since its absence disrupted his collection's continuity; the gap in Blum's display case was an aesthetic insult. Latch yielded to his colleague's demand, pledging to surrender the prized head after one more experiment.

On the morning of his final day with the head, exhausted after a long and restless night, Marvin Latch relaxed his usual cautions and somehow allowed his unprotected thumb to dip into a beaker filled with primitive embalming fluid and a mixture of cobra venom, alum and ear effluvia he'd extracted from the overdue skull. By noon he noticed his thumbnail blacken, crack and separate from its cuticle anchors. By mid-afternoon the thumb was half its normal size.

While Latch saw no connection between digital shrinkage and the manipulation of cotton, rayon or polyester fiber, after lunch he decided to report the event to a superior. Marvin Latch had no inkling that he'd be named Employee of the Month, albeit in absentia. By five P.M. he'd experienced total subtraction, vanished without a trace. The compound Latch discovered was named *Thumicsk* in his honor.

In New York City, Regis Van Clay was being ministered to by his lovely Trilby in a tub filled with hot cocoa, listening to Bix

Biederbek play "In a Mist" through a submersible speaker powerful enough to send vibrations rippling through the warm brew.

Regis liked what Trilby called their mocha meanderings. The girl was endlessly creative. She was gently inserting the nozzle of a Ready Whip can into his expectant anus when the extension phone he'd had installed in her apartment signaled emergency.

"This better be good," Regis said into the receiver. He knew he was talking to Thurston Blek, his Senior Executive Assistant. Nobody else had the number.

"Exciting news from the front," Blek said. "The boys downstairs just disappeared a pig. It only took one infusion of *Thumicsk* and sucrose, what we call the Canadian cocktail. Nothing left but the echo of an oink. We know the result was a tad extreme, sir, but we feel confident that we're zeroing in on a breakthrough in Operation Reduction. Our boys and girls are back at the drawing board—we've got two whole teams working simultaneously around the clock. One on inhibiting tissue contraction, the awful reaction to *Thumicsk* that caused Marvin Latch, and the poor pig, to vanish. The other on reversing chronic tissue expansion, the Patient X problem. They're absolutely bewildered about operating at cross purposes not knowing about Latch or Patient X, and both teams are ready to drop from fatigue."

"Don't tell me about their whining," Regis said. "More time is not an option. If they complain, threaten the lot of them with immediate extinction. And please remember that utmost secrecy is the golden rule. Any further word on Patient X?"

"Not good, sir. Dr. Merriweather called from the Intensive Care Unit. A certain young man is fading fast. She's quoting the Hippocratic Oath, insisting you give her permission to amputate."

"Permission denied," Regis said. "Listen, I want you to run some of that shrinking juice over to Merriweather right now. Carry it yourself. Tell her to use it immediately."

"Too much too soon could be overkill. We can't control the degree of shrinkage. When we tried it on the pig, well, *poof*, no more pig, not even a stain. Before human trials, more tests are definitely—"

"No time. We've got to roll the dice, Thurston. If the boy dies, he dies. But he must be kept alive and intact while there's a hangnail of a chance to get him back to normal, near normal or reasonably normal proportion. Call my bitch of a sister-in-law and tell her to put away the cutlery. Tell her the latest results with *Thumicsk* strongly suggest we've found a safe, effective antidote for her favorite patient. Say we've gotten Phase One approval from the FDA. Tell her anything. Remind her that *Solacitrex*, diluted with *Thumicsk*, could be a rain shower in the parched forest of unleavened penises. Millions of them! And forchrissakes, do not mention that pig of blessed memory. And call our office in Brazil to see about finding a dependable supply of shrunken heads."

"Will do."

"Have our admen begin to think about repositioning the *Solacitrex* image before a certain side effect goes public. Christen an amalgam of *Thumicsk* and *Solacitrex* with a memorable name. I'm thinking *Stalagamide*. The perfect combination of Stalactite and Stalagmite—two stones for one, shall we say, troubled bird. And don't ignore the subconscious suggestion of a shaft entering a cave. A nice warm, wet tunnel of pleasure."

"Like Howe Caverns? That's positively lubricious. *Stalagamide*. The elevator drug. Up and Down. Works both ways. I'm hearing the word *organic*. Can we use the word organic?"

"Yes, definitely organic. Let's line up the actor who played Rocky for our spokesperson. Damn, I wish his name wasn't Sylvester."

"Consider it done. Your mind is a steel trap, Mr. Van Clay."

"God, there's so much to do and I end up doing it all myself," Regis said when he ended the call.

"You work too hard, dear," Trilby said.

"It's true," Regis said. "Some Wall Street eunuch is always yowling about my *quote*, excessive compensation package *unquote*, but what do they know about my daily anguish? What do they know about excessive?"

"What were you saying about a rain shower for a certain parched forest? Should I buy more stock, baby Regis?"

"Ask me in a couple of days," Regis said.

A week later, when she heard good news, Trilby bought a thousand shares.

Solacitrex (500 mg)
Trade Name: *Silentush*
*The famous windbreaker that now offers an extra benefit . . .
strategic inflation when you want it most!*

Now combines with:

Thumicsk (.001%)
Trade name: *Retdema*
*Big news for anything swollen, from Regis Pharmaceuticals.
We bring your troubles down to size!*

Now, together! Presenting:

Stalagamide
*The ointment that helps you rise to the occasion . . .inch ahead of the
competition . . . then go home smiling. Finally, no more worries about
those four-hour—or even four-year—erections!
Because Regis Pharmaceuticals raises your horizons . . .
and reduces your concerns!*

65

"A peanut? Jellybeans?" Simon had said a month after his first dose of *Thumicsk*.

"A few weeks ago you couldn't get around without the help of a crane. Now you're more portable, mobile, trim, perfectly healthy, and still complaining." Dr. Merriweather said.

"I need a magnifying glass to see my johnson. I'm Pan without his peter."

"Size isn't everything. Let's not forget the importance of technique. I grant you, appearance may affect first impressions. But think about how much has been achieved by others with far worse physical challenges than yours. Take the case of the Elephant Man, or Napoleon."

"Right now being the Elephant Man or Napoleon doesn't sound so bad. So, this is it?"

"We don't know. *Thumicsk* did its job. It reversed the unpleasant *Solacitrex* side effect. That we do know. You're back at a manageable size. We have no indication of any negative side effects."

"Manageable if I lived under a mushroom. Is there a chance for future growth?"

"There's always a chance," Dr. Merriweather said. "I once had a hibiscus that lost all its leaves but I kept those bare stems alive through an awful winter and the following spring it produced a whole bouquet of the most beautiful—"

"What about the ads I see for *Stalagamide?* Those 'Inch ahead of the competition' commercials? The ones with the dancing ruler. Wouldn't that help me add a few centimeters?"

"*Stalagamide* is a derivative of *Solacitrex* combined with *Thumicsk.* We could try it in small doses. It's a drug that might cause a relapse. You're highly allergic to *Solacitrex* as we know. Maybe you should thank your stars for *Thumicsk* and let it go at that. Something is better than nothing. You dodged another bullet, son. You'll never know how close you came to castration."

"I have a pretty good idea." Simon said. "I saw the twinkle in your eyes, Dr. Merriweather. How many times did you ask me to sign those permission forms?"

"I acted in your own interest, Simon. To keep you alive. And here you are, spared instead of spayed, cured and ready to go home. What ever happened to gratitude? It would be nice if you offered some small token of appreciation, a simple thank you, doctor. Not to mention your debt to Regis Pharmaceuticals."

"Thank you, doctor, I think. As for Regis Pharmaceuticals . . ."

"I think my brother-in-law acted very well in a delicate situation. He demonstrated a real concern for public safety by acknowledging the remote possibility that *Solacitrex* might induce *erectotesticular phalusial goliathism.* That warning isn't hidden in small print. It's right out front on every label."

"Don't forget the part about seeing your health care provider if your erection lasts more than a century. They're crowing, not warning."

"That consumer alert is entirely gratuitous. There's no proof that *Solacitrex* caused your problem, no statistical evidence that would stand up in a court of law. And you did sign an ironclad document absolving the company of liability. And you weren't charged a red cent for your hospitalization or my services. I wouldn't leave here bearing any grudge toward Regis Pharmaceuticals."

"I admit to mixed feelings," Simon said.

"You'll be dismissed today," Dr. Merriweather said. "Don't over exert. Eat a balanced diet. Get plenty of rest. I'm going to give you this tape measure. If you notice any change in your dimensions, either way, please let me know immediately."

"Either way?" Simon said. "Is there a chance we haven't touched bottom?"

"I'm going to give you a few tablets of *Stalagamide*. If you detect any sign of swelling or more shrinkage, call me immediately. You should know that I've been told in no uncertain terms that you are not to be allowed access to any product produced by Regis Pharmaceuticals or its subsidiaries. So please tell nobody the drug came from me."

"I heard I was persona non grata at Regis. I'll keep this quiet," Simon said.

"And don't expect overnight miracles. Reversing the *Thumicsk* effect might take time. Or it might not work at all."

66

When his cell door opened, Simon saw a short, full-bearded man in a black business suit, white shirt, navy blue tie decorated with quill pens, cowboy hat and western style high-heeled boots. Simon thought he must be another one of the multitude of lawyers who had filed appeals on his behalf over the years, some for altruistic reasons, most to get their names mentioned in the few newspapers that bothered to carry such reports.

Now that the death penalty was back in vogue, the only lawyer who came around was Marvin Klipstein, mostly out of habit. Whoever he was, this visitor had to have some clout to be allowed a private audience, face-to-face, instead of under glass in the reception area.

While a guard secured the door, the man identified himself in a deep bass voice, lifting Simon's limp hand to shake it vigorously. "My name is Anson Tellerude. I suspect you might be familiar with my books and articles."

"I can't place the name," Simon said. "Which is not to say I never read what you wrote. I hardly ever remember an author's name. It's a problem that goes back to my formative years when I thought everything good was written by somebody named Arthur Unknown. It was years before somebody told me that I'd misread Author Unknown. That said, why are you here?"

"I'm here representing Caged Creators, a group of volunteers devoted to encouraging the incarcerated to explore and share their experiences with the world outside the walls. My specialty is collecting the prose, poetry, essays or diaries of the condemned. A shit job you say? Naturally, most of us would rather cater to those with the slightest chance of redemption. However, I feel it's never too late to help an inmate seek personal insight into a turgid past and gain the satisfaction that comes through reaching out to potential perpetrators in time to help them change their ways.

"And there's what I call the final triumph of the otherwise anonymous—the pleasure of leaving something of oneself behind that's both signed and fully protected by copyright law. Of course, not everything written gets published. On the other hand, a rejection slip can't be too traumatic a disappointment to the already executed.

"Each year we sponsor publication of a collection called *Dignity of the Damned*—a powerful title, don't you think? Where permissible, each contributor's estate is paid a generous royalty. If you live in a jurisdiction that restricts profits from subsidiary rights to capital crime, the money goes to victim families."

"I did mean to write my memoirs but I never got around to it," Simon said. "I do have a few hours left. Maybe I should get busy before too much longer."

"We meant to contact you sooner," Anson Tellerude said. "You know how it is with volunteers. Oversight prevails. You fell through the cracks. I was hoping you might have a few scribbled scraps or doodles to offer for consideration. You could still make our deadline."

"I don't expect you'd like anything of mine," Simon said, "since the truth is, I'm not guilty in the traditional sense. And I'm not sure you'd be allowed to print anything I might write. My case is very complicated."

Simon saw the guard yawn and wander down the corridor.

Tellerude's beard brushed Simon's face as he leaned close to whisper, "I know you're not guilty of what *Sixty Minutes* called 'Cold-Blooded Monkicide.' "

"You know that?" Simon said. "Sometimes even I'm not sure."

"Look at me," Tellerude said. "Take a slow look."

Simon studied the face hovering near enough for him to tell that his visitor had eaten a pastrami sandwich for lunch. Otherwise, there was no recognition.

"The eyes? The chin?"

"You have me at a disadvantage," Simon said.

"They did an incredible job," Tellerude said. "You've got to hand it to them."

"I'm sorry if I seem impatient," Simon said, "but I'd planned to use the time I have left to touch base with a few memories, so . . ."

Tellerude positioned his mouth an inch from Simon's left ear. "I'm Brother Lucas, the one you killed. Does that ring a bell?"

"Yes, well, thanks for dropping in," Simon said. "But you'd better go now or you'll miss your spaceship."

"It's the truth. I wanted you to know how things are. You can face your maker with a clear conscience."

"My conscience is clear. I know what's going down and why. I suspect my maker has some knowledge of economics, gross national product, the flow of goods and services, the balance of trade, the cost of every side effect in the highly competitive global pharmaceutical marketplace, the need to sacrifice one lousy life in the interest of America's place in the new world order. I have no problem with that so why should my maker?"

"You're the perfect patsy. They broke the mold when they made you."

"If you're Brother Lucas, how come they reeled in your body?"

"They found *a* body. Some poor bastard on their generic hit list. Or snatched from an undertaker's parlor."

"And what about your Digital Shadows? Are they alive too?"

"I wish. That was a real shame. Nice people. Very sincere. Call their demise a case of friendly fire. Collateral damage."

"I'm tempted to believe you. But a certain highly placed and well-informed person told me how you were shot, then carted away and dumped in Long Island Sound."

"Who? Brian Beem? Did he take credit for being the shooter? I love Brian but he couldn't hit Dolly Parton's tits with a heat-seeking missile. No, the spook establishment hated the fact that a Company dropout found spiritual fulfillment, financial security, and produced a pretty good pinot noir.

"Plus they needed me—their dark star if I may say so—to deliver a few delicate messages in the Middle East. So Brother Lucas was resurrected, reinvented and reinstated. Under duress. By the way, Simon, never believe a word Beem tells you. Frankly, I'm amazed he bothered to tell you anything. Though I did hear that the President feels a little queasy about this whole affair. Or is it the First Lady? They're both Born Agains. Once would have been enough. Beem must have been sent to ease your mind, the same reason I came. In case they had you wondering if you really are guilty of advanced Monkicide."

"To ease my mind and your conscience. No, I know I'm not Monkicidal. What was all that gibberish about Caged Creators? *The Dignity of the Damned?*"

"Amos Tellerude's official credentials these days. Talk about born again. The organization and book are real. A front for Special Ops. The condemned enjoy the idea of getting into print so we pick up a lot of valuable last-minute information they won't even confess to a chaplain. Incidentally, if you're interested, I can get you published. A letter to your mom. A prayer for peace. A childhood memory. Recriminations and regrets, always welcome. Something upbeat. Nothing controversial. No? Well, if you change your mind, have your people call my people. Meanwhile, sweet dreams, Simon Apple. Regards to my Shadows."

67

The immediate success of *Stalagamide*—to be taken under careful medical supervision—the first successful drug guaranteeing on-demand penis enlargement while combating excessive erectile size and duration—sent the stock of Regis Pharmaceuticals to new highs despite a cautionary warning on the new drug's label that alerted consumers to watch for rare but possible episodes of *errectotesticular phalusial goliathism* and/or *retractial priatic davidilate*. Recommended dosage was three capsules daily for life, at a cost of two hundred eighty dollars per week. The stock split 3-1 and increased its dividend by 17 percent.

Regis Van Clay's reputation turned platinum, his face graced the covers of *Fortune, Time, Business Week, U.S. News.* Under Regis's guidance, a drug with a potentially deadly side effect had been transformed into a marketing monster.

Simon Apple was informed by Robert J. that some 5000 options to buy that stock, held in trust for him since the *Cripthalizine* settlement negotiated by Marvin Klipstein, Esq., represented a substantial windfall. That was all news to Simon who never read the fine print. Now that he'd reached age twenty-five (which Regis's actuaries had bet against) he was eligible to receive an annual stipend sufficient to ease his way in the world. Quarterly dividends from his stock, plus the income from a moderately decent job, would allow him to live comfortably. Klipstein's deal had one possible drawback—he also had an aversion to small print—the lawyer neglected to contest a provision stipulating that the stock could never be sold and that the shares would revert back to the company upon Simon Apple's death.

With the help of a bank loan, Robert J. exercised the options. Simon got his first dividend check in the mail along with a copy of the Regis Pharmaceuticals annual report, its cover featuring a detailed model of Voltan Zerminsky's proposed tribute to the CEO. Inside the booklet, among columns of numbers and an impressive array of bar charts and mounting curves, there was a picture of the sculptor and his wife, Victoria.

When Simon saw the photograph of Zerminsky's spouse, who he did not consciously recognize, he began to weep for no reason he could explain. There was something haunting about that woman's aura.

The money came at a good time. Simon was still far from feeling his old self despite Dr. Merriweather's pronouncement that his vital signs were better than normal. The use of *Stalagamide* did him no good. When he fumbled to find his pimple of a penis in order to urinate, he was throttled by crushing depression. He avoided showers and baths, covered every mirror that might reflect his mortification and moved about the city in constant fear that he'd be forced to seek out a public urinal and find himself standing next to a cucumber.

Following his doctor's advice, Simon tried to focus on the bright side, counting his blessings, repeating the bromide that less is more. Considering his liberation from the sling-sack-and-walker, things were looking up, but accepting the reality that he couldn't satisfy the sexual appetite of a Munchkin or even a sugar ant diminished his sense of worth. Having already been circumcised once, Simon was further burdened by the anxious echo of *déjà vu*.

Dr. Merriweather championed psychological counseling or membership in a support group as a good idea but Simon was more reluctant to expose himself emotionally than physically. The doctor tried to buoy his spirits by walking him through the hospital's trauma unit before Simon was discharged, but that attempt at shock therapy backfired. Watching others struggle with their assorted miseries gave some solace; being empathetic was like being a philanthropist—it was definitely better to give than to receive—but that brief comfort was tempered by survivor's guilt. Any residual benefit from the experience was lost when Dr. Merriweather took a wrong turn leading Simon through the hospital's sex change clinic.

He decided it was time to find refuge from the city's concrete pressure—a place without skyscrapers, a horizontal place where he could cope with his abridged anatomy in relative privacy. Dr. Merriweather agreed. She thought a vacation might be just the thing to mitigate his chronic depression.

Returning home to Glenda was no option. Robert J. and Rowena deserved better than a sulking visitor, what with their new twin toddlers, Zachary and Rebecca, to cope with.

Meeting his father, Rowena and siblings in his deleted condition was an unattractive prospect. He was a walking time bomb, medically speaking. Any day things could get worse and not only because of further shrinkage. Dr. Merriweather explained that if Simon was resistant to *Stalagamide*, and, since the drug's *Thumicsk* component that had so drastically shrunken his privates contained a heavy concentration of estrogen, there was a good chance that Simon's voice might revert to its pre-adolescent soprano. He didn't relish meeting old acquaintances back home sounding like a squealing gerbil.

Besides, Glenda seemed as far away as Saturn, banded by impenetrable rings of crystallized time, circled by moons with quizzical faces. Going home was not a viable choice for rest and relaxation.

Finding a cabin somewhere in a desert sounded feasible but Simon had a strong affection for trees and changing seasons. There was also the practical need to consider medical emergencies that would require quick access to Dr. Mercy Merriweather. It made more sense for Simon to study escapes within a hundred-mile radius of Manhattan.

After browsing countless articles in *The Sunday Times* and *Travel & Leisure*, Simon's imagination was captivated by a town called Serene Harbor near the tip of Long Island, described as "a quaint hamlet, an unpretentious neighbor to the posh Hamptons, once an important 19th Century port of call, back then a lusty mix of itinerant merchant seamen, whalers fresh ashore after five-year voyages from the South Pacific to the Beaufort Sea, whores, gamblers, Bible thumping widows of captains swallowed by the waves, peddlers and land speculators, Serene Harbor was transformed by receding 20th-century economic tides into a quiet village populated largely by fishermen, farmers and blue collar workers serving the needs and whims of elite Southampton, East Hampton and Bridgehampton society."

Serene Harbor sounded like a perfect location for rehabilitation, thankfully undiscovered, solidly anchored by carpenters, plumbers, masons, salt-of-the-earth citizens struggling to make a living in a community of no possible interest to tourists or the trendy creative. A town tempered by a long history, an anvil of repair for the flotsam and jetsam of a smithereened spirit.

In the months of his treatment, first with *Thumicsk* and now with *Stalagamide, The Windchime Concerto* along with the cluster of feelings for Polly Moon had entered the gray limbo of nostalgia. Now Simon saw a TV infomercial listing Placebo's recording of the song as a Golden Oldie available with thirty others for $12.95, +S&H. His fears for Placebo proved justified. When her name plummeted off rock 'n' roll's Olympus her moment of glory fizzled. In the torrid pace of American Evolution, generations with tastes and preferences of their own emerged on a daily, if not hourly, basis. The morning's hatch hadn't the slightest interest in what came before; the past was a playground for arthritic clowns and the past meant yesterday. Its music was certainly not worth retail price.

Nobody cared about *The Windchime Concerto*.

There was no further need for Sinbad Green.

So Simon dropped the pseudonym and became Simon Apple again.

It was hard to let Sinbad sail away into the sunset. Simon felt as if he was losing a loyal friend. But, as Dr. Merriweather said, it was time to move on toward whatever horizon there was for the only known survivor of *erectotesticular phalusial goliathism*.

68

The first day of September, Simon bought an ancient minibus covered with paintings of flowers, peace symbols and slogans like SAVE THE RAIN FOREST! SPARE THE CONDOR! FREE TIBET! YOKO GO HOME! KRISHNA LIVES! LITTER NOT THE STARS! IF IT'S GOT TITS OR WHEELS YOU'RE IN BIG TROUBLE! I BRAKE FOR WHIMS! BURNING GAS AND HAULING ASS! and left New York behind, heading due east.

Emerging from the Queens Midtown Tunnel was yet another rebirth for him. Being forced to pay a toll to leave the city and begin a new voyage of discovery seemed oddly appropriate. It was like buying a ticket to the future. When Simon dropped his coins into the EXACT CHANGE basket, a barrier bar lifted and a green light signaled GO. He experienced a sensation of release, the purging, purification and catharsis he'd heard joggers and devout churchgoers describe.

Simon drove his minibus through a corridor of factories and warehouses, under advertising billboards tempting him with pictures of happy people eating, drinking, sunbathing, loving, traveling, playing, enjoying the world's limitless bounty. Between the billboards, he looked out past huge fields of stone tombstones, statues of cherubs and angels, acres of dead New Yorkers arranged as neatly as crops of wheat and corn. That affluent group of cadavers were fortunate enough to be buried with a reasonably good view of the city's fabulous phallus, the Empire State Building (which the shrunken Simon didn't begrudge; the city deserved its big dick), though it was sad that they'd expired before the plots they now occupied had become choice real estate.

He drove past a clot of apartment houses flying a banner that read: IF YOU LIVED HERE YOU'D BE HOME ALREADY; then a cluster of senior citizen residences where he could see the ambulatory inmates staring from their balconies, looking down at the Long Island Expressway—a river of traffic as eternal as the Mississippi, deserving of its own Mark Twain. He drove through suburbs he recognized from watching *All in the Family* where Archie and Edith Bunker huddled together, worried sick about dark-skinned invaders next door. He passed exits to Forest Hills, Great Neck, Roslyn and Glen Cove—havens where the rich kept their families warm and safe in lush houses tucked among lawns and giant trees.

His minibus sputtered and clunked in the slow lane, getting the finger from passing truckers, until he drove beyond Westbury and Smithtown, where the tidal surge of traffic thinned to a trickle, where there were still a few acres of empty space, where dust hovered in clouds over potato farms. He watched tractors pull wagons full of migrants toward shacks and sheds marked by smoke trails rising from their tin chimneys. He turned toward the south shore then east again, skirting towns called Bayshore and Patchogue, and caught the first clammy scent of the ocean.

Old Montauk Highway took him through Quogue and Hampton Bays to Westhampton Beach, then Southampton—a mythic enclave, a sleepy WASP's nest where *Vogue* and *Harper's Bazaar* said the blessed people went to the beach in gowns and tuxedos.

Beyond Southampton he stopped at a roadside diner, fed himself with a hamburger and fries, gulped a cup of sludgy coffee, pulled into a Mobile station, filled his gas tank, checked his dipstick, poured a quart of oil into the minibus's gut, topped off the radiator's reservoir with distilled water and hit the road again, man and car nourished and expectant. The station's attendant told him to keep a sharp eye out for a sign pointing the way to Serene Harbor, only a mile or so after the Carvel ice cream hut.

Simon found the sign and followed a rutted back road that skirted Southampton's asshole. The route to Serene Harbor was lined with humble cottages, junk yards, a marina that rented Sunfish and kayaks, a string of battered motel cabins, a garbage dump where a thousand yelping gulls gave broken appliances and piles of trash the look of snowdrifts, a local deli, a bar and grill that sold pizza pies, empty fruit and flower stands, a field where two horses stood watching the sunset, a real estate office, an overgrown graveyard across from an abandoned church with a caved-in roof and fire-blackened timbers. The road curved along a long stretch with no visible evidence of human habitation, bridged a swampy pond, curled around groves of maple, oak and pine and ended at a REDUCE SPEED! CHILDREN AT PLAY! sign that marked the outskirts of Serene Harbor, Founded in 1752.

At last light, Simon pulled his minibus onto an empty field, found a spot camouflaged from the police by a hedge of yew, unrolled a mat he'd bought at a Salvation Army thrift shop, lay himself down under a bedspread he'd found stuffed under the driver's seat, and fell into the best sleep he'd had in months, allowing that he jerked awake a few times during the night expecting to find a hovering nurse holding a can of Ensure and a bowl of generic hospital Jell-O, to hear pillow-muffled moans and groans floating through disinfected air, but when he realized there was no nurse, no Jell-O and the only sound was the sorrowful chirp of cicadas and tree frogs, he smiled and slept again.

69

Regis Van Clay, along with his wife, Lucille, and their three children—Price, 19, Anthony, 14, and Sheridan, 9—were about enter the Waldorf Astoria Hotel where Regis Pharmaceuticals held its annual meeting. With them was David Huffner, Regis's speechwriter, scribbling a few last-minute changes in the final text of the CEO's remarks to what promised to be a huge and ebullient turnout of stockholders, financial analysts, and the business press.

Regis's speech summarized the incredible achievements of the previous year. Profits were at an all-time high and rising. The numbers were a rousing endorsement of the company's global strategy. With acquisitions in thirty-two countries spanning every continent, the future was more than bright.

Wonder drugs like *Stalagamide, Thumicsk, Xanelul* and *Expeloton* demonstrated the company's continuing commitment to research and development. Unexpected uses for those drugs had reversed a moribund profit picture and more than compensated for tremendous losses in *Cripthalizine, Nonacripthae, Viloxidril* and *Aquathaline* due to what Regis had come to call Apple Effects.

The Regis product spectrum had grown to include point-of-sale items for personal hygiene, cosmetics, dental care, first aid, pain relief, fertilizers and pet remedies, the manufacture of specialized equipment for doctors, dentists, veterinarians, laboratories and hospitals, devices for implants, transplants, instruments ranging from scalpels to colon scopes, a whole new pantheon of tests for pressure, pregnancy, blood sugar, viruses, bacteria, and top secret projects for the military. Huffner wrote: "Regis Pharmaceuticals has boxed the proverbial compass. Skill! Dedication! Imagination!—these energize our company's tireless labors. Amazing new discoveries are steppingstones toward the alleviation and elimination of illness, disability and, someday, morbidity. We are ever in the vanguard of the war against aging—and, yes, death itself!"

A powerhouse speech.

In the limo driving to the Waldorf, Huffner had been told by Lucille Van Clay to add the word *scintillating* somewhere, anywhere, into the text. He'd already used luminous, incandescent and coruscating (edited to sparkling). Lucille explained that her husband had a special fondness for scintillating, arguing that it was a word too seldom used in an age of false modesty. Huffner said it would be wrong for Regis to give the impression that he was gloating, too cocky. Lucille blunted that argument with the truism affirming a rooster's right to crow when the sun rose. Her husband concurred.

As the party was about to enter the hotel, a revolving door discharged a short, bald, bent old man with red eyes, blue lips and skin the color of wilted lettuce. He clutched a 38-caliber pistol in a trembling hand. The gun was aimed at Regis's chest. "Don't move, don't breathe," the man said, pausing to wheeze and cough. "Stop doodling," he yelled at Dave Huffner who hadn't noticed him. "Get the lady and the kids out of the way," the man snarled at Regis. "You're the one I'm here to assassinate. Don't think I can't shoot straight even with the glaucoma."

"What do you want?" Regis said.

"I want you dead is what I want."

"That's Regis Van Clay," Dave Huffner said.

"I know who he is, thank you very much. You seem to be the speechwriter. Here's a text for today's speech: So long, it's been good t'know ya." The man spit black phlegm. "Pray for yourself, Mr. Big Shot. You have thirty seconds."

"Would you please try to stop your hand from shaking," Regis said. "What's your problem? Why me?"

"Why you? You see what I got in my hand? The other one, not the one with the gun."

"A piece of paper," Dave Huffner said. "He's got a piece of paper."

"Stay out of this, hack," the assassin said. "A piece of paper that happens to be a prescription from Dr. Samuel Evinbaum who practices on Johnson Avenue, in Riverdale, The Bronx. You want to know what it's for? *Tonlara XL*. The yellow pills shaped like pyramids."

"*Tonlara XL?* That's one of ours. A vasodilator." Huffner said.

"I know it's yours. I know what it is. It keeps me alive. You know how much it costs?"

"Full price or co-pay?" Huffner said.

"Sixteen dollars a pill. You ever hear of a fixed income?"

"Hold your horses," Regis said. "Do you know what it costs me to make those pills?"

"Not sixteen bucks," the man said. "I know that much. Every morning I get to choose between having a heart attack and having

breakfast. Every night I get to ask myself if I want food, electric, rent
or a pulse. Do I freeze in the dark, starve, move into a cardboard box
on the street or drop dead? Enough with the choices. Have a good
long nap."

"You idiot," Huffner said. "I'm surprised at you. You're going to
kill Regis Van Clay because he makes the drug that keeps you alive?"

"You're calling me an idiot?"

"He didn't mean it," Lucille said. "He's excitable. You know
how writers are."

"He meant it," Regis said. "Didn't anybody ever tell you that the
price of a drug is directly related to its effectiveness? Don't you know
there are hundreds of studies proving that cutting the price of a medication reduces its potency?"

"This is not about potency."

"He means a discounted drug doesn't work as well as the full
price one," Huffner said.

"Thanks for translating," the man said. "I never heard such bullshit."

"If you're set on killing me, kill me." Regis said, "but get your
facts straight. I laugh when I hear people complaining about the cost
of an item as scintillating, yes, I said scintillating, as *Tonlara XL*.
Because I know if I lower the price, it could kill you. Don't ask me
to explain it. It has something to do with human nature. I'm not saying generic drugs don't work for some people. But whatever the reason, the cheaper the pill, the more work for the undertaker. You
think I want to charge sixteen dollars a pill retail?"

"This is crazy," the man said, thrusting his gun against Regis's
belly. "You're saying you're doing me a favor by charging sixteen dollars for one lousy pill?"

"Absolutely. Do I want you to starve? Do I want you homeless?
Do I want you in intensive care? Do I want that on my conscience?
This is my wife standing there. Those are my children clinging together. Do I want them to think of their husband and father as a callous
human being? But there is proof. Tons of proof to back me up."

"You're saying you have statistics?" the man said.

"Reams of statistics," Regis said. "Before you pull that trigger,
take a minute to think things over. How about I arrange for you to get

a month's supply of *Tonlara XL.* Free samples. Huffner, make the arrangements. And send this man a copy of those reports on the lethal results of excessive price reduction in places like Canada, Israel and emerging nations in Africa. Send him those reports and the samples even if he does kill me."

"Yes, sir," Huffner said. "A month's worth of free samples and the stats."

"How come I never heard about such a report?" the man said. "I watch the news."

"Blame the liberal media." Regis said. "Not me."

"What about free samples?" the man said. "If discounts are dangerous, what do your statistics say about free samples?"

"Uncertain. If you want to take the risk, be my guest. You know, it's ironic. Did you ever ask yourself why my company is called Regis Pharmaceuticals and not Van Clay Pharmaceuticals?"

"I did wonder about that," the man said. "It kept me up all night."

"Let me tell him," Huffner said. "Because Regis's father, August Van Clay, our beloved founder, may he rest in peace, was a greedy old bastard who would have denied a Q-Tip to a bleeding orphan who didn't have the penny to pay for it. Yes, the company was originally called Van Clay Pharmaceuticals. The minute Regis here inherited controlling interest, he changed its name to forever erase the memory of his price-gouging biological progenitor. Regis Van Clay swore an oath to dedicate himself to humanity."

"I'm confused," the gunman said. "But I'm going to kill him anyhow. How much can it cost to make those *Tonlara XL* pills?"

"Actually, thirty-four cents," Regis said the instant a sniper from the NYPD Swat Team dropped the would-be assassin with a single clean shot to the head.

"You were amazing," Huffner said. "That spiel about statistics was brilliant. Incredible."

"We probably have numbers like that in a file cabinet someplace," Regis said. "If we don't, make sure we get some. As for your spiel about my father, I have to say I resented your references to the finest man I ever knew. Changing the name to Regis Pharmaceuticals was a way to fuck the IRS."

"I was trying to save your life, boss."

"Hand me my speech. Lucille, Price, Anthony, Sheridan, get your tails in gear. Listen to that murmur from inside the auditorium. The sheep are bleating for their shepherd."

70

Serene Harbor proved to be everything Simon hoped it would be — a forgotten *cul de sac*, proud of its past but comfortable with a shabby present. Simon's eyes, glazed by the jumbled sights of New York, suddenly cleared. He focused on every separate detail of the tiny town's anatomy.

Serene Harbor was built along a waterfront where a few sailboats bobbed on waves tamed by long stone jetties. An old barn painted with a sign, SERENE HARBOR YACHT CLUB (there were no yachts, only a few dinghies and a Boston Whaler), sat on an inlet across from a barbered park, mostly lawn, that hosted a few stately trees, a playground with a slide and swings, a picnic table and well-spaced wooden slat benches facing the bay. Each bench was marked with a brass plaque engraved in memory of someone who'd once walked on local earth but now danced among angels: THIS BENCH IS DEDICATED TO MRS. JULIA BOWSTICLER — NOW SHE SMILES DOWN FROM THE STARS.

Across from the park, an abandoned factory building loomed over the landscape, looking displaced and a bit menacing, like the homeless men and bag ladies Simon had seen crouched in Manhattan doorways. A sign near the factory's roof read: INTERNATIONAL TIME in flaking gold letters.

A block inland, Revolution Street, the town's commercial center, was bracketed on one end by a Civil War cannon and a flagpole, on the other by a windmill with its arms locked in place. Between those landmarks were a market, a pharmacy, a general store, a post office, a library that had once been a mansion, two antique shops, a hardware store, the three-story Union Hotel, Bob's Fish Market, The Skull & Crossbones Bar, the cube-shaped Commodore Cinema, and the Town Hall.

Side streets named for the nation's founding fathers were divided into small lots where Serene Harbor's citizens lived in decrepit houses, many dating back to the 18th century. Scrubby gardens struggled to grow in sandy soil. Roses, hydrangeas, daises, impatiens, poppies, hostis, beach plums, yews and wisteria all bespoke noble attempts at preserving order and elegance.

Other houses, more decrepit, forsook useless blooms and greenery; their lawns cultivated more practical crops of auto parts, stacks of tires, boats on trailer beds, the skeletons of cannibalized appliances, stone elves, sundials, birdbaths, claw-footed bathtubs, sinks, broken toilets, and assorted pieces of abandoned furniture, many missing parts like drawers or legs. Rusted bedsprings protruded metal tentacles that curled like overgrown weeds.

Among those junk piles was a wide assortment of broken tricycles and bicycles, many plastic toys and, here and there, a battered doll. Simon let himself wonder if those dolls had been dropped by children rushing off to school that morning or if they'd been abandoned by changelings now with adult bodies and kids of their own.

Cars, some dating back to the heyday of chrome trim and tail fins — Fords and Chevys with an occasional Buick, Studebaker, Kaiser or Caddy shell in the mix, ex-army Jeeps and pickup trucks were parked in pebble driveways or along low, crumbling curbs.

On higher ground, Victorian fossils, once the homes of whaling captains and kings of commerce, advertised ROOMS FOR RENT, offered BED & BREAKFAST accommodations, displayed FOR SALE signs tacked shamelessly onto tipping wrought iron gates.

At the tiny library, Simon leafed through a pamphlet on Serene Harbor's polyglot population and its reputation as "a model for tolerance." The booklet mentioned that "the Caucasian community coexisted on excellent terms with two Black enclaves, each with a distinct demographic. One, an inland community, was made up of modest shacks once populated by whalers many of whom had been Indians and Africans." A footnote said that area was nicknamed Lionel Hampton. "The second Black area spread along a strip of beach where affluent Negroes built summer cottages in the booming decade of the 1920s then passed them along to their fortunate descendants."

The booklet emphasized Serene Harbor's spirituality. There were churches for Methodists, Presbyterians, Episcopalians, Roman Catholics, Pentecostals and Baptists. There was even a synagogue built by Jewish factory workers; the sprinkle of Jews dated back to the existence of a factory built early in the 20th century when industry made a feeble attempt to replace the vanishing whaling trade as Serene Harbor's chief economic engine.

Each race and religion had its own hallowed ground: the black cemetery, tucked among maple and oak trees, was a mile from the beautifully landscaped Protestant burial field where butchers, bakers and candlestick makers shared choice territory with the wealthy nabobs of Serene Harbor's halcyon days. In that fancy bone yard, mausoleums and obelisks stood beside splitting tombstones with weather-erased inscriptions that marked the graves of heroes of the Revolution, 1812, the Civil War, Teddy Roosevelt's wars, two World Wars, and the "police action" in Korea. The Catholics had their resting place nearer to the ocean, a peaceful gathering place for stone saints and cherubs. The small, crowded Jewish cemetery outside town was almost entirely hidden from the highway by a collapsing fence and a few skimpy evergreens.

Visionaries had long since sensed that Serene Harbor was a candidate for inevitable gentrification; the abandoned factory, with a fine water view, was the obvious key to upgrading the community. The International Time Company had built their ill-fated clock and watch factory on land (originally bought for a song) where whale blubber was once processed into lamp oil and candles. In those days it was easy enough to find cheap labor—immigrants were recruited on Ellis Island, transported to Serene Harbor on a railroad spur that no longer existed, and quickly taught to manufacture metal casings and paint luminous dials.

After a few years of success, that business folded during the Depression; International Time went bankrupt leaving the local workers and imported Jews to fend for themselves.

What was left of the factory—a few acres of rotting cement, cracking brick and broken glass surrounded by rusty barbed wire— cluttered the landscape just beyond what was left of the once proud pier. There were perpetual rumors that the watch factory would be converted into upscale apartments for summer tenants, an ambitious plan complicated by the annoying discovery that its site was officially designated as highly toxic—corrupted by machine oils, acids, radioactive paint and other chemical carcinogens.

Shortly before Simon's arrival, the government had paid for an attempt to remove a plume of sludge shaped like an octopus from under the factory's foundation, and had certified that the building and its site were safe for human and animal habitation. Construction was about to begin on the new incarnation.

Oddly, Serene Harbor's old-timers didn't relish the idea of an apartment house replacing their town hulk; the factory was an eyesore, a poisonous mushroom, but it was their eyesore with a certain nostalgic appeal, something like having an ugly cousin in the family. They hired an independent testing company whose findings contradicted the government's engineers, and all plans for the factory's conversion were put on hold pending further study.

Despite the eidolon of bitter litigation, because of its valuable water view and the new popularity of Long Island's South Fork, investors bought and sold the property many times. Every attempt at reconstruction had been blocked. Defending what was left of the watch factory was a classic example of the passion with which Serene Harbor defended its bullyweed identity. Unlike its neighboring postcard settlements—East Hampton, Amaganset, Water Mill and Sagaponack—Serene Harbor battled to avoid becoming a prime destination for the summer elite.

Within a few days of his arrival, Simon landed a part-time job at the Better Days Antique Shoppe on Revolution Street. He'd gone into the store to browse, having nothing better to do, lured by its collage-from-hell window display—a kaleidoscope of discards ranging from a decapitated Howdy Doody puppet to a collection of German beer mugs decorated with fat peasant girls dancing with assorted beasts from the Black Forest.

There were cracked stained-glass window panes, a school desk missing its seat, a rusty cow bell, a pile of lobster traps, paint-flecked duck decoys, a fireman's helmet, a ship model without its masts, a torn crazy quilt made from flour and burlap sacks, a bucket of marbles, an iron tractor saddle, a bronze crucifix dangling from a red, white and blue ribbon, a stuffed frog, a box of utensils, seltzer bottles in pastel colors, an assortment of bracelets, necklaces and rings in the cubicles of a wooden type-setter's tray.

Simon remembered his favorite academic, Ms. Tabitha Ulman, explaining the lure and allure of antiques, urging her students to consider that every object contained a numen, the trapped spirit of a former owner. Ms. Ulman carried an antique mirror in her purse claiming she could see shadows staring out at her through its oval of smoky beveled glass. Since then, Simon was respectful of what he'd once considered deified junk; he gave antiques the benefit of the doubt and listened for their whispers.

The inside of Better Times was like its window, filled floor to ceiling with rescued leftovers. At the back of the shop, sitting in an armchair behind a rolltop desk, reading a copy of *Life* magazine under light from a gooseneck lamp with a green shade, a large woman sat pretending to ignore him. Simon sensed that he was being closely watched, wondering what the woman thought he might steal. He was examining a photograph of Clark Gable framed inside a toilet seat when she pushed herself up from the chair on flabby arms and waddled toward him. "If you need any help, don't be afraid to ask," she said. "It's what I'm here for."

"Thanks," Simon said.

"You're the one who lives in the bus," she said.

"How would you know that?"

"Everybody here knows everything. You wonder why we haven't kicked you out of town? Curiosity. What are you doing in this part of the world?"

"Getting a feel for the place," Simon said.

"Are you some kind of leftover hippie?"

"Why? You want to put me in the window?"

"A drag on the market."

"I'm looking for a place to settle, at least for the time being. I like your town. It's got good vibes."

"Talk English if you don't mind. What's your name?"

"Simon Apple."

"Wanda Hubbard. I own this store. And the rest of the house. I've lived here all my life. How old do I look to you?"

"Twenty-one," Simon said.

"Close. Seventy-eight in the shade. Let's not crap around. You want a job? Here's the deal. Wednesday to Friday you watch the store while I go scouting for merchandise or just lay around upstairs playing with my vibrator. Saturday mornings you hold the fort while I drive around to scavenge yard sales. Sunday nights we both drive out to the county dump because you wouldn't believe what the weekend people who live in those McMansions, the ones you read about in *New York Magazine*, call garbage.

"You get a room upstairs, utilities included, with kitchen privileges and space in my fridge. You can use the washer-dryer if you ever decide to change your underwear. You get paid thirty bucks a week by check on the books, or twenty-five cash, off. Your choice. Oh, you help with odd jobs like shoveling snow, mowing the lawn, bagging leaves, putting up Halloween and Christmas decorations, and delivering what needs to be delivered or picking up what needs to be picked up.

"Did I mention you don't screw around with my granddaughter, Martha Marie, when she comes out to visit which is usually every few months because if you do I feed you to the gulls. Think it over before you agree. It won't be easy. Martha Marie is a doll, a sweet tempered girl, all body and no brains, hot as a barbecue. She's a former virgin who backs into doorknobs for kicks. You're gonna be the first guy who backs away. Understood?"

"Understood."

"Besides, I do not allow any form of spawning in my house under any circumstances because the thumping and moaning brings back too many happy memories that give me indigestion. My slogan is keep the past at arm's length which might sound confusing coming from the mouth of a lady who sells antiques but life throws curves. I inherited this business from my mother and nothing better came along including Mr. Hubbard, may he rest in peace, and my two daughters they should drop dead. So those are my terms and conditions. Unless you're a plumber, carpenter or a doctor you won't get a better offer, not in Serene Harbor, not at this time of year."

"Sounds like a once-in-a-lifetime opportunity," Simon said.

"Oh, I should have asked you if you're in any trouble with the cops."

"No trouble."

"Drugs?"

"Nothing illegal."

"Booze?"

"Maybe a few beers. After five."

"Republican?"

"Independent."

"Diseases?"

"Not that I know about."

"Here's a broom. Sweep the sidewalk. Then skip over to the market and get me a pack of Camels and a box of Oreos. They're on special, one to a customer. I already filled my quota. Take this fiver. Count your change."

71

Simon's days at Better Times had a dreamlike quality. As winter closed in, very few customers jingled the bell hanging from the shop's door. Most came because they were lost, looking for the way back to Route 27 that led to east to Montauk or west to New York. A handful were genuine antique addicts who explored every store that might hold hidden treasure.

He learned quickly to let the browsers browse in silence and to meet suspicious eyes wary of reproductions—not that there was much in the store anyone in China or Thailand would bother reproducing—with a cordial grin. Wanda Hubbard gave him leeway to drop any item's price up to 40 percent, but only after acting like he was a rube being raped by bargain hunters.

He invited shoppers to take their time, repeated stories about somebody finding an original copy of the "Gettysburg Address" glued to the back of some innocuous picture like the one of Clark Gable framed inside the well-used toilet seat, or an original Michelangelo sketch tucked inside a child's picture book. "The other day I saw an article about a teacup from the Ming Dynasty, bought for fifty cents at the Brimfield flea market in Massachusetts, that brought a hundred thousand at auction!"

When wives and husbands disagreed about paying even the sale price for something like a salad bowl with ceramic ducks circling its rim, Simon would say, "Well, money is important but this bowl will give you pleasure for years and if you divide the dollars you spend by all those years, we're talking about a few inflated dollars a year and you'll own something that can be proudly displayed, and then passed down to future generations." He found he had a real gift for salesmanship and won Wanda's sincere praise when she tallied the day's receipts, however meager. Meager was better than nothing in winter, and nothing was what she'd expected until the sun returned.

When the shop was as empty as its cash register, which was most of the time, Simon read books with warped covers that smelled like swamp water: novels, biographies, histories, volumes of poetry, cook books, comic books, anything handy. He opened brown, flaking newspapers with urgent headlines about crises as obsolete as hula-hoops that reminded him of his ancient *Britannica*. He studied sheet music, his fingers trying to follow notes and clefs that lay like drunks sleeping on railroad tracks. He sang their lyrics, gleeful and sentimental, about love in Paris, rain in London, rivers, including the mighty Mississippi, seductive Swanee and sensual Wabash, laments for soldiers fighting forgotten wars, hits from Fred Astaire movies and Broadway blockbusters, patriotic ballads, gospel favorites, standards by Crosby, Sinatra, Presley or the Beatles. Simon sang to amuse himself but also to test his voice against Dr. Mercy Merriweather's warning that his use of *Thumicsk* might leach testosterone from his vocal cords and leave him sounding like a plucked pullet. Since *Stalagamide* had no effect on his condition, Simon's hopes for recovery were fading fast.

On his days off, Simon drove out to Montauk, climbed to the top of its famous lighthouse and watched the ocean, nostalgic about his *Viloxidril* days and what might have been if he'd followed through on his plan to live under a sky of waves; he could have been in a meaningful relationship with a pike, wrapped in the tentacles of a giant squid, lolling on The Great Barrier Reef or lounging on a deck chair from the *Titanic*, trading war stories with a retired shark. He might have found Atlantis, the ultimate antique shop, and been hailed as a savior by a population of tuna, stingrays, sardines, shrimp, clams and crabs.

If he'd become a full-time sea creature before *Aquathaline* had erased his gills, after a few good years he'd probably have found himself skimming aimlessly through the world's basement hardly noticing its bounty of bones and treasure, wondering about life among the air breathers, denied memory of the sweet wet furnace simmering between Polly Moon's endless legs. Spiritually speaking, salmon sex had to leave something wanting.

Simon realized that second-guessing the past squandered the present, but so did watching television. Staring at the ocean—never changing, never the same, a puddle of liquefied eternity—linked Simon to a sense of mystery, tantalized him with unanswered questions, mingled hope with despair, roiled what he assumed was his soul, kindled hopes of immortality even as its corpse-laden beaches confirmed mortality, celebrated transience and permanence, echoed sentiments of awe and wonder, forced him to consider that even the sea was a slave to the pull of the moon. Looking out at that which seemed limitless conjured a brutal awareness of limitation.

Existence was a no-win situation. Without the foundation of logic, lacking any splinter of proof, with no crumb of circumstantial evidence to convince himself that creation was anything but the whim of a demented atom, Simon decided he'd rather be a living witness to ongoing mayhem than a drifting empty shell.

When he wasn't watching the contradiction of tides, Simon walked the Hampton beaches, rode past cornfields and potato farms, watched horses jump and roll in thick grass, gaped at the castles of the super rich on estates the size of Central Park.

After work, he learned to play a passing game of pool at the Skull & Crossbones, the town's off-season social center. Serene Harbor's natives accepted his presence without obvious acrimony. If Simon was OK with "Mother" Hubbard, he was OK with them.

While there were usually a few women who hung out at the Skull & Crossbones bar, most of the patrons were big muscled laborers, and fishermen sporting tattoos of hot babes, angry lions, eagles in flight, wind-blown flags, and the names of wives or sweethearts current or former. They drank beers or boilermakers, smoked cigarettes, chewed cigar butts, talked sports, jobs, weather.

What surprised Simon was that the closest thing to serious conversation—the verbal glue stronger than the usual blather about lousy bosses or the good old days—were complaints about sprained backs, leg cramps, neck spasms, constipated guts, or the occasional busted stitch, broken bone or upcoming hernia operation. The citizens of Serene Harbor, descendants of Ahab and Starbuck, saw themselves as walking wounded.

While he listened to the click of pool balls scattering helter-skelter across dragon green table turf, Simon often had the feeling he was back in the hospital under intensive care instead of standing with a cue in his hand surrounded by jocks built like boulders. He hadn't realized that even the frightened fragile wear tattoos, a truth hidden from the overprotected sons and daughters of Glenda.

That insight was both pleasing (he felt less of a freak, more one of the boys) and disappointing; Simon would have preferred not knowing that the resident hulks needed glycerin suppositories to coax what he would have guessed were industrial-strength rectums.

Another favorite topic was sudden death, sometimes from a heart attack that exploded the healthiest, hairiest chest but most often the result of a head-on collision down the highway toward Riverhead. If the victim was a distant relation, or only a slight acquaintance, there'd be no mourning at the bar beyond a moment of respectful silence. If the corpse was a regular at the Skull & Crossbones, then there were toasts, reminiscences, and a collection taken for the bereaved family. The really popular victims had their pictures posted on a bulletin board, and an American flag the size of a table centerpiece was lowered to half-mast.

For Simon, the great lesson of the Skull & Crossbones was that nobody is immune from things that go bump in the night or during the average day. As for things that go bump given half a chance, Wanda Hubbard's granddaughter, Martha Marie, arrived in Serene Harbor on an evening when the first snow surprised the town.

Her unexpected visit came the week before Halloween. In the spirit of the season, dangling straw men, spiders with glittering eyes, cardboard skeletons, paper ghosts and goblins, pumpkins with candle-lit grins decorated doorways and windows. Somebody'd hung a large black bat from the tallest chimney of the abandoned watch factory. The window of Better Times displayed a mannequin from the 1940s wrapped in mummy rags.

When Martha Marie showed up, light from a wispy moon had turned a thin veil of snowflakes to what Simon saw as a shower of rhinestones. Serene Harbor wasn't ready for the gift of diamonds. Mother Hubbard dispatched him to pick up Martha Marie at the Long Island Railroad station in Bridgehampton. Simon's minibus skidded along frozen roads, its windshield wipers squeaking, its bald tires fighting for traction. When he reached the station, the train had already pulled out.

Simon wondered how he'd recognize his passenger. That concern was wasted. There was only one person waiting on the platform, a young woman standing close to a tilted lamppost. She was bundled into a ponderous fake fur that made her look like a porcupine. Simon honked his alto horn; the porcupine lifted a small shoulder bag, struggled with a large donut-shaped canvas case on wheels, and moved toward the sound. Simon climbed down from the driver's seat to help with her baggage. "You must be Red Riding Hood," Simon said. "Your grandmother can't wait to see you."

"You must be the new person. Sorry to drag you out on a night like this."

"Not a problem. Where I grew up this weather would be considered tropical. Hand me your stuff. I'll stow it in back."

"Be careful of my drums. They're heavier than they look."

"So, you're a drummer? Interesting," Simon said.

"Not very. Not yet."

Inside the minibus, Simon waited while Martha Marie tried to buckle her seat belt. It wouldn't fit around her coat. "Let it go," she said. "Better a fiery death than dishonor. I got this stupid coat at a thrift shop in Brooklyn. It makes me look like a horse."

"Porcupine," Simon said.

"I'd rather a horse if you don't mind."

"A horse then. A Clydesdale. No disrespect intended. At least you're a warm horse."

"Tell me, new person, how can you stand working for my sweet Granny Hitler?"

"We get along fine," Simon said.

"I never heard anybody say that. Are you from Tibet or what?"

"Or what," Simon said. "This new person's name is Simon Apple."

"I'm Martha Marie Hoffer."

"That I know. You mind if I smoke?"

"Why should I mind? Or was that a rhetorical question?"

In the light from a wooden match, Simon got his first clear look at Martha Marie. She was no beauty but she had a pleasant face. Under a barrage of frizzy yellow hair he saw large brown eyes and a wide mouth. A turned-up nose had been badly fixed—it had the pointy look of a high-heeled shoe with nostrils nearly large enough to inhale acorns, the product of assembly line surgery. Simon knew that identical nose from scores of coeds at Celadon College. That nose made her seem like an old friend.

It wasn't until they reached home that Simon understood why his employer's list of terms and conditions had included a taboo on any fiddling with Martha Marie. When she took off the porcupine coat, he confronted a perfect body: lovely thrusting breasts, a small waist, trim thighs connected to endless legs. He had to stop himself from floating toward that nirvana of curves and crevices, like a space-walking astronaut pulled by the sudden gravity of a shooting star.

The realization that lying with this incarnation of Aphrodite was denied him for reasons light-years beyond the mere obstacle of the oath imposed by Wanda Hubbard was unbearable. Simon's sad excuse for a penis, the inch worm bequeathed to him by Dr. Merriweather and *Thumicsk*, tingled with the intensity of a tuning fork. Feeling dizzy, blaming fatigue, Simon said his good nights and went to his room. From the stairs he heard Martha Marie tell Grandma she planned to stay for a full week, weather or no weather.

72

By the next day, Simon's frustration had eased somewhat. The untouchable intruder was a terrible drummer, absolutely anti-aphrodisiac. Martha Marie banged and clanged at her bass, kettle and cymbals with no perceptible sense of rhythm.

Her racket began after breakfast and continued for most of the day, loud enough to penetrate downstairs to the store where Simon sat trying to read. The banging made Wanda's antiques tremble in sympathetic vibration; it made them seem alive. As much as he winced from those grating drumbeats, he was happy that they beat the shreds of lust from his mind like dust paddled from a mangy rug. But her pernicious percussion also reminded him that Martha Marie was there, one short flight above his head, her breasts and bottom, arms and legs delicious in perpetual motion.

That same evening, Simon learned that Martha Marie was an incorrigible flirt who'd probably stained the seat of every pickup truck in Serene Harbor. When she came with him to the Skull & Crossbones, the few female regulars went silent as zombies. They resigned from combat, outclassed and outflanked. While the women froze, every man in the place, including old Marco the bartender, turned into an erection.

While Martha Marie worked the room, renewing acquaintances, Simons's skin wrinkled with raging envy. Envy turned to jealousy when he saw thirty eyes, usually as expressive as boiled eggs, focus lasers on her cleavage, and when she bent over the pool table, the rump crease clearly outlined against her spandex slacks, Simon knew his reaction was way out of proportion. Martha Marie wasn't exactly his date, but he felt as possessive toward her as if she were his wallet.

He also learned that this generic object of desire was more planet than star; she shone by reflected light. The girl was a shameless narcissist—tossing her reflection at every mirror, drinking glass, and bit of metal trim along the bar, even half-full ashtrays. He watched her blatantly evaluate how effectively those reflections reflected in eyeglasses, empty bottles, light fixtures, jacket buttons, the juke box's chrome coin slot, the silver metal knobs on the cigarette machine, anything capable of capturing her image.

The jealous agonies Simon endured at the Skull & Crossbones were ant bites compared to the traumas he suffered late at night or in the early morning when Martha Marie headed for the only upstairs bathroom in bikini panties, using her arms for a bra, or, still steaming from a hot, perfumed tub, headed for her room, wrapped in a tight Turkish towel. By choice or chance she left her door open wide enough for Simon to catch flashes of her naked knee bends, stretches and—most excruciating of all—doing push-ups that allowed her nipples to brush the stripes on an authentic 19th-century zebra rug.

To avoid going completely berserk, Simon kept his focus on that designer nose with its humongous set of nostrils whenever Martha Marie teased him with wide-eyed stares, adorable grins, pouting lips, and an acrobatic tongue that licked ice cream or chocolate sauce off her spoon after one of Wanda Hubbard's elaborate dinners.

Grandma had commanded Simon to share evening meals during Martha Marie's stay in order to keep her company. Home cooking was a welcome change from his usual diet of spaghetti and meatballs or fried chicken at the Skull & Crossbones, but the price in personal anguish was high. That Simon hadn't openly demonstrated any interest in bedding Martha Marie threatened her self-image as the Empress of Ripe, succulent as a honeydew from Eden. At the dinner table, her advances became more and more tantalizing; he felt his defenses cracking like castle walls pummeled by catapulted boulders. He identified with the watch factory's shaky façade, holding together but on the verge of collapse.

When Wanda left the pair alone while she went into the kitchen to check her pot roast, stir a sauce or top a warm pie with swirls of frosting, Simon would feel a shoeless foot slide up his leg and grab for his lap napkin with an educated toe. He'd watch his tablemate dip her pinky into a honey jar and suck it like a lollypop. She'd complain about the heat from the stone fireplace, fish an ice cube from her water glass and reach into her blouse, massaging her breasts to cool down. Martha Marie monitored her stunts in the shiny belly of a water pitcher, then measured Simon's response by any telltale wince, twitch or facial spasm.

During that interplay, the two of them kept a soundtrack going for Wanda's benefit, casual conversation as innocuous as the bleating of diplomats. Martha Marie did most of the talking, commenting on movies Simon had never seen and celebrities he'd never heard of. "You two are such chatterboxes," Granny Hubbard would say or, "How can you young people eat and talk at the same time?" Wanda seemed oblivious to the fact that her granddaughter was driving Simon Apple crazy with temptation while his unshakable resistance left Martha Marie in private panic, but Simon had the eerie feeling that Granny enjoyed their torment, tender chickens turning slowly on a spit.

Five days into Martha Marie's visit, in the dead of night, he woke to find her tugging at the blanket covering his naked body. His eyes popped open just in time to roll himself over to conceal his miniaturized equipment. "What are you doing?" Simon said, sounding like a hopeless idiot.

"I want you," Martha Marie said, rubbing Simon's bare bottom, "and I know you want me. Well there you are and here I am. So let's get on with it because my affection is already turning to anger and what could be something beautiful might end as one of those grotesque memories of what might have been."

Simon defended himself with a top sheet, sat up and snapped on a flashlight he kept on his night table. Martha Marie was wearing a black lace-trimmed teddy held together by bowed ribbons and a few uncomplicated hooks. "You've got to understand," Simon said, "I made a solemn promise to your grandmother. I swore on the Holy Book to avoid any physical contact with you. This is not only a matter of honor, it's about keeping my job."

"We could be quiet as consenting adult mice."

"No," Simon said. "I'm a screamer. A very noisy fucker. I'm famous for that."

"You are a strange boy. Move over. Let me climb in with you. I'm cold out here. Cold and lonely."

"Martha Marie, I can't deny that you are a very desirable woman. I'm flattered that you find me worth a second look. Aside from betrayal, giving in to your considerable charms would leave me homeless and broke. Go back to your room. We can have an abstract fusion like phone sex."

"You're telling me to get myself off? I can do that right here if it turns you on."

"Not here, not tonight. Martha Marie, there are other factors."

"You have a girlfriend? So what? I have a boyfriend. We can pretend to move back in time, long before we met them. Say this is the first century B.C."

"Now that you mentioned it, I do have a girlfriend. Did have. She recently died. I'm still in mourning," Simon said.

"She'd want you to get on with your life. I can't accept that as your reason for being so nasty to me. Is there something else? Like for example herpes or clap? Is that it? Are you being protective? Don't worry. I have a fabulous immune system and a pack of rubbers."

"It could be worse. My tests haven't come back yet. I'm not going to move over and that's that so don't make it harder for me."

"Haven't I made it harder for you? I'll bet it's nice and hard, Simon. I need to be held. I need you inside me."

"I know rejection is hard for you to take. I'm not rejecting. There are things I can't explain. I'm having a nervous breakdown here. Shoo. Go away."

"You won't get another chance," Martha Marie said. "Because now I am furious."

"I accept that," Simon said, "and I don't blame you. We can still be good friends."

"I get the picture. You're queer. That's it, isn't it? You're in the closet."

"I can understand why you might think that," Simon said. "Give me Rock Hudson or give me death."

"Up yours," Martha Marie said and stormed back to her room. She left Simon bathed in drenching sweat, cursing out God, the Devil and the new bottle of *Stalagamide*, sent by Dr. Merriweather. He was in no mood for sleep so he dressed as quietly as he could, pulled a heavy sweater over a woolen shirt and went out for a walk around the town, taking deep, burning breaths of frigid air to erase the tenacious traces of Martha Marie's perfume that managed to get past his sinuses and lodge in his brain.

The humiliation of refusing the most precious of gifts, even from a nympho-narcissist, made Simon cringe under the umbrella of winter stars. Whole constellations sang lamentations, as they must have for Tabitha Ulman's favorite hero, Hemingway's *macho castrato*, Jake Barnes, in *The Sun Also Rises*. At least Jake's truncated tower was the result of fighting a good war. Simon Apple had done nothing but swallow a pill to counteract a pill to counteract a pill to counteract a pill to counteract a pill to counteract a pill to counteract a pill.

He walked east, eager to meet Serene Harbor's next sunrise. Dawn's early light had a way of routing the vultures of despair, albeit temporarily; dawn was Simon's only ally, but walk as fast as he might through a fresh carpet of crunching snow, dawn was still an hour away.

Simon's itinerary took him along the waterfront to where the abandoned watch factory loomed like a decaying cadaver. He welcomed the chance to inhale its toxic emanations, an odorless essence less malevolent than Martha Marie's delicious Opium by Yves St. Laurent. Simon would have been relieved to have his flesh fall off in clumps, leaving a radioactive skeleton, free of recrimination and regret, striding jauntily toward the arm-locked relic of a windmill at the end of Revolution Street.

Simon stopped abruptly. He thought he saw a dull gleam of yellow light dribbling from behind a boarded window on the factory's top floor. It had to be an illusion or reflection but there was nothing to reflect; there were no lampposts rooted near that building, no security lights; the last remnant of a waning moon was stifled by a Brillo pad of clouds.

Yet there was definitely something luminous up there—a soft, steady glow. Simon wondered if it could be from the residue of radium paint soaked into the factory's brick-and-mortar skin. If that was the source, why wasn't the whole structure beaming like a beacon? No, it was definitely bulb-mothered light confined to a single window. Simon stopped to ponder that mystery when he was grabbed from behind.

"So what are you looking at?" said a crumpled cellophane voice with the same accent as Hyman Vornik's, Glenda's best and only tailor, a refugee from Romania.

The arms wrapped around Simon's jacket were thin as insect legs. He easily freed himself and whirled, buoyed by a rush of adrenalin, his own startled arms ready for a fight. Before he threw a punch, Simon saw that his enemy was the oldest vertical human he'd ever encountered, a man hardly five feet tall dressed in infantry camouflage with a wrinkled face the size of a dime.

That little face peered out from behind the white foliage of an enormous beard, linked by a bush of sideburns to wisps of hair hanging from underneath a Brooklyn Dodgers baseball cap. Simon realized if he'd thrown a punch at the sprouting head supporting that face, the whole skull would have snapped off a neck no wider than a heron's and rolled into a snowdrift. "Answer my question," the man said. "What are you looking at?"

"Before I answer any questions, can I make a suggestion? It's not a good idea to sneak up behind a person in the dark."

"I scared you, right?" the man said, laughing. "You nearly pissed your pants, right?"

"You mind telling me what this is about?" Simon said.

"He answers my question with a question," the man said.

"Who are you, the night watchman?" Simon said.

"The night watchman? That's good. Ha ha. You got a sense of humor. Before I get nasty, take some advice, go home because I got no time for a conversation."

The man headed for a heavy door at the side of the factory marked KEEP OUT! PRIVATE PROPERTY! TRESPASSERS WILL BE PROSE-CUTED! The door was bolted shut by an iron bar and a lock the size of a fist. The wispy man didn't reach for a key; he pulled at the knob using his legs for leverage. After a few tugs, the bar and lock moved with the door, leaving a wedge of space. The man squeezed inside and pulled the door shut behind him. Simon went to investigate and saw that the massive lock was attached to nothing; the bolts that once anchored it to brick had corroded to stubs. Simon looked up at the window that first caught his attention. The light flickered and went out.

73

Later that morning, Simon gulped his third cup of coffee, trying to keep awake behind the counter of Better Times. Wanda Hubbard came down to the store to do some quick dusting. She threw a rag and a spray can of Lysol in Simon's direction, pointing toward a wall filled with a newly acquired cache of terrible circus paintings by an anonymous artist with a fondness for clowns, dwarfs and acrobats. The pictures, in faded oils under glass, were bordered by mildew-stained mats surrounded by thick, warped gilded frames. Wanda bought the collection for a song at a barn sale.

"I heard a lot of noise last night," Wanda said. "The patter of little feet. Doors opening and closing. What was going on, Simon? You remember what you swore to me about Martha Marie?"

"I didn't hear a thing. I slept like a log," Simon said, spraying and wiping around a trapeze flier in free fall grasping for his catcher's bulging arm. "I haven't seen Martha Marie since last night's marvelous dinner."

"Sure, sure," Wanda said. "But if she happens to get knocked up, consider yourself a bridegroom. One way or another, you must have rolled off that log you slept like because I heard you go out around five o'clock."

"Oh, that," Simon said, "yes, well, I did get the urge to snort some fresh air. Which brings me to something I wanted to ask about. I was ambling along down by the factory and I swear I saw a light up on the top floor. That struck me as pretty odd in itself but it gets more interesting. There was this little old man with a beard . . ."

"Last night I saw upon the stair a little man who wasn't there. He wasn't there again today. Oh how I wish he'd go away," Wanda said. "You know that poem?"

"My father used to recite it," Simon said, "but the little man upon the stair didn't have a Jewish accent and he wasn't dressed like a commando."

"I doubt you saw any lighted windows in the factory. Everything there is long since disconnected. And why would a little man with a beard be wandering around in the cold at five in the morning? I'd forget the whole thing if I were you. You must have been hallucinating. Did Martha Marie feed you some of her mushrooms? I thought she was off that stuff."

"No mushrooms," Simon said. "No Martha Marie."

"No lights, no wandering Jews," Wanda said. "You're a good man, Simon. I'm very pleased with your work. I know you won't abuse my hospitality. I trust you. A word to the wise. Several people have mentioned to me that you fit in nicely here in Serene Harbor. This is a sturdy old town but it balances on a fragile ecology. It's best not to rock any boats. Now I've got to get over to an estate sale in Wainscott. When you finish with the frames leave the window open for a while. The shop smells like an armpit."

From upstairs, Simon heard a symbol crash and the rat-tat boom-bang of Martha Marie's drums. He pretended not to notice. "Good hunting," Simon said. "I hope you find something fabulous."

"Listen to her," Wanda said. "She don't sound too happy. She's a lot like her mother. My sister. Some people like to make noise. If by some miracle a customer walks in tell them we're doing construction."

An hour later, when the doorbell jingled and a lanky middle-aged man who looked to Simon as if he were assembled from a Leggo kit walked in, the drums were still beating. "If you have any questions, it's what I'm here for," Simon said over the banging. "I hope all that racket isn't too much of a bother. We have a crazy person upstairs. Locked in the west wing. Harmless, though."

"I'm not a shopper," the man said. "I'm a close personal friend of Mother Hubbard. I gather she's being a doting Granny this week."

"The boss lady is out looking for product," Simon said. "I don't know how long she'll be away."

"I came to talk to you, Simon Apple. You are Simon Apple?"

"Talk to me?"

"I'm Evan Crimmins. Does the name mean anything to you?"

"It certainly does, Mr. Mayor."

"So, you keep up with town politics. Impressive."

"You're mentioned in every issue of the *Star Express*."

"I own the paper. And half the property on Revolution Street including this building. Which is to say Evan Crimmins has a large investment in the future of Serene Harbor. I have every faith that we're on the verge of an explosive period of growth and development. This is tomorrow's boom-town." Martha Marie's playing added punctuating volume.

Simon had to shout: "Considering the town's location, a few miles from the richest territory in America, it's amazing the explosion hasn't happened yet. Did you know that during the Cold War the Reds had a nuclear missile programmed to hit the Hamptons? The highest form of flattery. They knew where the power was. And here's Serene Harbor, a trot from ground zero, and still affordable. If I were in real estate, I'd say this area is a goldmine, Mayor Crimmins. The thing is, I like Serene Harbor the way it is but I suppose nobody can stop the future from happening."

"Wanda said you were a smart kid. She was right. You've got perspective." Mayor Crimmins sat on a Coca Cola case from the forties. "She also told me you were asking questions about lights and ghosts near the watch factory."

"Word does travel fast," Simon said.

"She stopped by my office for a quick chat on her way to Wainscott. I thought maybe you and I should discuss the matter further."

"All I know is what I saw. I didn't mean to make too much of it. As far as I'm concerned, it's a non-event. There's no reason for anybody to get nervous."

"Nervous? Who said anything about nervous?"

"I just got the impression that you're a little fidgety," Simon said. "I know I am. It's those drums. They sound like a heart from an Edgar Allen Poe story."

"I own the watch factory," Mayor Crimmins said. "It's easily the most valuable piece of real estate in Serene Harbor. Centrally located, water view. For two decades I've planned to turn it into a complex of condominiums. Top of the line. But my dream has been frustrated by pussy-brained environmentalists and a senile historical society."

"You mean just because it's a toxic site and a landmark?"

"See? You've been here a few months and already you're indoctrinated. Spreading false rumors. The factory and its surrounding lands have been cleaned and declared safe by the EPA. It was one of the first allegedly contaminated facilities reclaimed by Superfund monies."

"I heard the neighbors paid for an independent survey that showed radiation levels a little lower than downtown Chernobyl. Isn't the whole matter in the courts?"

"It is," Mayor Crimmins said. "It has been for the better part of fifteen years. At this rate it will be for another fifty. And every day I walk past that building instead of seeing a beautiful harmony of homes I'm forced to look at a shit pile."

"I'm sorry," Simon said. "But however it happened, I did see a light in a window up near the roof. And I did meet a very small old man who ran inside the factory."

"Which is what I came to talk about," Mayor Crimmins said. "I wouldn't want you to discuss your fantasy with anybody else."

"It wasn't a fantasy," Simon said. "And I didn't plan to discuss it with anybody. I just mentioned it to Mrs. Hubbard. Then you showed up."

"Let's not make too much of this," Mayor Crimmins said.

"Good Lord, that noise is unbearable. No wonder you're seeing things."

"I am not seeing things. There was a light and a kind of pygmy in fatigues wearing a Brooklyn Dodgers cap who ran inside your building."

"We'll continue this conversation at some future date," Mayor Crimmins said. "My head is swimming. In the meantime, Simon, remember that loose lips sink ships."

"Excuse me?"

"A World War Two expression. I mean it would be best to shut up about—"

"I've got the message," Simon said.

Martha Marie accented the mayor's departure with a series of elephant hoof beats that rattled the cups, dinner plates and ironstone pitchers that once gave pleasure to the residents of Serene Harbor's cemeteries. One flower-covered cup, nearest the lip of the shelf it shared with seven identical siblings, surrendered to the assault of vibrations, teetered, tipped, and fell toward a box of rusty farm tools. Simon made a dive for it but missed the rescue by the length of a finger. It smashed against an iron wrench and dissolved into a shower of porcelain chips.

After he cleaned up the pieces, Simon sucked at a few drops of blood dribbling from a slash across his palm. The cut was nothing deep or serious, but enough of a gash to add insult to injury. Seven demitasse cups violated a basic tenet of antique lore; when it came to cups, service for eight added huge value. Service for seven was damn near impossible to sell even at a gigantic discount.

Wanda Hubbard would be livid when she saw the damage and Simon knew she'd vent her venom at him. She might even insist on deducting value-lost from his pay and she could make a reasonable case for the subtraction. Simon had been left in charge of the store— Wanda's trusted guard dog—and he'd failed in his duty. Blaming Martha Marie's heavy hands was a waste of time. Granny would never turn on her precious visitor.

Simon braced to take the jolt in the Cup Tragedy. He wrapped an embroidered linen dish towel around his bleeding wound, put the BACK IN FIVE MINUTES sign on the store's outer door, and dashed upstairs to where Martha Marie clashed cymbals as if she were executing imps between the brass spheres. He found her sitting on a stool in her room, stark naked except for a blindfold fashioned from one of Wanda Hubbard's good napkins—the ones she used for special dinner parties, emblazoned with hibiscus blooms in reds and pinks.

"You've got to quit being the little drummer girl," Simon said. "Things are breaking down in the store. You're driving everybody crazy including the mayor."

Martha Marie lowered her volume, brushed her cymbals with soft strokes, and threw her head forward so that her blonde hair fell like rain covering her breasts and mingling with her pubic garden. "I hear a voice," Martha Marie said, "but I can't place it."

"Take the napkin off and you'll place it," Simon said.

"It doesn't matter," Martha Marie said. "What matters is that my music drew whoever you are to the source of sound." She upped the beat again. This time she tossed her head backward so yellow hair flew in all directions. At that moment it occurred to Simon that he was talking to a naked woman except for her fancy blindfold. Somehow that significant fact hadn't struck home before. He was concentrated on the ruined service-for-eight set of demitasse cups.

Martha Marie's whole body, bouncing breasts to swaying shoulders, twitching thighs to flaring nostrils, moved in counterpoint to the measured thunder of her bass drum. In a seamless motion she somehow managed to flip her long legs over the bass and straddle them around a large bongo that must have come from a closet or attic in the Hubbard house. She traded her drumsticks for hands and slapped the bongo with so much force Simon could swear he saw smoke rise from its punished hide though he realized it had to be dust.

Simon wondered how many cups and saucers were abandoning inertia for flight from their shelves downstairs. It was the last rational thought he had.

Simon felt a terrific pain between his legs. His scrotum filled with syrup. He heard a pop much louder than Martha Marie's drum, more like the insolent sonic boom of a jet fighter. The *Stalagamide*, with an assist from the drummer, fulfilled its promise. The drug kicked in with a vengeance.

Simon Apple's penis stiffened and shot out of some anatomical

cave where it had been hiding—it presented itself with such conviction that it managed to split apart the metal teeth that zippered his fly.

The next thing Simon remembered was riding Martha Marie
like a surfer on a Hawaiian wave.

"I knew you had to have me," Martha Marie yelled on a note of
triumph. His own yell, "Thank you!" matched Martha Marie's
enthusiasm and pleased her greatly. She had no way of knowing
Simon Apple was addressing a pantheon of gods and goddesses. She
said, "You're welcome," as if he was talking to her. She began to slap
his head in a jungle rhythm. Simon, a willing bongo, heard himself
making sounds he recognized from a movie about agitated Zulus.

At the exact moment Simon and Martha Marie came together,
radio and television signals in Serene Harbor lost coherence.

TV pictures turned to white dots streaming across a black abyss
of screen. AM and FM radio reception became the howl of feral cats.

Telephones still worked but carried fading voices barely perceptible through a mesh of static.

Calls went out to the cable company, local stations, the police
and fire departments. Serene Harbor was off the grid, denied access
to its soap operas, talk shows, popular music, news anchors, wrestling,
even the balm of *Mr. Rogers Neighborhood* and *Sesame Street*.

This terrible electronic separation from the world beyond their
ice-bound town was unknown to Martha Marie and Simon. They
fucked like lions through the afternoon and into evening.

When Wanda Hubbard returned from her scouting trip she
stepped over wrecked sets of china and glass, climbing two steps at a
time, following the squeak of exhausted bedsprings where Simon
and Martha Marie still copulated, oblivious to her ranting and
protests.

"You signed an oath of premarital celibacy in church," Wanda
said. "In *church*! This doesn't look like celibate behavior to me."

"He seduced me, he inflicted himself upon me," Martha Marie
said peering out from between Simon's legs. "He ravaged me. Call
the cops."

"You slept with the cops last year," Wanda said. "Local and
State."

"Well, I feel misused," Martha Marie said.

"Can I get a word in edgewise?" Simon said. "This isn't what it looks like, Mrs. Hubbard. I mean, it isn't sex so much as it is affirmation. Martha Marie needs to prove to herself that she exists and the only way she can prove it is to bed any man or boy in the hemisphere. I know I made you a promise and I tried to keep it. God knows, I tried. But there's only so much temptation a normal human being can resist. As for the broken crockery, I'm perfectly willing to pay for half the damage." Simon reached down to make sure his genitals retained their suddenly impressive size. They did. "In fact, I'll pay for all the breakage. And glad to do it. Because miracles have occurred here this afternoon."

"I suppose it could be so stated," Martha Marie said.

"Good. Because before you leave my house I plan to present you with a bill for the heirlooms you destroyed," Wanda Hubbard said.

"Heirlooms?" Simon said. "That's a huge word to describe your inventory. I felt guilty selling that junk."

"Would you mind if we put some clothes on before continuing this conversation?" Martha Marie said to her grandmother. "Whatever romance there was in this assignation is already slipping away from me."

"Assignation?" Simon said. "That's a huge word. What trace of romance there might have been was pulverized by the beat of your tom-toms. However, for all that, you did me a service I can never forget. Don't worry. They probably won't use your real name in the medical journals."

"What's he talking about? And who won't use my real name?"

"Leave this house, Simon Apple," Wanda Hubbard said. "Leave Serene Harbor. Get in your bus and drive away. And don't stop at the Skull & Crossbones to gloat about penetrating my granddaughter. That won't come as any news. She's been doing the town since she was fourteen. Like mother, like daughter. She's a carbon copy of my daughter."

"I have no intention of gloating," Simon said, "except inwardly. But before I go I'd like to make one phone call. Long distance to New York City. You can add time and charges to my breakage bill."

When Simon tried to phone Dr. Mercy Merriweather he got

nothing but the crackle of static on the receiver. The lines were out, not unusual on icy days. When he hung up the phone, he heard Mother Hubbard cursing out her TV set. There was no sound or picture. She was missing *General Hospital*. At the same time, Martha Marie was yelling at her radio for its kittenish whining; at first she thought it was New Age music but she quickly realized there was a major problem.

Telephone, TV, radio—there was some kind of media plague blanketing Serene Harbor.

When he heard about the disturbance, Simon assumed those astronomical freckles called sunspots were to blame or possibly some nuclear riot in outer space or a seizure in Earth's magnetic field— one of those phenomena beyond control that periodically remind humans of shared insignificance in a screw-you universe.

Whatever the cause, it probably didn't signify the end of the world; the problem would soon abate—wires, transmitters, receivers would hum again, invisible signals would fill the air with the usual mix of sustaining gibberish.

Before he became fully aware of Serene Harbor's communications deprivation, Simon knew only that Wanda Hubbard's phone was having one of its frequent winter tantrums. No big deal. He could contact Dr. Merriweather later with the amazing news of his restored, actually improved, dimensions. His magnificent erection was still intact; Simon was thankful that Granny didn't make a fuss about that though she couldn't help noticing.

Simon wasn't particularly sorry about failing to reach the doctor's office. She would insist on dissecting the miracle of Simon's second puberty. There was plenty of time for blood tests, X-rays and probes. Before relegating his rescue to impersonal explanation, Simon was happy to feel the immediate poetry of redemption.

74

Simon left Wanda Hubbard's house that evening before dinner. There was no time to say goodbye to Martha Marie who was asleep, in recovery. When Simon had settled accounts with his employer—

low on cash after paying her damages but high on the bulge that still filled his pants—he walked outside to his minibus carrying his things in a duffel bag slung over his shoulder.

It was snowing again, the temperature well below zero. Simon turned the ignition key, relieved when the old battery coughed and drooled enough power to wake the icy engine and animate the windshield wipers.

He had no idea of where to find accommodations he could afford on such short notice. His first thought was to head for the Skull & Crossbones where one of the regulars might have a room to let. Chances were nobody in Serene Harbor would rent to him, not if they asked Mother Hubbard for a reference which they would. The natives circled their wagons where loyalty was concerned and Simon was outside the circle. Besides, in that dreary weather the bar would close early.

A mound of snow already blocked the entrance to the park where Simon had camped when he first drove into town. With no obvious options, the Skull & Crossbones was worth a try.

Luckily, there was a sign of life at the town oasis. Simon could see bodies moving behind the bar's steaming window. He parked across the street and jumped down from the bus into a slapping wind and slush deeper than the tops of his boots. As he was about to yank at the brass fishtail knob of the Skull & Crossbones storm door, Simon reminded himself that he still carried a boner in his pants. He hunched forward and arranged his sheepskin coat to conceal the obelisk as best as he could.

Inside, it didn't take long for Simon to realize he was already branded as an outcast. The only sign of recognition came from carrot-shaped Mayor Evan Crimmins, bent over a game of pinball called Silent Cinema Hits or Misses. The mayor was trying to guide a silver ball toward a hole between the waving legs of a girl tied across a railroad track as a streamlined locomotive roared toward her. The girl was labeled Save the Starlet—5000 Points! Her bare legs flapped back and forth while the locomotive's whistle blended with her recorded screams.

Mayor Crimmins smacked the sides of the pinball machine but the jolts couldn't stop his ball getting kicked across the game board by her flailing legs toward another hole marked Gone with the Wind. As the ball rimmed that ominous abyss and fell inside, Mayor Crimmins kicked at the machine. A siren wailed and the glass screen flashed Tilt!! The End!! "Damn," the mayor said, "fuck me."

He gave Simon a limp wave. Simon waved back, grateful for the attention. "Look who just walked in here," the mayor said. "The little drummer's boy." The three men and one woman bellied up to the bar laughed and made wet noises. "I hear you had some trouble with your landlady," Mayor Crimmins said while he made a circle with the thumb and forefinger of his left hand and penetrated it with the index finger of his right.

"So the word is out," Simon said. "And I thought the phones were kaput."

"We have our ways," the mayor said. "Kid, you've got to understand that Martha Marie is someone we hold near and dear in Serene Harbor. She's like a church or a war monument—a gift from above, a rallying point, a place where us simple guys and gals can come to be reminded of better weather. We feel a geographical and spiritual kinship with Martha Marie. She stirs sweet memories."

"He means she's equal opportunity twat," the woman at the bar said.

"That was vulgar," Mayor Crimmins said. "Uncalled for."

"I don't think you'll sue me," the woman said. "You been there once or twice, Your Honor."

"How long have you been a guest in Serene Harbor?" the mayor said to Simon who was wiping his wet face with a paper napkin.

"A few months."

"It was Wanda Hubbard who took you in. And you forced yourself on her beloved granddaughter contrary to a verbal contract between you and the aforesaid."

"I wouldn't put it that way. Wanda, Mother, Granny, whatever, Mrs. Hubbard didn't exactly offer sanctuary. She gave me a job below minimum wage and let me park my minibus on her property. You know damn well I didn't force myself on Martha Marie Hoffer. You were in the shop today. You heard those drums. It was like a cannibal office party. That wasn't music we heard; it was palpitating. There are just so many palpitations a man can endure. I won't go into details, sorry to disappoint you, but I am telling you that what transpired between myself and a certain young lady was entirely consensual. Add to that, inspirational. I was bone again, nothing less."

"The expression is born again," Mayor Crimmins said. "Lad, whatever claims you make, it's better that you leave Serene Harbor. We have no tolerance for sexual predators. Wanda Hubbard's accusation is tantamount to condemnation and conviction. We would prefer to keep our daughters pure for as long as possible, as naive as that may sound to someone devoid of morals."

"Fine," Simon said. "But where can I go on a night like this? Don't worry, I'm willing to pay for a bed."

"How much?" a tubby man at the bar said.

"Stay out of this," Mayor Crimmins snapped. "Mind your own business. Simon, come sit down in the corner there. We'll talk about your predicament."

Simon got himself a bottle of Bud and squeezed between a wooden bench and table.

"You look wedged in," the mayor said. "I call this table the John Wilkes booth. It's the quietest spot in this dive but it is a narrow squeeze. Take off your jacket. Stay a while."

"I'll keep the jacket on," Simon said, "because something tells me I won't be welcome here for very long."

"Well, you never know. You could go out and collide with an iceberg. Then again, you might leave town with a nice bundle of severance pay in your wallet, enough to pay for a classy motel room. "

"How might that happen? Do you know somebody buying lost souls?

"Please lower your voice. What is about to be said is entirely confidential. Understood?"

"You have my full attention."

"A shame those losers at the bar don't have their TV to watch. You heard all the TVs quit? It's a terrible deprivation. Our conversation is the only amusement in town."

"And no drug commercials."

"This isn't funny, Simon. You don't have to comment on everything I say. Just sit and absorb. Now, let's weigh your options. You could drive off into the sunset with nothing but lint in your pocket.

Or you could choose another direction. Free will is the Lord's greatest gift. Unfortunately not much else is free. Did I mention to you that I happen to own the former watch factory?"

"You mentioned it. You want to build Condo Nirvana but there's the small matter of a toxic waste dump."

"It's a rotten feeling to have your vision put on hold by misinformed zealots. Tell me, do I strike you as a person indifferent to the health and safety of family, friends, tenants, cats, dogs, birds? Evan Crimmins, a devoted public servant? Yet he stands accused of putting profit ahead of his humanity. It's such nonsense. To be victimized by the toxic phobia of those idiots who dare cast themselves as saviors of the race. That site is entirely safe."

"A batch of independent experts said—"

"There are always so-called independent experts ready to question everything. As much as I admire our justice system I cannot keep from feeling utter disgust at the corrupted process of appeal after appeal after appeal that results in nothing but social stagnation. And let us not forget the shameful matter of inflated income for shyster lawyers. The cycle must be broken."

"Is this relevant to where I might sack out tonight?" Simon said, shifting his weight to take pressure off his erect penis; the extended tumescence didn't alarm Simon; after so many months in Limpville it was no wonder his organ refused to relinquish its newfound splendor.

"Very relevant. I've been waiting for someone like you. Bright, alert, but at the end of his tether. A desperate hunter, if you will. And I've been waiting for a night exactly like this when in just a few hours nothing with wheels will be able to move out there."

"Mayor Crimmins, I still don't make the connection to—"

"That factory has got to vanish. It must burn. Fire is my only ally, the great purifier. There is nothing like flame to resolve irresolvable conflict. The building must be transformed into ashes."

"I thought your plan was to convert what's left of the factory into—"

"Better to start from scratch, build a new tower and endure endless frustration in the courts. Even a five-alarm blaze would leave some of the foundation intact, possibly even usable sections of brick. That structure is built like a fortress. Here's the irony: the minute the factory collapses, the same Serene Harbor preservation crowd that's been driving me insane with their nostalgia will beg me to clear the lot of whatever debris remains in the interest of civic pride."

"What about the land underneath the building?" Simon said. "Isn't there some cherub-dissolving syrup flowing toward the bay?"

"I'd be the first to admit, that was once true. But American know-how came up with techniques to neutralize that slop." Mayor Crimmins's eyes blazed with passion. "Simon, I'm tired of praying for a stray bolt of lightning to do my work for me. A man must create his own opportunity."

"Are we talking arson?" Simon said. "Because if we are . . ."

"Arson is a vile word. Vile. We're discussing assisted conflagration. We're talking about a clever but destitute young man who can do the modest hamlet of Serene Harbor an enormous favor in exchange for the welcome extended to a shabby stranger who violated the trust of his benefactor. Expiation is in order. All it would take is one match accidentally dropped onto a strategically placed pile of oily fabric or newspaper. Notice that I used the word accidentally. I certainly would never ask anyone to deliberately destroy a cherished landmark. What would happen on a night when our phones are out of order and our streets are snowbound? A night when fire trucks are moribund. Poof! No more factory, no more experts, no more lawyers, new prosperity for this forgotten neo-Hampton. Simon, you can leave here absolved of guilt, flame-laundered, your possibly shady past cremated. And you'd go richer than you were when you came. There are decisions to be made motivated by informed impulse. And made quickly."

"For the sake of argument, Mr. Mayor, before informed decisions are made, suppose somebody like me did decide to accidentally drop that match. You said yourself the roads would be impassable. How would a conflagration-assister avoid, say, ten years in jail?"

"If a tiny fire were kindled in a remote corner of that enormous building it would take hours for the flames to spread. The main highway is still negotiable. I've arranged for certain side streets to be plowed. A person could be miles away from here before the first curl of smoke was visible."

"Before I say anything, I want to repeat that my business with Martha Marie was two hundred percent consensual. I swear she levitated off her seat and literally flew across the room and landed on my privates."

"You could tell that story to a judge when they charge you with statutory rape."

Mayor Crimmins reached into his jacket and pulled out a blue envelope stuffed almost as full as Simon's underwear. "There's two thousand dollars here, all in small bills. I don't usually pay in advance for services rendered but I believe you're an honest young scoundrel with a great future. Getting inside the factory shouldn't be too much of a problem. The doors are hanging by a thread. But you already know that."

"How do I know? Because I saw what I saw. There's somebody living in there."

"Are we back to that nonsense? Let's suppose you're right. If there is some kind of phantom, some impish creature residing in that ruin, wouldn't it be out of there at the first hint of danger?"

Simon hesitated, then reached for the envelope and peeked under its open flap.

It was filled with currency enough to pay for a lot of life. He picked up the hoard and slipped it into his jacket.

"I'd offer to buy you a drink," Mayor Crimmins said, "but my feeling is you should get the show on the road while there is a road." The mayor pushed a pack of Skull & Crossbones matches across the table.

Simon, whose erection remained rigid as a tree trunk, stood, discreetly bent, and headed for the door. The feel of all that cash against his chest was amazingly comforting. Any barbed qualms gave way, tilted like the pinball machine in an incendiary direction.

75

Arctic air that migrated from the polar cap came whistling over Long Island Sound freezing breaking surf into shapes that lined the jetties like letters from a dead alphabet as Simon's minibus crunched over cracked pavement and black ice, dipping and skidding toward a hidden corner of the factory lot where a wooden fence that guarded its perimeter had split apart leaving a gap the bus could easily exploit. That fence was papered with NO PARKING NO LOITERING NO TRES-

PASSING VIOLATORS WILL BE TOWED warnings but Simon was pretty
sure he was safe from the pair of police guarding the town. They
were probably loading up on anti-freeze, playing gin rummy in the
converted warehouse on Lincoln Lane they used for a station.

Simon squeezed the pack of matches in his pocket, coping with
second thoughts. He lit one of the midget torches and watched it
flare, consume itself, and fail, leaving a twisted black worm of ash
between his fingers. He needed more time to think things over so he
settled back in the driver's seat watching snowflakes the size of moths
cover the minibus windshield. A half-hour of drowsy meditation
might enforce or demolish his shaky resolve to *burn baby, burn*. A
brief delay wouldn't make much difference, whatever he decided.

Without warning, Simon's thirty-minute nesting plan was rendered null and void. His minibus heater gave out an asthmatic
wheeze, then a metallic shriek, and died. Thin, tin ribbons of wind,
sharp as the flaps on sardine cans, were already slicing into the bus's
air vents and slashing through cracks where windows and doors
never did seal shut.

Simon tried to insulate the leaks with bits of newspaper and rags
from a backseat mound of junk he'd meant to discard someday but
nothing stopped the thuggish cold. He pulled the remains of a beach
blanket around his shoulders and over his head. In minutes his eye-
lids drooped; in twilight sleep he imagining himself stored inside
Polly Moon's automatic ice maker, waiting his turn to slide down its
chute and plop into a martini shaker. Inside his dream, a voice told
Simon that if he let himself doze he could easily freeze to a cube that
wouldn't thaw until late spring.

Hearing his teeth rattle like dice snapped him awake. Simon
quit his mobile ice tray and tried his luck at finding a warm, dry place
inside the factory. Despite Wanda Hubbard's and Mayor Crimmins's
strong efforts to convince him that he must have been hallucinating,
Simon knew he'd been attacked by a spindly ancient who'd skittered
inside the condemned pile of brick, mortar, wood and radioactive
debris, rushing toward someplace hospitable enough to sustain his
peculiar combination of flesh, bone and beard; there had to be sanctuary someplace inside that disaster of a ruin.

Simon scanned the building, trying to remember which window it was that had caught his eyes, but there wasn't a clue. Every

pane was broken or blacked out. He searched through rising drifts and snow devils until he found the door that had swallowed up the feisty goblin who'd challenged him. Like that apparition, Simon forced the door open as far as he could, inhaled deeply enough to flatten his gut, pushed aside his persistent hard-on and managed to squeeze his way inside.

The factory inside wasn't much warmer than the winter world outside but at least it provided protection from stinging snow needles and offered a shield, however porous, against the diabolical winds that moaned down from the Northland.

The shivering intruder followed a beam of yellow light from a flashlight he kept for just such emergencies in the Volkswagen's glove compartment. That battery-drained wand had barely enough strength to define the obstacle course he faced.

Simon saw that he stood at the foot of a steep staircase lined with broken crates, pieces of rusted machinery, burnt-out motor parts, and a line of barrels, bottles and steel drums that must have held ingredients for the virulent soup now oozing below the tidy shops on Revolution Street. Those abandoned containers—the barrels, the bottles wrapped in moldy burlap sacking—looked like stragglers from a beaten army attempting a vestige of symmetry in numb retreat from wherever it was that staircase led.

Simon headed up the flight of narrow steps, testing their stability before committing his full weight, feeling the factory's carcass shudder and groan under his boots. While he climbed, he covered his nose against malevolent fumes—sinister genies peering from the jugs and tubs of stinking chemicals that fueled the polluted plume corrupting the roots of Serene Harbor's struggling gardens and curdling the sea.

Mayor Crimmins had assured Simon that money from the Superfund was used to reclaim the tainted real estate by sucking up all traces of radioactive muck, trucking away a residue of sludge deadly enough to melt the planet. Crimmins insisted that any opposition to his plan to transform that wasteland into upscale housing was based on fear and superstition, not scientific fact. But Simon couldn't shake the acrid smell of death from his nostrils. It was a heavy smell of vomit. Like sniffing the armpits of angry ghosts.

When he reached the second story landing, Simon's cautious

feet began to detect a subtle vibration, a tremor, a purr, as if the building had turned into a giant alley cat. At first he attributed the buzz to some quirk of the winds slapping at the factory's walls, sneaking through broken window glass and the cracks between rotting bricks, prowling abandoned corridors. But the hum was too regular, too deliberate to blame on nature's whims. The higher he climbed, the more intense the *ohmmm*; the soles of his feet tingled as if he were stepping over a carpet of angry bees.

On the third floor, halfway along a hall as cluttered as the staircase, behind a massive double door, the sensation peaked. Simon heard a sound like the whine of a dental drill cutting through a molar. He switched off his flashlight and searched the door's border for some hint of light, but a tight seal blocked any spark from escape. Simon was sure the source of sound was a machine, but that was impossible—the factory was a dead building, doomed, disconnected, deserted for nearly half a century.

According to the burghers of Serene Harbor, Simon's story about seeing a gnome vanish into the factory's embrace was the prattle of a lunatic. To be fair, Simon had to allow that it was logical for Wanda and the mayor to conclude that the little man who wasn't there wasn't there. He had almost been ready to accept that, in his agitated state, the meeting was a mirage brought on by stress. Reaching for a more mystical explanation, Simon considered that his boggled mind could have conjured up a rescuing ancestor from deep within a troubled half-Jewish subconscious—some really distant robed relative might have come forward to offer the balm of Old Testament wisdom, a wisdom marinated in time's mellowing brine for over five thousand years. Any explanation of his encounter, however bizarre, was more reasonable than its reality.

Simon knew he might have lost touch with sanity, but he also knew what a drill sounded like from his days in metal shop at Glenda High. Somebody was definitely doing something behind that door. And that somebody was a smoker.

The high, sweet smell of a cheap cigar managed to waft into the corridor. Robert J. smoked the same brand in the days when everybody past puberty puffed on something before the habit became taboo. Serene Harbor's founders, who once rowed little dories toward thrashing whales, hurling harpoons at frenzied mountains of rage, now skulked outside in every weather to take a drag on a Marlboro. The factory could be a gathering place for smokers plotting a strategy of return, like early Christians in an above ground catacomb. Simon discarded that theory as too exotic for such a quiet town.

He grabbed the doorknob, turned it, and pulled hard. The door was locked tight. He knocked with a fist, then yelled a loud "anybody in there?" He got back nothing but a hollow echo. Scanning the hall with the fading beam from his flashlight, his eye caught sight of a rusting crowbar the size of a baseball bat and he went for it. The weight of iron felt good; he took a few swings with it as if he were back at Munchkin Academy hitting fungoes during recess.

Simon found a slight crack in the door's frame. He jammed one end of the crowbar into the sliver and leaned his weight against it. Nothing happened. He tried again and again, using all his strength, his foot propped against a cement wall for leverage. The crowbar bowed, but the door didn't budge. From some trench of instinct, Simon cupped his hand around his mouth and screamed, "Delivery!"

The machine stopped. He thought he heard movement behind the barrier.

"Delivery!" Simon yelled again.

"I didn't order nothing," said a crinkled voice. "Get lost."

"I can't stand here all night," Simon yelled. "I got other stops to make."

"Hold your horses."

Curiosity triumphed over caution. Simon heard footsteps creaking closer to the door, then the abrupt snap of a metal bolt. The door opened slowly. A pink face like a bearded peach appeared in the crevice between the door and its frame. Squinting eyes looked Simon over, up and down. "What's your business with me? What did you bring? Italian? Chinese? Who sent it? Mayor Putz? Who told you I was here? Is it paid for? I never tip."

"It's my turn to ask a few questions," Simon said. "Can I come in? It's freezing out here."

"I suppose," the elf said. "I hope you didn't bring dried fruit. I got enough apricots and prunes to last a year."

Simon pushed his way past the door. He was in a room with ceilings twenty feet high. A bank of windows, boarded or covered with heavy curtains, lined a wall. One of those windows must have leaked the faint light that Simon had seen. The source of that light was a square of hanging fluorescent tubes. A line of kerosene heaters rimmed a square table, their heat as intense as a slap. Simon unzipped his jacket and watched the little man who wasn't there jump back in horror. "Don't worry, this erection has nothing to do with you," Simon said.

"That's good news," Simon's hallucination said, relighting a thick cigar.

"You've got light and heat in here. All the amenities. At least I know I'm not crazy."

"Nobody knows that about themself. What's with the boner? You always walk around like that?"

"I think it has to do with a medication I take called *Stalaga-mide.*"

"You got any extra?"

"Not funny."

"Funny. Hard-ons are always funny. Ask Milton Berle."

"I want you to know I was sent here—"

"By Mayor Cocksucker, right? To burn me out? Your friends call you Nero?"

"My name is Simon Apple. And you happen to be exactly right. I'm a professional arsonist."

"I expected to see you back here. I was warned to vacate. Tell your boss I'll drop dead before I vacate."

"Ah, there's the drill I heard," Simon said. "What's that you're working on? A pocket watch? And while we're at it, who the hell are you?"

"Simbok. Hyman Simbok. So, did Crimmins give you a Zippo or a Dunhill? I'd bet a Zippo, the cheap bastard."

"How did you know why I'm here? What's with you and Mayor Crimmins?"

"Mayor my *tuchis.* I know him before he was born. Look at me. Would you believe Hyman Simbok is nearly a hundred years old? It seems like a few minutes ago when Crimmins's father, Abel, signed me up to make clocks and watches. Me and my family, may they rest in peace. He got us right off the boat from Ellis Island. We didn't have unions in those days. I did it all. Casings, hands, glass, mechanisms, everything, but my specialty is faces. Including the numbers—Arabic, Roman, American, name it. Every face hand-painted by Hyman Simbok has a different expression. No two alike. And I'm talking thousands. They glow in the dark. Reddish, bluish, greenish, name it. You want to know what they paid me? Shit. You want to see my work?"

"No," Simon said.

"At least Abel Crimmins was a gentleman. He made me a manager. We got to be good friends when I learned some English. He liked to play chess. He wrote me into his will. Just before he died: 'Hyman Simbok has a job for life. He is entitled to live in the factory dormitory in perpetuity.' Perpetuity! I didn't even know what it meant until I found out when those sonsofabitches closed the place. Then his kid bought it to make apartments. He offered me plenty to get out, even a house. I told him this is where I live and this is where I work and this is where I stay. He tried to break his own father's will by having me committed. Can you imagine? The judge threw out his case. And he made Big Shot Mayor give me heat and electric in perpetuity. Perpetuity. I got my own generator. Before you start lighting matches, come over here, Apple."

Simon was pulled across the room by an arm as thick as a thread. "Look here at the wall. And look up at the ceiling." Simon looked. He was staring at hundreds of watch and clock faces pasted to cinder block and plaster. "Makes the Sistine Chapel a kindergarten, eh?" Simbok said. "This isn't my only museum. In some rooms I ran out of space, walls to ceilings. Every inch is covered. You want to see?"

"What's the point?" Simon said.

"It's my talent. What else can I do? Sit back and collect social security and my pension plus interest from the few bucks Abel Crimmins put away for me?"

"The factory has been closed for half a century."

"Tell me something I don't know," Simbok said.

"Faces without watches?"

"Every one with a different expression. Listen, what goes around comes around. When hand-painted watches and clocks come back in style who has the best inventory? Answer me that. Naturally, if Mayor Scumbag finds somebody to burn me out, that changes things. So far he hasn't found the right person but I see a glint in your eyes that makes me edgy. Did he pay you in advance?"

"He did. Two thousand."

"Two? He must like you. I am going to offer you a 10 percent interest in my inventory for one thousand. It could be worth millions. Who in Switzerland can do better? You ever see a Rolex face looking back at you like a Simbok face?"

"I'd suggest you pack what you want to take with you before this building is ancient history, Mr. Simbok. I need the money I got for this job and I can't let sentiment get in the way. You have fifteen minutes to get ready. I'll even drive you to a motel. If you're thinking of calling for help, forget it because all the telephones are out."

"I have no telephone. Only a color TV."

"TVs are out too."

"No TV? Not good. People must be pissing in their pants."

"Fifteen minutes and counting."

"You're forcing me to call Mengele," Simbok said, blowing a tunnel of smoke rings.

"You can't call anybody. I just said—"

"Mengele. A pit bull. If I ask her in a nice way she tears your balls off along with that wiseguy prick. When she's finished with you, I bury what's left in the basement. You want to meet the bitch personally? You wouldn't be the first. One snap of those beautiful jaws and—"

"An attack dog? You really expect me to swallow that?"

"Mengele does the swallowing. If I was you, I'd settle for the 10 percent."

"I said I would set fire to this abomination, do Serene Harbor a favor, and I will," Simon said.

"A favor? This town was once blessed with piss-and-vinegar wild men. Sailors. They went for whales and boiled their blubber for lamp oil and ambergris for perfume. Then they stripped the bones for corset stays and scratched pictures of wives and girlfriends on their teeth. If they lived through years on the ocean and Neptune spit them back out on land, they headed for a whorehouse or a whiskey bar. What have we got now? Did you see the lousy paintings they sell downtown? You hear any echoes of the drowned men cursing, or weeping widows? You catch the stink of rendered fish fat? And after, when the fish business collapsed, the town built this factory that gave jobs to a thousand greenhorns who came to America without a pot, without the language, with no education, maybe with a wife and kids, maybe with a pair of shoes. And they worked fifteen-hour shifts. The ones who got poisoned from the paint, you hear their howls from the graveyard. You got a Jewish nose, kid. I can tell. Did you ever think that, if one of those wanderers didn't have the guts to come to this country, at least half of you would be a bar of laundry soap or a lampshade? I don't know why Hyman Simbok was left alive. Maybe as a witness. Maybe to keep this factory a monument. Which I intend to do. So make up your mind, Simon Apple. Mengele ain't a vegetarian, he ain't a gourmet, but he's always hungry. Here doggy! Dinner time!"

Simon heard a hungry growl from deep in the building. He watched Hyman Simbok reach under his work table, come out with a shotgun and aim it at Simon's recently activated crotch.

"Make it 15 percent," Simon said.

"Ten," Simbok said. "But I'll throw in a watch face that's the spitting image of Martha Marie. I heard how you violated that girl. And a cigar, practically from Havana."

Simon managed to get the minibus going and find one of the plowed roads Mayor Crimmins had promised. He drove past a few widely spaced houses—saltboxes dating back to the 19th century. Several were wrapped in scaffolding, others had fresh siding, patched roofs, deck and patio extensions. The wood that was added or recently replaced hadn't taken on the reddish-brown barn color of Serene Harbor's older salt-whipped homes.

Alongside the works in progress, pyramids of black earth, sand and clay had been gouged from the rocky landscape to make room for swimming pools and tennis courts. Hedges of privet walled off what Simon guessed were new lawns. He could see the tops of ornate birdbaths, sundials, ceramic tubs, stone nymphs, and an army of dwarfs and trolls watching over FOR SALE signs tacked to neat fences. The gentrification of the Serene Harbor that Evan Crimmins predicted was proceeding apace.

76

When the prison nurse entered his cell, she reminded Simon of the palm trees he'd seen in Florida. The long-bodied nurse leaned like a palm herself. Her mop of hair looked like a crown of palm leaves. Her head could have been a coconut, ripe and ready to drop. Simon thought she fitted nicely into a crisp blue uniform.

"Nurse Flok is my name." She tapped a photo ID tag pinned to her collar.

Simon watched her survey his cell, displeased by the chaos of cards, letters, newspapers and magazines that surrounded the prisoner on three sides. Nurse Flok held a clipboard and a ballpoint pen.

"I need to ask you a few questions. I'm here to develop a medical profile of Simon Apple before—well, you know."

"I think I already signed a pledge of confidentiality."

"Nobody mentioned anything about a pledge. Any history of heart disease?"

"None."

"Diabetes?"

"No."

"Cancer?"

"No."

"Allergies?"

"That's a long story," Simon said. "Just write that I'm allergic to Boston cream pie."

"This isn't a time for humor, Mr. Apple," Nurse Flok said. "Please try to be cooperative."

"If it doesn't violate a confidence or endanger the nation in any way, say I'm allergic to every prescription drug ever approved for consumption by the Food and Drug Administration."

"Unresponsive," Nurse Flok wrote on a form clipped to her board.

"That's unfair," Simon said. "I've never been called unresponsive. I'm a very responsive person by nature."

"Have you ever undergone surgery?"

"I've had my share."

"Could you be a bit more specific?"

"Just a little surgery. All my organs, muscles, tendons, sinews etcetera, etcetera have been removed. I'm hollow." Simon patted his chest. " Except for this noble heart."

"Unresponsive," Nurse Flok wrote. "Have you ever consulted a mental health professional?"

"Once or twice," Simon said. "About two million dollars worth."

"Unresponsive."

"I wish you'd stop using that word."

"If you quit displaying a childish attitude. You're not helping me or yourself, Mr. Apple. We like to keep complete and accurate files on our terminal guests. Your medical profile will be added to a growing pool of knowledge that might help offer insight into the causes of extreme antisocial behavior. Some day a familiar constellation of symptoms emerging in very young children, perhaps babies, even fetuses, will trigger alarms resulting in the administration of powerful medications designed to ameliorate or eliminate hostile proclivities."

"What about side effects?"

"Excuse me?"

"Generated by those powerful medications designed to ameliorate or eliminate. Let's suppose they stimulate and exacerbate. Take the case of this monster standing before you. Could I use the Devil-made-me-do-it defense in good conscience when I know my whole life is a side effect? It was a cocktail of very expensive drugs that brought me here."

"Moving right along, have you ever suffered from headaches, dizziness, black stools, constipation, gastrointestinal distress or visual disturbances including the ink-blotty things we call floaters, ulcers, hernia, tinnitus, hearing loss?"

"I can't remember."

"Unresponsive," Nurse Flok wrote. "I'd think a person guilty of monk murder, followed by aiding and abetting congregational suicide, might welcome the chance to expunge his guilt by helping with our research."

"Just tell the kiddies not to try that at home," Simon said.

"I heard you agreed to donate your body parts to save others but your offer was refused due to fears of genetic and chemical contamination. Here's a second chance to do a good deed. You might consider donating your medical history to the same good cause."

"Here's my contribution to your information pool," Simon said. "Shake well before and after using."

"Ambiguity killed the cat," Nurse Flok said. She wrote, "Subject unresponsive."

77

Simon's minibus managed to reach Route 27, then followed a Suffolk County snow plow toward the town of Manorville just south of the Long Island Expressway. The minibus bounced over swelling drifts and into the parking lot of a roadside mall with a McDonald's as its centerpiece.

There was method to the stopover. Simon was starved—hungry enough to tolerate a cardboard burger dripping special sauce, oily fries, and a chalky chocolate milkshake. If the Expressway was closed by the blizzard, he could spend the night in a warm place near a convenient approximation of a food supply. Simon paid for his order, and left a dollar tip for the teenage clerk who served him, appreciating the courage it took for her to show up at work in such hellish weather. He felt sudden affection for the golden arches that signaled a greasy port in any storm.

While he chewed his food, Simon thought about the thousand dollars, all cash in his jacket pocket. He considered it a loan from Evan Crimmins and planned to pay it back as soon as he turned more affluent. The thousand he'd paid to Hyman Simbok in exchange for ten percent of Simbok's trove of watch faces, along with a free sample, an Admiration cigar, and the immediate dividend of safe passage past Mengele's fangs was another matter—arguably not part of his obligation to the mayor.

When he finished eating, Simon lit the Admiration with one of the Skull & Crossbones matches. The smoke did an excellent job of squelching the chemical aftertaste left by his milkshake, replacing it with the preferable flavor of over-roasted chestnuts. That pleasure was cut short by a busboy calling attention to the NO SMOKING sign over the restaurant's revolving door.

As Simon drowned the cigar's smoldering tip in the dregs of his shake, he watched the blizzard through a large foggy window. Icicles dangled from a blocked drain that ran along the roof. They looked like the bars of a cage. Webs of frost made much of the window glass opaque but left a few transparent islands.

Through one of those islands Simon saw what he thought must be a new kind of snow blower flashing red and yellow warning lights as it moved slowly into the parking area. He'd never encountered anything quite like it—a vehicle the size of a tractor-trailer with ten pairs of brutal tires. The flashing thug of a machine prowling outside McDonald's could easily have qualified as one of the merciless machines used to crush opponents in a war of monster trucks.

As the behemoth came to a stop, Simon saw searching arms of a radar scanner on top of its cab. He watched a bank of satellite dishes aimed at distant stars as they bent, turned and changed focus. They seemed to point at him.

His peripheral vision caught sight of other huge vans and a string of police cars circling the mall in tighter and tighter arcs until the bizarre parade nearly strangled the oasis where he sat. Simon thought of an old joke Chirp Bennet used to tell about a stupid bird that flew in ever diminishing circles until it disappeared up its own asshole.

Dozens of men emerged from the trucks with a horde of police officers, guns drawn, following close behind. The point men in the group that spun through McDonald's revolving door were dressed in orange biohazard suits and carried black boxes that sprouted insect-like antennae. Others surrounded the building.

Simon realized there must be a major problem; he doubted it was the food or his attempt at smoking. Besides Simon, there were five other patrons in the dining area, all with anxious faces. The clerks behind the counter didn't look too happy either. What came

to Simon's mind was a leak in a gas main that could blow the
Manorville Mall into legend. Lighting his cigar could have caused
Armageddon. The blatant irony of that possible outcome made him
smile. Hyman Simbok's revenge.

More orange-suited invaders entered the building, each waving
a metal rod. A few ran toward the kitchen. Others took up positions
behind the counter. Every customer and employee in the place was
herded toward the restaurant's center. Several of the displaced
clutched unfinished Big Macs, wedges of hot apple pie and containers of coffee or soda.

Simon grabbed for his jacket, ready to evacuate on command.
His concern deepened when he saw the metal rods aim at his waist
quiver and vibrate. The black boxes peeped like electronic chickens.

"What the fuck?" said one of the orange men who seemed to be
their leader. "What's he got in his pants? Whatever it is, it's between
his legs—You!" he said to Simon, "step away from the group. Stretch
your arms out in the Jesus position. Spread your legs. What the fuck
is your name and what the fuck is your game?"

"Do I need a lawyer?" Simon said.

78

Looking into Regis Van Clay's eyes was like staring at twin tor-
nados trapped inside a pair of snow globes. Brian Beem could see
flickering bolts of pure fury. He wondered what a brain scan would
show.

"You say they found Apple at McDonald's?" Regis said. Even his
voice sounded as if it was boiling.

"In a town called Manorville about forty miles from the Hamptons. Eating junk food. That stuff can be lethal."

"From your mouth to God's ear," Regis said. "Could we skip the
comments about nutrition and get to the point."

"The thing is, the FCC's Triangulation Unit traced the source
of the communications fuckup to Apple. More specifically, to his
prick. They said he was afflicted by *Priapus Magnitus*, a very rare
symptom. It seems the erect penis transmits a disruptive ionic wave
that causes magnetic turmoil."

"He had a hard-on at McDonald's?" Regis said.

"I gather it was a doozie. He'd been taking *Stalagamide* prescribed by Dr. Mercy Merriweather. To counteract some kind of severe shrinkage. Seems Apple was screwing this woman in Serene Harbor, the epicenter of the electronic disturbance, when he heard a loud pop and suddenly—"

"Pop goes the weasel. Is that when the trouble started?"

"Exactly," Beem said. "Some areas in Serene Harbor never lost electricity and automobiles remained functional, but for a huge area most telephones, radios, CBs, shortwave transmitters went dead—"

"What did any of that have to do with *Stalagamide?*"

"You could say nothing directly. But the FCC report concluded that it was responsible for setting off the nano magnetic molecular eruption because of interaction between the drug, the woman, Simon Apple's body chemistry and barometric instability. It was a lousy night, weather-wise."

"Did I ask for a weather report?" Regis said.

"I'm only the messenger," Beem said. "Bottom line, the scientists feel pretty sure that Apple's organ transformed into the equivalent of a mini-microwave tower radiating chaos in all directions. The feeling was confirmed when that tower was demagnetized using an experimental substance developed at your Nanotower Initiatives Division."

"Nanotower Initiatives? I don't recall being involved with . . ."

"It must be impossible to keep current with every plum in the corporate cake," Beem said. "Credit for coming up with the demagnetizing agent goes to Dr. Joshua Vine, a Regis Pharmaceuticals team leader on a top secret project funded by the Air Force as a component of AMDD&D. That's Advanced Missile Defense, Disinformation and Disorientation."

"It still doesn't ring a bell," Regis said. "What's the stuff called?"

"*Compassarate Dioxide.* It was never meant to be an antidote for genital magnetified electro-intrusion. It was designed as a next-generation stealth weapon, a colorless paint to be applied to the fuselage of military aircraft. With demagnetization properties effective in confusing enemy radar pulsations."

"And how did this Joshua Vine happen to think this *Compassarate Dioxide* would work on a stiff prick?"

"Ah, interesting story. He says he was reaching for a tube of K-Y lubricant during a midnight tryst in his lab with . . ."

"Who he was fucking is irrelevant, Beem. Keep your focus."

"His hand dipped into a Petrie dish holding a few ounces of the newly distilled substance and a drop or two must have gotten into the condom—"

"I pay these people to get laid on company time," Regis said. "Paid to get laid. And they want to unionize."

"His performance was neutralized. But he noticed a marked improvement in the quality of his stereo system's performance. The sound level—"

"His stereo system? Who is this idiot? And how did he dare offer a hush-hush preparation for use on Simon Apple? There's a picture of that jinx with red slash over his face pasted over every desk at Regis Pharmaceuticals. I assume *every* includes that Nano . . .whatever—"

"Initiatives," Beem said. Nanotower Initiatives Division."

"Oh, shut up," Regis said. "Every department head has been instructed to deny access to any of our products by . . . What's the use? Nobody pays attention to anything I say."

"In defense of Dr. Vine, he may not have known that the transmitting penis was attached to Simon Apple. They don't reveal names. Civil liberties and all that."

"And now the FCC and the Department of Defense have petitioned the FDA to recall *Stalagamide?*"

"They feel the drug might pose a danger to its users and to the entire nation's communications network and the power grid."

"We're going to be forced to black box another of our fattest cash cows," Regis said. "*Stalagamide* brought in six point two billion dollars last year, and there are no reports of *Priapus Magnitus*. Not one."

"Well, now there is one," Beem said. "Better safe than sorry."

"I can't believe you said that to my face!" Regis yelled.

"I'm sorry. It slipped out."

"It slipped out. Like Apple did. You people had him in your hands. I'm trying to keep my blood pressure from splitting my skull. How could you lose him?"

"In all the confusion, he just walked out the door of Building C at Brookhaven National Laboratory where they'd taken him for further study. We found his minibus under a snowdrift. We had it chained to a tow truck but somehow he managed rip off his bumper and drive the damn thing toward the Long Island Expressway. Its tire tracks were obliterated by blowing snow. Wherever he went, trust me, he couldn't have gotten far. We'll have him in a matter of days."

"I'm suffering from palpitations," Regis said, sliding a *Xanelul* tablet under his tongue. "Leave me now, Brian."

After Brian Beem said his good nights and quit the room, Regis Van Clay reached for his private line and called Belladonna.

"Heavy pain," Regis said when she answered.

"Pain rules," Belladonna said. "Pain soothes the brain."

"Vine said it improved the performance of his stereo system," Regis said.

"Excuse me?"

"Rhetorical comment," Regis said. "Forget it."

"I'm worried about you," Belladonna said.

"Just make me holler bloody murder," Regis said. "Tonight, anything goes."

79

Simon waited out the blizzard in a Flatbush Avenue flophouse in downtown Brooklyn, wondering about his next destination on life's curvy road. He knew he had to leave New York again and find refuge someplace so obscure that the hounds of authority could never catch his scent. This time he had no specific idea of why he was on the run but something said he'd better keep running.

It was entirely possible that a vindictive Martha Marie Hoffer might file a charge of statutory rape against him. But the greatest probability of prosecution was his delectable escape from detention after the scientists at Brookhaven National Laboratory determined his world-class erection was the cause of communications mayhem on the trendy South Fork of Long Island.

While government agents argued with local police over the right to custody, or whether, in fact, any crime had been committed,

Simon simply walked out the front door. He found his minibus sand-wiched between a dozen police cruisers and three huge rigs with gigantic tires, topped by outstretched metal arms Simon guessed were radar scanners. The little bus's rusty bumper had been chained to a tow truck. Simon got the bus started, threw it into reverse, slammed his foot onto the gas peddle, left the bumper behind, swerved a sharp left, followed an exit ramp, and drove a staggered route to Brooklyn.

Simon had more to worry about when, next morning, he picked up a coffee-stained copy of the *New York Post* lying on a diner count-er. On page six, a daily chronicle of celebrity motion, obsessed with anything to do with Hampton lifestyles, he found an item about Serene Harbor. There was a picture of a supermodel (who boarded her Arabian stallion at a Serene Harbor farm) standing wide-eyed, hypnotized by a greedy blaze that was swallowing the town's aban-doned watch factory.

The story reported that there was hardly anything left of the industrial fossil. Firemen blamed the burnout on a cigar stub, still hot, found in a box of half-melted watch faces. One firefighter was quoted as saying, "They each had their own expression. One looked exactly like the Virgin Mary."

There were signs that a squatter had been living inside the fac-tory but no body was found. Simon wondered what happened to Hyman Simbok, a man so frail he wouldn't leave an ashtray's worth of proof that he ever existed.

Simon realized that even if Simbok managed to escape and find shelter in one of the empty summer cottages around the town, he would know it was dangerous for him to admit he was alive and pos-sibly still an obstacle to Mayor Crimmins's building plans; better to cut his losses and head for Miami. If a resurrected Simbok declared himself, accused the mayor of arson or laid claim to the factory's site, the mayor would have him committed or worse.

Most likely, Crimmins assumed that Simon Apple had earned his money honestly and was probably responsible for accidentally barbecuing an unwanted tenant. Still, if word of Simon's deal with the mayor was ever leaked by some pinball freak at the Skull & Crossbones with twenty-twenty ears, the charges against him would be a lot worse than screwing a nympho drummer, blanking out a few thousand TV screens, juke boxes and phones, then evading custody by the Feds.

After breakfast, Simon took a subway to the root of the George Washington Bridge, hiked across that span to Fort Lee, New Jersey, waved his thumb at the passing parade of traffic and took the first ride he could get heading anyplace. His benefactor, in a pickup, dropped him at an intersection where a major highway met whatever road he'd been traveling, so, following the map of pure chance, Simon positioned himself facing north and west on Route 17, and waited for another Samaritan.

His next ride came in a sleek red Porche driven by a dapper young Asian man. Simon, wearing a battered jacket, plaid shirt, Levi jeans, slush-caked K-Mart boots and a knitted hat pulled down over his ears, felt rumpled and mangy sitting in such an elegant car with its leather seats and a custom-crafted wooden dashboard. The driver's outfit—a Burberry raincoat, Aussie outback hat, and rust-dyed alligator shoes—was a collage of designer fashions, a cutout from GQ Magazine. Simon had the feeling he sat inside a rolling mansion in the presence of a modern incarnation of Kubla Khan.

That impression was enforced by the way the driver handled his designer wheels—hitting near ninety, cutting in, out and around traffic, gliding through a skid over black ice that spun the Porche like a blowing leaf. The man drove with absolute confidence. Simon rode the rocket, his body speed-glued against the posh passenger seat. He considered making some comment about slowing down after the car sliced across the highway on a diagonal cut between an oil tanker and a huge moving van but kept his mouth shut, remembering the dependable admonition that beggars can't be choosers.

Not a word had passed between the hitchhiker and his latest savior. That struck Simon as unusual since, in his experience, the mandatory duty of an automotive freeloader was to listen, listen and listen to everything from political opinions to ancient jokes to the most intimate revelations—stories about baby-sitter blowjobs, fucking a field hockey princess, plowing a cheerleader after the pep rally, popping somebody's wife with Alpine tits in the church basement—listening to the endless monologues of proud or sorry souls who were vibrated to confession by the hum of four, six or eight cylinders (but holding the wheel, in control), eager to spill the beans to an easy priest, a transient stranger headed toward some unknown destination.

After twenty miles of silence, Simon's silent driver said, in accented English, "I hope you not catching."

"Catching what?"

"Catching me. You face purple blotches. Swollen like wonton. Earlobes like big moth wings."

Simon twisted his head so he could see himself in the rearview mirror. It was true, he looked terrible, like a bug on steroids, ready to fly.

"You allergic?"

"I do have a problem in that area," Simon said. "I reacted badly to this salve. But I don't feel sick or feverish. I don't think it's anything you have to worry about. But I don't want you to feel uncomfortable, like you picked up a leper, so you can drop me off right here."

"How far you go?"

"As far as you'll take me."

"I go Montibello. Little town. Sullivan County. Catskill Mountains. About a hundred mile."

"A hundred miles sounds hunky-dory. Are there any jobs up there?"

"Maybe some. Pump gas. Clean horseshit at racetrack. But those jobs snapped up by people who live there for many generations. Place used to be full of Jew hotels and bungalows. Jew families come up from hot summer city to breathe some air. Was called Borscht Belt. No more. Now Jew kids go for vacation to Paris, Rome, hey, even Beijing. No business left, not much anyhow. They keep horse track open nights for trotting horses who move legs snip-snap like scissor blades, pull little wagons around a circle. Used to be big sport, plenty money. Not many customers go there anymore. Place falling apart. It's there mostly to scrape what's left in sweaty pockets of Off Track Betting freaks who need something to bet on when sun goes down.

"There must be some work at the track like selling mutual tickets," Simon said.

"Sure. Good jobs in town go to insiders. Everybody somebody's cousin. Sad situation. But things could get a lot better for Montibello. Maybe gambling casinos allowed up there if they can find any genuine Native Americans from some Borscht Belt tribe. A smart Red Indian with connected bulldozer attorney—wham, wham, wham—who gets around the politics and end up with casino license. I hope a few Geronimos turn up. I wouldn't mind seeing it happen. I'm telling you, it wouldn't be bad for me if land prices balloon because I just happen to own few hundred acres."

For the next twenty miles Simon wondered why his face had puffed up. The only thing he could think of was a bad reaction to *Compassarate Dioxide*. He carried a tube of the stuff he'd lifted off a table before he trotted out of the Brookhaven Lab. It was another one of those weird tradeoffs: Simon wasn't walking around with the Eiffel Tower between his legs, but looking like a year-old eggplant wouldn't inspire anybody to hire him, not even for pumping gas. What was left from the Crimmins money wouldn't last forever.

"If you need work, maybe I help you," the driver said.

"Help me how?"

"I have little business going up there. You ever work in garment center? Rag trade?"

"No."

"Experience good but not necessary. You could learn."

"Learn what?"

"Your way around. I like you even with your fat face." A few miles later the driver said, "I get feel I know you from someplace. Were you famous?"

"I doubt it could be called famous," Simon said. "But I did get some publicity a long time ago. You might have seen pictures in—"

"Give me your whole name."

"Simon Apple." Simon meant to reincarnate Sinbad Green but he didn't have the energy.

"Ah! Ah! Simon Apple. Yes! The fish boy?"

"How would you know that?" Simon said, flexing. He thought that memory was long dead and buried.

"You don't recognize Shen Wa? Fish boy pull me out of the water down in Florida."

"Shen Wa? The illegal? That's fantastic. But they deported you to China."

"And Shen Wa bounce back again inside packing crate filled with snappy sneakers. Now he's a big American success. Fish boy, I owe you plenty. You need a job? You got a job. You work for Shen Wa right now."

80

Shen Wa drove through downtown Montibello, a battered playground whose centerpiece was the Broadway Diner; its façade thankfully outlined in flickering green neon, the only proof that the world wasn't all black and white. A block from the diner he turned off Main Street, drove a another quarter-mile, then swung the Porche onto an unmarked dirt road hugging the desolate shore of a frozen lake. Another sharp left aimed the car up a long driveway lined by two rows of ratty-looking pines.

At the end of the driveway, Simon saw a huge building in the style of a Swiss chalet that reminded him of the flame-licked watch factory. Half the building was roofless, with broken walls held up by charred black timbers. The other half was intact, hanging together from force of habit. The only sign of habitation was a potted pink cyclamen in an upstairs window.

"Welcome to Feinberg's Pine Lake Villa," Shen Wa said, parking his Porche near what looked like the main entrance. "This was some big hotel way back when. Boy oh boy! Hollywood stars got started here. Famous athletes played ball here. Doctors, dentists, lawyers, businessmen, gangsters came here. Famous place for whoring or getting married. Pretty girls saved up all year to come for a week and find rich husband or just get laid. Great food, all strict Kosher, entertainment every night. I get the information from guy who used to be bellhop here. After people stop coming, the owner held onto property waiting for gambling to happen but never happened. After old man Feinberg die—rest in peace—his kids sold it for peanuts to my syndicate. Dumb move. Soon gambling. "

"And you're holding out for Tonto to open a casino?" Simon said.

"Who is Tonto?"

"Doesn't matter."

"The gambling will come. Why should New York State give away all that tax to strangers? Meanwhile, we use the place for other purposes."

"What purposes would they be?"

"Come inside. I want you to meet some people."

"Could I wait a few days? Until my face looks less like crumpled gift wrap? And my earlobes scare me. When I look in my magic mirror it says, 'Who the fuck are you?' "

"Listen, Fish Boy, you look fine compared to who's in there. Your face is no big deal at former Feinberg now Shen Wa's Villa. Not even worth second glance. Who do you think works here now, hotsy totsies? Mostly illegals who can't speak English paying off their transportation from China, Korea, Vietnam, Philippines even Cuba. Plus a few mental cases from here and there. Nice people but wounded. You understand what I'm saying? All in the same boat as your face, Simon Apple."

Shen Wa led the way past what must have been the hotel's reception desk, then through an archway leading to a gigantic room with a chandelier larger than the one at Glenda's Lombard Cinema. Like the sun, that crystal fixture was surrounded by paintings of the twelve signs of the zodiac. "Pretty fancy, eh" Shen Wa said. Simon nodded. "Now we get serious."

They went through a pair of swinging doors into an empty restaurant kitchen, walking along a bank of stripped-down refrigerators that dangled loose plugs like snakes with pronged fangs, then turned past a wrought iron wood-burning stove that half-concealed another door with an EXIT sign taped to its frame.

Shen Wa opened the door and gestured. Simon entered his new workplace, startled by a sea of whirring sewing machines run by an assorted band of operators representing every race, color, creed, and gender Simon ever heard of and a few he couldn't begin to identify.

Beyond the battalion of sewing machines were rows of men and women with spines shaped like shrimp hunched over heavy equipment, carefully guiding menacing embroidery needles that stitched adornments onto women's coats, blouses, skirts and slacks or decorating men's glossy club jackets with the logos of football, basketball and baseball teams.

Behind the embroiderers were the pleaters, steaming fabric into accordion shapes, then, behind them, long tables where cutters followed templates of patterns drawn on brown paper. Off to one side, a cadre of punchers slammed buttonholes into blouses and shirts. On the other, a dozen workers followed white chalk trails, stapling blank sweaters and tank tops with glittering rhinestones.

Teenagers on roller skates pushing supermarket carts flew between the rows of machines, reaching into deep bins, filling their carts with loads of partially finished garments and rushing those pieces to other stations in the sweatshop's assembly line.

Far in the rear of the barnlike structure, workers pressed finished suits, dresses and slacks, hung them on movable racks that were pushed to where labels were carefully added with names like Ralph Lauren, Donna Karan, Calvin Klein, Tommy Hilfiger, Yves Saint Laurent, Gianni Versace, Liz Claiborne, the whole spectrum of trendy brands.

In the farthest part of the room, workers steamed, pinned and folded dresses, suits, shirts, ties, T-shirts, gloves, scarves—every conceivable kind of apparel, then loaded it into large cardboard cartons. The plant opened onto a loading dock where the cartons were forklifted onto trucks and vans that came and went non-stop.

"This where you work. At desk in corner. Preparing invoices and keeping track of our shipments. I count on you to set good example for others. In no time you advance to a foreman. Most of my workers live upstairs in dormitories. Smelly, tiny cubicles. Not for you. For you I rent room in Montibello on Huckleberry Street where Fish Boy can enjoy privacy. Don't thank me, Simon. I am always in your debt. And, oh, I am sending you a tube of Tiger Balm for your strange affliction."

81

Because Warden Donal was a devoted fan of Wallace Waldo's radio show, Wallace, Benny Valaris and Rosy Freeman were brought to Simon Apple's cell without the traditional courtesy of asking permission from the condemned man. Though Simon was deep in philosophical thought, he was glad to see what he'd come to call The

Nairobi Trio in a tribute to the monkey band created by the late comedian, Ernie Kovacs.

"Who did the set design?" Waldo said, examining the cot, sink and toilet. "I like it. There's a stark realism, a post-modern minimalist expressionism."

"Probably," Simon said.

"So, our own Sinbad Green turns out to be a killer," Benny Valaris said. "I always thought there was something a tad holier than thou about you. But I wish you'd confided in me. If you had, you'd be living somewhere in the Caribbean or maybe Budapest. I'm like a conductor on the Underground Railroad and just for the hell of it. I like helping deviants."

"Sinbad, er, Simon, knows you have a good heart," Rosy said. "Is there anything you need, baby? Anything we can do for you?"

"Nothing," Simon said. "The fact that you bothered to drop in is more than enough. So, Benny, how's life in the theater?"

"Not what it was. The ingenues are into karate these days. My total score is down but the quality is up. I think it's the Actor's Studio thing."

"You know what I think about some nights?" Simon said. "The piano store downstairs."

"That's curious," Rosy said. "I dream about the place."

"Unplayed pianos make marvelous music," Waldo said.

"Very profound," Benny said. "A line like that could make the Buddhist edition of the Bullshit Times. Listen, Sinbad, the thing is, you're a real celebrity."

"Until midnight," Simon said.

"Right," Benny said. "After twelve you're just another ghost. But I was wondering if you might say something to the news ghouls who come to witness the last crap you let fly into the diaper they wrap you in because the sphincter lets go when that heavenly white light switches on. Personally, I always thought the twenty-one grams of soul the New Age undertakers write about exit the body through the same back door. But enough of that. Hey, good buddy, for old times sake, if you'd drop a plug for Beaver Beer before you start gagging on phlegm, like, *Christ, wouldn't a can of Beaver Beer taste great about now, made from pure mountain spring water?* It would mean a lot to us, especially Wallace here because frankly the business hasn't been doing so great. Right, Rosy? I know you believe Rosy."

"He promised he wouldn't ask you," Rose said.

"He can't help himself," Simon said.

"Pure mountain spring water tumbling over ice cold rocks," Waldo said. "Beautiful message except for the fact that fishes fuck in pure mountain spring water."

"It's been nice seeing you all," Simon said. "But I'm a little tired now, so—"

"Yeah," Benny Valaris said. "Later."

82

FROM THE DESK OF MARVIN KLIPSTEIN, ESQ.

To: The Honorable Taylor Sturgeon
    Chief Justice of the United States Supreme Court

Dear Justice Sturgeon,

My name is Marvin Klipstein, who, as you may recall, was privileged to plead for clemency (which the Court unanimously denied) in the landmark case of *The United States of America v. Simon Apple* earlier this afternoon.

There are certain truths I wish to share with you, anticipating the remote possibility of some future opportunity, however unlikely, to face the Supreme Court at some future date. It is my fervent hope that you and your colleagues will not harbor any ill will toward me for presuming to attempt any delay in the scheduled execution of my client, Simon Apple, by lethal injection this evening.

My usual legal energies involve less noteworthy cases, often drawn from the underbelly of the Law: I specialize in accidents, insurance claims, real estate closings, Civil Court proceedings, traffic violations and similar humble assignments. It is obviously no secret, to

you or to myself, that Marvin Klipstein, Esq., is absolutely unqualified to appear before you.

I hope you will realize that I accepted the mandate to represent Mr.
Apple *pro bono* that was thrust upon me by Judge Harrison
Theodore Bane of the First District Court in Glenda, Minnesota.

Judge Bane assured me that all proceedings would be *pro forma*,
that your verdict was inevitable. Of course, clemency is out of the
question here.

I believe that even a country lawyer like myself who never wanted
to be part of this profession, who was goaded into attending law
school by a brutal father who hit me with prayer books when I hesitated to honor his will, should bring a modicum of passion to his
efforts on behalf of any client.

I did not want Simon Apple to feel, in that awful second before the
chemicals seize his heart, that he was badly represented by counsel. I was obliged to mount a strong argument on behalf of the very
idea of compassion.

I myself would never condone postponing this execution. But the
process must be served. In our democracy even a Simon Apple,
may he soon find peace, has the right to one last gasp of—or grasp
at—hope even if the condemned man has renounced that right
time and again.

Simon Apple was given a rousing defense (allowing for the absence
of certain highly sensitive information concerning extenuating circumstances which might have confused deliberations). Presented
with overwhelming evidence, the men and women of the jury ago-
nized for the better part of an hour before finding him guilty.

Nine of the twelve jurors in that courtroom shed a waterfall of tears
even as they rose to their duty and demanded Apple's demise! They
wept for the victims and possibly for the accused as well, once a
good person, turned somehow in a fiendish direction.

Since the day of his sentencing some twenty years ago, no less
than thirty-six appeals have been filed on his behalf by interested
parties, this despite the fact that before each appeal the condemned
man requested no further action be taken to spare or to prolong his

life. Simon Apple knows full well that he represents a clear and present danger to the economic welfare of our blessed nation and the way of life we so cherish!

We can justly say that we have given Mr. Apple his due as an American citizen. And I can say to you that Lawyer Klipstein, repulsive as the task was, did his best to stay the scythe of the reaper. I hope you can forgive me if my efforts to save my client appeared too zealous and I want to apologize if the Court felt I wasted your precious time and taxpayer money indulging some frivolous whim.

Eternally grateful for your understanding, I remain,

Sincerely yours,
Marvin Klipstein, Esq.

83

Simon's first responsibilities at Shen Wa's high-end counterfeit clothing factory—checking manifests and mailing out invoices— were repetitious and boring, exactly what he needed to rest and regroup an addled brain. After the hectic flight from Long Island, Simon wanted a mental vacation; he enjoyed every vacuous minute of the peace that comes with mindlessness.

Each day he left his rooming house on Huckleberry Street at dawn. As promised, Simon's boss had arranged for him to be driven to Feinberg's Pine Lake Villa. His driver was the mechanic responsible for maintaining the motors, belts and pulleys that kept the factory going—a native of Montibello who called himself Thunderclap Bald Bird and claimed to be the last member of an obscure branch of the Mohawk Nation.

In addition to his mechanical acuity, Thunderclap was Shen Wa's ace in the hole in his fight to turn the area into another Las Vegas. If the government ruled that a large portion of Sullivan County was the rightful property of Thunderclap's family and therefore entitled to reservation status, there was no law to prevent slot machines, crap tables and roulette wheels from bringing new prosperity to the tribe.

"The Great Spirit works in mysterious ways" was a favorite and frequent observation of Thunderclap in the brief conversations he had with Simon. Mostly they talked about the lousy coffee they regularly picked up at the Broadway Diner or the odds spread on the following Sunday's football games. That ritual of comfortable non-communication was repeated every night, when Simon was driven back to Huckleberry.

After work, it was Simon's daily habit to stop in at a bar called The Irish Smile. The place had known better days; adapting to its collapsed location, the eponymous Smile had drooped to a forlorn frown. The place was falling apart. Like his numbing job and those anesthetic chats with Thunderclap Bald Bird, the scene dovetailed perfectly with Simon's mood. He'd have a solitary beer while he watched Vanna White cross back and forth turning consonants and vowels on *Wheel of Fortune,* then cross over to the Broadway Diner to order the Blue Plate Special, whatever it happened to be.

Henry Sharp, a huge black man, the diner's owner and chef, had cooked for hotels like Grossingers, The Concord, Laurel's Country Club, Feinbergs Pine Lake Villa, The President, and Kutcher's—elite establishments that catered to a strictly kosher crowd. His specialty was preparing dishes that tasted like something else: kosher bacon, kosher chow mein, kosher prawns, kosher oyster stew—forbidden foods miraculously transformed to conform to orthodox standards. He accomplished that magic using certified meat, fish, vegetables and a dazzling array of spices. One of Henry's most valuable talents was to visit a table that ordered some pseudo *goyish* delicacy and take an oath that no gourmet could distinguish his ersatz dishes from the real thing; what Shen Wa's operation did for clothing, Henry Sharp did for recipes. When Simon ordered a dish like crab cakes or meatloaf at the Broadway Diner he could never be sure it wasn't made from leftover flounder heads, collard greens or sheep's kidneys decimated then married in a Waring Blender; reasonable doubt remained even if Henry put his hand on his heart and swore to its authenticity. But the food was generally edible and the price was right.

After dinner, Simon would pick up a newspaper or a magazine at Iggy's Convenience Store on the corner of Broadway and Huckleberry, then head back to his room.

He wished desperately to call Robert J. and Rowena, to hear familiar voices, but he knew better; if Simon Apple was a fugitive from Federal Communications Commission investigators, an accused arsonist, a homicide suspect, or a candidate for medical research wanted for stealing a precious tube of *Compassarate Dioxide*, the phones back in Glenda were surely tapped.

None of that would matter if the peculiar skin condition that began with his first *Compassarate Dioxide* massage got much worse. Simon had the feeling his life was coming to an end. By spring, Simon quit shaving because the touch of a blade was agonizing and looking into a mirror even more painful. The beard he sprouted helped hide his face but not his earlobes which had graduated from moth-sized flaps to bat wings.

Even the gathering of chronic depressives and bond slaves at the knock-off factory, The Irish Smile drunks, the Broadway Diner regulars with spirits like wilted lettuce, the inmates at the boarding house on Huckleberry Street looked away when Simon passed through their field of vision. Mornings and evenings, Thunderclap plastered himself against his driver's door, sitting as far from Simon as the car allowed.

It was Henry Sharp who directed him to the office of Dr. Franklin Milkowitz on Cherry Lane. Milkowitz, a retired family physician, took on a few interesting patients just to keep his hand in. Simon postponed making an appointment for as long as he could, then arranged for a consultation.

"Are you a real doctor or one of Henry's concoctions?" Simon said to a round, energetic man wearing a stethoscope that hung like a necklace.

"I'm the only game in town," Dr. Milkowitz said. "You're lucky you got here before an owl tried to eat you. When did you first notice you had a problem?"

"It's a long story," Simon said. "It might have something to do with an ointment called *Compassarate Dioxide*."

"Coincidence," Dr. Milkowitz said. "A sales representative from Regis Pharmaceuticals mentioned that to me only earlier today. Said that the stuff was way off-the-record, but he thought I'd hear about it from my son if I hadn't already. I got the idea it has something to do with electronics and might be harmful to magnetic resonance imaging equipment, not that there's an MRI in Montibello, and probably a danger to pacemakers. How did you happen to get your hands on a restricted designer chemical? Are you involved in some kind of test?"

"I'm not part of any test. How I fit into the picture is a very long story," Simon said.

"I need time to noodle this out," Dr. Milkowitz said. "Meanwhile, I could give you some wonder drug but you might end up wondering why I used a hydrogen bomb before trying a sparkler. One of my mother's magic potions might help. Whenever I had a rash on my *pipick*, she headed for the kitchen, not the drugstore. I suggest you buy a large box of Quaker Oats at the market and large patches of loose surgical gauze from the pharmacy. Staple the gauze into small pouches, fill them with uncooked oatmeal flakes and dangle a few of the bags in a hot bath. Soak in the tub at least twice a day for an hour or more. When you finish bathing, squeeze the wet oatmeal bags over a glass like tea and wash your face and ears in oatmeal soup."

"That's disgusting," Simon said. "It sounds like witch medicine. I think my nanny, Victoria, did something like that to me when I was a baby. She was very holistic. And she hated to waste food."

"I'll take a scraping to see if we're dealing with a fungus, a virus, bacteria or just another one of God's little jokes," Dr. Milkowitz said, reaching for something shiny and sharp.

84

FROM WALL STREET WHISPERS—
YOUR INSIDER MARKET REPORT

ARE WE HEARING RIGHT? IS REGIS PHARMACEUTICALS ABOUT TO UNLEASH A GIANT? IS REGIS'S NEW VENTURE, MUSE HORIZONS, A "SOUND" INVESTMENT? LISTEN UP . . .

Dire predictions downgrading the future of Regis Pharmaceuticals, resulting from the dramatic loss of revenue caused by the governmental ban on *Stalagamide*, might prove premature. Word on the Street is that the company is about to release a blockbuster new product—*HypaVibe*/The Miracle Module—under the mantle of a new division, Muse Horizons.

Strange as it may seem, *HypaVibe*, far outside Regis Pharmaceuticals usual product mix, is aimed at the burgeoning consumer electronics market!

When quizzed about very loud buzz predicting a fifty-point jump in Regis Pharmaceuticals stock, analysts point to very optimistic remarks by Mr. Van Clay at a gathering of Pop Culture mavens in the sparkling new Regis Auditorium in Hollywood.

"Regis Muse Horizons, our newest division, will quickly establish itself as a leader in all aspects of sound technology ranging from a new generation of hearing aids to speakers with unparalleled fidelity. Our involvement in the pop and classical music scene will blend the technical with the creative. We will engage in the production of CD albums and videos featuring multiple Grammy Award–winning musical groups, top singing stars and the world's great orchestras. The transition from LP and VCR to CD formats can only be compared to the inevitable decline of Neanderthal culture and the exciting transition to Cro-Magnon dominance. Who can say what the future will bring?"

When asked about Regis Pharmaceuticals sudden entry into the music business, Mr. Van Clay explained that his entire working life has focused on curing illness and decrepitude. "Awareness of those horrors has increased my appreciation for the gift of music. The old saying that 'music hath charms to soothe the savage breast'—or is it beast?—is absolutely accurate. So I will do my best to put aside thoughts of virulent viruses for a moment and allow time and energy for our company to contribute to the hearing, and listening , pleasure of millions. *HypaVibe* improves the performance of any speaker system, telephone to stereo."

Along with talk of Regis's sudden interest in sound transmission, there are also several unanswered questions floating around concerning the "Miracle Module's" role as a "miracle molecule" with future medical and military applications. The company refuses to confirm or deny the validity of any such claims. Our attempts to investigate reports of a whopping contract awarded to Muse Horizons by the Department of Defense proved futile. One wonders if the military has developed a sudden interest in attack dancing—or if something else is afoot?

WALL STREET WHISPERS has upgraded Regis Pharmaceuticals stock to a magnetically attractive BUY NOW.

85

When Simon left his office, Dr. Milkowitz made a slide from the scraping and shipped it down to the National Institutes of Health in Washington. His son, Milton, worked at NIH researching the mounting national death toll from legally prescribed medications, a worthwhile field of study considering that multiple thousands of victims are wiped out annually (and more thousands of cases go unreported). Those statistics result in billions of dollars in lawsuits filed against doctors and drug companies by widows, widowers, and occasional orphans. The vindictive lawsuits cause real inconvenience to health care practitioners forced to pay astronomical insurance premiums (passed on to their surviving patients) and, worse yet, to cope with mounds of time-consuming paperwork.

Dr. Milkowitz thought his son might be able to dig around and find out about any adverse side effects associated with a compound called *Compassarate Dioxide*. He asked Milton for a quick reply since he gave Simon Apple no more than a few weeks to live at his present rate since he suspected that Simon suffered from a rare case of *Fractus Epidermal Magneticia Detritum* complicated by *Multilobal Oculap Exaggeritus* with signs of AAN (*Attendant Aural Neuropathy*).

The reply he got was not from his son; it came from a smooth talking woman who identified herself as Captain Ginger Flytrap, a public relations officer with the North American Air Defense Command. She informed Dr. Milkowitz that his inquiry about *Compassarate Dioxide* impinged on a highly restricted area of profound military concern. The caller demanded to see all records pertaining to the patient designated *Apple, Simon*. When Dr. Milkowitz mentioned the issue of doctor-patient confidentiality, Captain Flytrap lowered her voice and told him to shove a sigmoid scope up his anal flexure.

An hour later, Milton called urging his father to "comply with NORAD's request without further delay and ask me no further questions." His son said, without further explanation, that the letter accompanying the slide Dr. Milkowitz sent for analysis hadn't helped his career.

An hour after that, the Regis sales rep called to apologize for prematurely mentioning *Compassarate Dioxide*. "The drug showed initial promise as an anti-inflammatory," the Regis rep said, "but all testing for human use has been suspended. In this business, you win some, you lose some."

"Products or patients?" Dr. Milkowitz said.

"A little of both," the salesman said. "Either way, for me, it comes down to income. I should have gone to med school."

Dr. Milkowitz hurried to send Simon's records to Washington before the post office closed, then he walked down to the Broadway Diner for a cup of decaf and a friendly chat with Henry Sharp.

"Thank you for recommending me to that young man, Henry. It turns out he's been exposed to a highly toxic substance. You may have saved his life."

"All in a day's work," Henry said, flipping a pancake.

What amused Dr. Milkowitz was Simon's comment about his nanny—what was her name? Victoria?—dipping him into oatmeal baths, the identical panacea his own mother forced on the Milkowitz brood in poison ivy season. "So much for super drugs," he told Henry Sharp. "There's still something to be said for the Old Faithfuls."

"Like roast chicken and mashed potatoes," Henry said.

86

Much to Dr. Milkowitz's surprise, by late spring Simon Apple reported that oatmeal immersion had worked wonders, that it was no longer necessary to hide his face behind a beard and his elephantine earlobes had significantly reduced in size. The doctor didn't know whether to credit Quaker Oats or nature's best healer, time itself.

He wanted to tell Milton about Simon's dramatic recovery but ruled out any further involvement with clandestine governmental experimentation. It was best for his son if the whole incident quietly faded away.

No longer a pariah, Simon was promoted to floor manager at Shen Wa's bogus boutique. Part of his new job involved thumbing through a ton of magazines each month, ripping out pages with photos of celebrity trendsetters. The trends they set often began in the least expected places before being swallowed by the ravenous marketing apparatus, sanctified in shopping malls and department stores soon to be copied by Shen Wa's elves.

Simon also watched the adolescents around Montibello with a detached, critical eye. If he saw something he thought might be imaginative, a harbinger of a future fashion fad, he'd snap a few quick Polaroids, then attach them to a report for Shen Wa.

Simon saw proof that the acorn doesn't all far from the tree; shades of Robert J., he was orchestrating what amounted to a peek-a-boo album of his own featuring a curious cast of local characters. Ironically, his interest was in the clothes and shoes that covered Montibello's beauties, not in intimate glimpses of their cleavage. Shen Wa's mantra was: "Big money in suits, not birthday suits." If Simon's photos and a few rough sketches piqued his boss's attention, the material was faxed to addresses in Thailand, Indonesia, Turkey, Pakistan, Egypt, Korea, the Philippines, Ecuador, Bolivia, Paraguay and Mexico—always with a blind copy marked for China.

One evening after work, Simon wandered into The Irish Song for his nightly bracer. Since his promotion and the raise that came with it, he'd switched from beer to vodka martinis. He noticed that the oasis had switched bartenders, a definite upgrade if the girl who'd replaced buxom Cyril Shaunessey looked as good from the front as she did from the back. Her neat bottom, really unusual for that depressed area, immediately caught Simon's eye and not for obvious reasons. There were two large daisies painted on the tight-fitting denim that framed her buns, their green stems running like seams down the backs of her pant legs, disappearing into the depths of her Ferragamo boots. He got out his Polaroid—flowering butts could be the wave of the future—and snapped a picture. The bright white flash made the new girl in town whirl around. Simon saw it was Polly Moon.

"If you asked I would have smiled for you," she said. "Do you have some kind of fetish or was hitting the button just another case of premature ejaculation?"

"It was the hills beyond," Simon said, astonished to see his Placebo mixing drinks in that piss-perfumed dive.

"It's peculiar but I think I know who you are," Polly said. "Give me a minute to zero in."

"More to the point, I know who you are. Why in hell is a rock star like Polly Moon mixing drinks in a joint like this?"

"Well, mister X, fame is fleeting. At the moment Polly's star needs a new battery. I've definitely seen you somewhere. A very long time ago. Jog my memory."

"Simon Apple. From Glenda."

"Simple Simon from back home? Of course I know you. Didn't we share our formative years?"

"You wouldn't share. But the truth is, we've seen each other much more recently. I guess you were too stressed out to remember."

"Stressed or stoned. I'm supposed to be working. Name your poison."

"Smirnoff martini on the rocks. With a twist."

"Chip chip. A nice boy like you drinking Smirnoff martinis in Six Pack Country? You win the lottery?"

"I work at Feinberg's Pine Lake Villa. It's a famous hotel."

"I once played the Concord. But I thought all the ritzy hotels were dead and buried."

"Not Feinberg's. It has a loyal clientele. Polly Moon, I'm very confused. The last time I saw you you'd just won a Pan for Record of the Year. You were riding the whirlwind."

"Long time ago, Simon."

"Not that long."

"You're talking about the music business. Wildest roller coaster in town. But I'll soon be ready for my first comeback."

"You will, Placebo. I know you will."

"Didn't you used to call me by that dumb name?"

"Polly. I meant Polly. Old habits die hard. So tell me, where are you staying?"

"I found a room in a boarding house on Huckleberry Street. A few blocks from here."

"No, what a fantastic coincidence. It's where I live. Huckleberry just off Broadway."

"Synchronicity," Polly said. "It's what makes the world go around. We never did have a chance to get to know one another. Maybe now we will."

87

Dearest Love,

Before now I never understood the Song of Solomon or the Rubaiyat of Omar Khayyám. If I met Sol and Omar, say for a drink, I could have asked about the problems of being the King of Israel or maybe the best carpet maker in Persia and told them something about Polo or DKNY knockoffs but I don't think I could have really related to them beyond a point and they'd know it.

All that changed this week. Now those guys and Simon Apple could have a one-on-one exchange of ideas concerning the outermost boundaries of love, time, luck and death. I do believe they would recognize me as a true peer, not as a king or carpet maker or duplicator of a Vuitton sack but, if I may say so without sounding pompous, smug, or self-satisfied—as a total human being in the making.

Before this week, I think my limit in the loving department was somewhere between the Kama Sutra and Frank Sinatra. Over the years I have had intimations of sensuality as a bridge to spirituality but few and far between. With you, when our bodies touch, I am catapulted over endless horizons, finally on the highway to realization—a road without toll booths or traffic lights.

Who would have thought nirvana was located on Huckleberry Street in Montibello, New York, a mile from the raceway? Certainly not me. You must know that since I first saw you pink and purr-fect in your pram, even the formidable barrier named Fritzel could not keep me from adoring you. Nor could your constant and brutal rejections i.e. all that spitting and vomiting, etc. Because I knew back then that behind those slings and arrows of repulsion lurked sweet ambivalence.

I was convinced that you were my destiny and remained so, though when you became a musical idol I admit to doubting our future together. Your beautiful rendition of The Windchime Concerto seemed to carry you out of reach.

You don't remember a certain delivery from Wallace Waldo Enterprises involving a refrigerator with the capacity to manufacture its own ice cubes, which I saw as a mechanical metaphor for the robotic person I felt you'd become.

I won't dwell on details of a certain afternoon encounter when a certain girl fell asleep before she was asked to write a receipt acknowledging said delivery (for which the delivery person took a mountain of flak) except to tell you that the incident was the closest a certain young man had ever come to heaven's gate. Still, for him it was a lonely experience. He could only hope that the certain girl's subconscious would remember something of the afternoon she'd spent in the arms of that certain young man if only in a dream, recognizing that the odds against such a miracle of synchronicity were about fifty-to-one, if not more.

And now, time-seasoned, we have come together!!! I think wiser; you could say tenderized by life's thumps and bumps, ready to accept the cosmic and comic experience of absolute fusion along with the terrifying prospect of inevitable fission which is the outrageous price we must pay for "following our bliss" (as Bill Moyers and Joseph Campbell advise we do on the Public Broadcasting System).

What we have discovered together is beyond any words that might possibly approach an adequate expression of gratitude except perhaps for a simple thank you, that most humble verbal daisy not unlike the flower blooming on the back of your jeans.

I cannot write anywhere nearly as well as Sol and/or Omar but you get the idea, you know your welcoming lips have devoured Simon Apple's heart with every kiss, and his befuddled soul is swallowed up when you allow him to enter the Rubaiyat of your deepest cave. Thou art fair, my beloved, and don't ever forget it—whatever the critics might say—and they will, they always do.

Totally yours,
Simon

"I shouldn't have let you read that," Polly said.

"No secrets between us," Agent Beem said. "Rest assured, it will be treated with the utmost discretion."

"I have everything you asked for in triplicate. Fingerprints from all ten of his fingers, hair clippings cranial and pubic, nail cuttings, whisker fragments, earwax, enough seminal fluid to float the *Andrea Doria* and this letter of which I'd like a Xerox copy. There's even a little vial of Simon Apple's tears. Now, do you have the signed contract? As per the terms of our agreement?"

"Two copies, both notarized," Brian Beem said. "Polly Moon is now the property of Regis Muse Horizons. They're committed to produce your next album and to promote the aforesaid with their best efforts, well in advance of next year's Grammys. In addition the company agrees to sponsor a live tour of no less than twenty major cities across the United States. Please sign your name on the lines marked with an X and return the second copy to me. After you hand over that case of goodies, as per—"

"As per," Polly Moon said. "What happens to Simon now?"

"No concern of yours. Oh, before I forget my nephew, Ronald, would appreciate your autograph. I promised to ask you. 'Best wishes, Ronnie' would be fine. When he heard me mention your name he got all excited but he couldn't remember why."

88

"I'm sorry it took me so long to get back," Brian Beem said. "As the poet might say, 'Things to do and miles to go before *you* sleep.' Scratch that remark. It was crass."

"I'm immune to dumb jokes," Simon said. "Living in limbo for two decades dulls the senses."

"*Tempis fugit.* Has it been twenty years since your trial? Time flies what with all the bleeding hearts filing appeals. Not to mention the Pope's letters, the Dali Lama's protests, and the countless demonstrations when your death sentence came down."

"Twenty years almost to the day," Simon said. "And after seven thousand three hundred and six days in a lethargic trance, I find myself in a hurry to die. You promised more details. We're moving right along toward zero hour and I still have no idea how you linked me to Brother Lucas's murder and a batch of tainted fish bladders. All I do know is that one balmy day in Montibello, I was chewing out a girl who'd sewed four hundred Gloria Vanderbilt labels onto Versace bikinis, a cardinal sin in the world of pseudo chic, when my boss came screaming down the factory aisles ordering everyone to quit whatever they were doing and make a dash for the rear fire exit. He was speaking about ten languages at once so I was a bit confused but the general idea was to get the hell out of the place ASAP. I ran with the rest. We made it outside and found ourselves on the set of a Dragnet film. There must have been a thousand cops surrounding Feinberg's Pine Lake Villa, supported by more ordnance than it took to track down my quasar-powered boner as the cause of *multimedia interupti* in and around Serene Harbor."

"Actually about five hundred cops," Beem said. "It was a lot of muscle. Possibly overkill. But the last shot we had at you was a dud. This time we were thinking Velcro. You weren't going to walk away like you did at Brookhaven."

"Shen Wa was pretty pissed since he'd made all his monthly payoffs on schedule. He naturally assumed the raid had something to do with his business practices. I was happy to see the look of relief cross his face when he heard it was only me you were after."

"Yes, I liked seeing his face transform from pinched and anxious to loose and peaceful when he got the message. His color came back too, from wilted grass to verdant arbor."

"Verdant arbor? I never thought I'd hear you use language so eloquently."

"You hardly know me, Simon."

"You could arrange for us to get to know one another better."

"I don't think that's in the cards this time around. When Shen Wa and his people refused to single you out and hand you over I was filled with emotion. For a global entrepreneur and his miserable, exploited and abused wage slaves to defend a non-entity like you with so much passion, when they stood to lose everything, was truly inspiring. And when you volunteered to give yourself up, well, what can I say? It was a beautiful thing."

"I think it was you who read me my rights after outlining the charges against me. I expected my crime would relate to trademark violation or maybe the watch factory fire and the fate of Hyman Simbok. Your voice sounded so confident, so rehearsed. I felt really close to you, considering it had been so long since we first met at Quikpix. The accusations didn't sink in until you had me inside that armored truck. Of course, knowing I was innocent, and being a fool, I assumed I'd be out of custody in twenty-four hours, not a hundred seventy-five thousand three hundred forty-four hours."

"You knew Hyman Simbok?"

"Slightly. Whatever happened to him?"

"He couldn't deny it was his cigar that set fire to the factory building though he tried to incriminate the mayor, Evan Crimmins. I heard he'd sold a bag of hand-painted watch faces to the Whitney Museum in New York. Then I think he went down to Key West and reconnected with a childhood sweetheart from the old country."

"I hope he took Mengele along," Simon said.

"You're losing me."

"His pooch from hell. Not important. I began to worry about

myself when your men hustled me into that helicopter. I'd never been in a whirlybird before."

"Amazing machines," Beem said.

"The blindfold wasn't necessary," Simon said. "Or the cuffs."

"Policy."

"I had no clue where we landed. I never expected—"

"You still can't be sure about where you were," Beem said.

"Please. Humor me, tonight of all nights."

"This isn't a conjugal visit. It's not even official. Certain information is still classified. Which reminds me. Your friend Polly did request a conjugal last week. She said you two were married in the eyes of God."

"More true than not except that God seems to have blinked," Simon said. "Why wasn't Polly allowed to—?"

"There was no record of any marriage license. We can't allow anybody a night of fun and games in the Death House just because they might feel the urge to conjugate."

"You could have given us one night together," Simon said.

"I know," Brian Beem said. "I was for it. But the warden felt what might be picked up by the security cameras might end up in every porno shop in America."

"Not just America. Placebo has fans around the world," Simon said. "She's an icon. Tarnished, but an icon."

"Who?"

"I meant Polly Moon."

"Getting back to Brother Lucas," Beem said, "Making that connection was easy, cut and dried. Courtesy of Ms. Moon, we had enough of your body fluids, hair samples, all kinds of markers you'd left on Brother Lucas's corpse, inside and outside. The jury was very impressed by the fingerprints on that slightly edited "Dearest Love" letter we found stuffed in Luke's anal cavity. The prosecutor couldn't say if Brother Lucas put it there to let us know who shot him or just for sentimental reasons."

"My valentine to Polly Moon? She showed you *that*?"

"Afraid so."

"It's a shame Polly's last album turned out to be such a bust. I liked some of the tracks."

"Nothing to hum or dance to, nothing to match *The Windchime*

Concerto," Brian Beem said. "That's what I call authentic New Age music."

"Thanks," Simon said. "You know, I never felt bitter toward Polly for working with you, Brian. I guess that's a measure of how I adore that woman. At the time, I did think it a bit coincidental that she turned up at The Irish Song the way she did, but somehow I just accepted that as part of the normal flow of events. Does that sound dumb or what?"

"Dumb but understandable," Beem said. "I believed my first wife when she said she was spending those Monday nights taking a course on Raising Healthy Hydrangeas. And there was the case of Veronica Lake, a major star who ended up as a hooker and boozer in some jerkwater town in New England. Or was that Betty Hutton? Or both? So we thought it was credible enough to ship Polly Moon to Montibello."

"And it worked. I bought her whole story. You know what the President said to me? He said, 'Simon, did you know the anatomy of women is the reason we're sitting in an oval office instead of a squared-off room? That the architect who built the White House was very much aware of the vaginal implications of interior design? Something called *Feng Shui.* Rumor has it he was spurred on by the First Lady. And she was right on target. This room generates enormous energy. It's an aphrodisiac. That helps explain some of the otherwise unforgivable hanky panky that's scandalized the Executive branch of government. I know you're blindfolded, but you must sense how history was forever changed by this ovular environment, clitorally speaking.' "

"You were never in the oval office," Brian Beem said. "You never spoke with the President."

"I'd know that voice anywhere. He was the one who convinced me to take my medicine, no pun intended. He was the one who brought Regis Van Clay into that room to spout the statistical disasters caused by my existence. Between the two of them, I was ready to run outside and lay down on the nearest guillotine."

"You were marvelously cooperative," Beem said.

"But humiliating my family by conjuring your monk-murder fabrication with that fugu fiasco. I didn't deserve that or expect such treatment, not after the President shook my hand and patted my shoulder. You do know they're awarding me a posthumous medal in a century or so? My lawyer, Marvin Klipstein, said he'd negotiated that deal. But who can say if they'll keep their promise?"

"Not me," Brian Beem said. "Well, I think you're up to speed now. I have nothing more to tell you that I can speak about. I hope it gives you some solace knowing that, albeit indirectly, you'll be memorialized on millions of warning labels in many languages until the end of time. Flagging those side effects has already saved more lives than secondhand smoking bans and seat belts combined. Of course, no thanks to you, the dollar hit new lows against those Yens and Euros but now that we've plugged the so-called Apple Gap, pharmaceutical exports are already tipping what I call the imbalance of trade. We'll make a comeback. We always do. We always will. And that's not hubris. It's guaranteed by the sacrifice of soldiers, sailors, airmen, spies and so-called ordinary citizens like Simon Apple."

"I suppose you know Brother Lucas came to visit me here. He looks better than he did before I murdered him."

"You saw Brother Lucas? Did you also see Jesus and Moses waiting to greet you when the ax falls?"

"It was no hallucination," Simon said. "He was here. You have to know Lucas is alive and well. He said he's on special assignment for the Company. You're incapable of telling me the whole truth and nothing but the truth."

"What a nasty accusation," Brian Beem said. "Simon, it's been an honor to know you. You're a jolly good fellow. I think that whenever I'm having a good dinner or fornicating with Mrs. Beem some part of me will feel a portion of my satisfaction is deservedly shared by a freckle-faced kid from Glenda, Minnesota."

"I never had freckles," Simon said.

"I didn't mean literal freckles," Agent Beem said. "I meant figurative freckles. Rest in peace."

89

Simon was told that his farewell dinner would soon be served. Living in a world without clocks, that news, not unexpected, still came as a surprise. His only connection with time, except through memory, came from a Hyman Simbok one-of-a-kind hand-painted watch face which he kept in the breast pocket of his saffron uniform stenciled U.S. GOVERNMENT ISSUE across the chest and back.

That watch face, a fat-cheeked imp with ringlets of curly hair, lecherous lips and a bulbous nose that served as hub for the hour, minute and second hands, had become a kind of talisman for Simon, his not-so-good luck charm, a disembodied souvenir from a world where people actually compartmentalized their days to chronicle the march toward oblivion.

In his section of the prison, always brightly lit for the eyes of security cameras watching for suicide attempts or the vaguest indication of any attempt at escape, the guards were forbidden to answer questions about calendars or clocks. Simon was so immersed in that timeless world he'd long since stopped asking visitors about the progress of the sun's daily journey or the phases of the moon. If someone like Marvin Klipstein, Esq., who Simon had enough reason to trust, violated house rules and said something like, "Got to get moving, the kids should be getting out of school soon," Simon didn't believe him. The only credible truth in the Death House was that only Death, tiptoeing softly over a goose-down path of minutes, knew the time.

"You have a visitor, not a relative. If you want to see him you'll have to see him under glass," the guard said.

While Simon shuffled down the long corridor leading to the visitor's room, downstairs, in the prison kitchen, a pound-and-a-half lobster, formerly of Ogonquit, Maine, wriggled on a chrome counter, straining against rubber bands, holding its pincers shut. A large steel pot of water simmered on the stove, sending up the first bubbles of what the cookbook described as a vigorous boil.

At first, Simon didn't recognize his meticulously dressed African American visitor, a man in his prime with silver-speckled hair framing a strong, composed face.

It always amazed Simon that when he caught reflected glimpses of himself in some liquid mirror in a plastic mug or soup bowl (glass and metal was forbidden), he'd see some ancient stranger looking back at him. It took a while to realize he was seeing himself. Whenever he thought about women he'd known, their faces were unchanged, their bodies young and supple. Then Simon was forced to perform the frightful addition of decades, the alchemy of a frenzied accountant correcting the balance sheet of a corporate cheat before an audit.

Using the same brutal math, he was forced to realize that his visitor was his high school buddy, Chirp Bennet. From Chirp's expression, Simon guessed the shock of recognition was mutual — they'd both time-traveled over a considerable distance.

"All these years," Simon said into the monitored telephone. "Chirp, you're looking fit as a fiddle."

"You too," Chirp said. "So what's new with the fabulous fucker from Glenda High?"

"Not much," Simon said. "I've been on hold for a while."

"So I heard. Tell me, are you guilty as charged?"

"No."

"I didn't think so."

While the two men checked each other's faces for wrinkles, Simon's lobster felt itself lifted through the air then dropped with a splash into the boiling cauldron. It lost all belief in omnipotence. It's shell turned from the color of sea bottom mud to a furious sunset red.

"What are you up to these days?" Simon said.

"I'm the Art Director for *Positive Outlook Magazine*. Wife, Zelda. Three kids, Malcom, Angela and Chirp Junior. We live in Fair Lawn, New Jersey just over the Washington Bridge. Life is good."

"Excellent," Simon said. "You know, that we lost touch is one of my biggest regrets."

"And mine. But you do accept that I could never forgive you for what you did to my Camaro. I still can't, so let's not pretend that the wound is healed. You sacrificed our friendship for a quick screw in the park."

"A quick screw in the park? Are you speaking of Tabitha Ulman? I loved that woman, head to tail. How could I know I was suffering from . . ."

The prison chef added a clove of garlic to a saucepan where a generous chunk of butter melted. Then he tossed a batch of potato slices into a pot of hissing oil. While the french fries cooked, he chopped a parsley garnish and filled a small plastic tub with coleslaw fresh from the refrigerator.

"There's no excuse for what you did to my wheels," Chirp said. "But I didn't come to talk about the past. I didn't plan to come at all. Zelda said it was the Christian thing to do. So here I am. How could you have fucked Miss Ulman in my backseat when you swore a blood oath?"

"Look, they're going to execute me in a few hours. Can't we kiss and make up? Isn't there anything I can say that—"

"No, damn it. Nothing. Listen, it was nice seeing you looking so composed."

"You too," Simon said. "My best to the little woman."

"Zelda is six two. She was once in the Olympics. Track and Field."

The cook was a religious man. He sensed his efforts were being judged by angels. When he squirted whipped cream on a wedge of key lime pie, he knew those angels grinned.

"I only slightly expected to get laid that night," Simon said.

"I wish I could just forgive and forget," Chirp said. "But every time I read about you I think 'Cragar wheels, 4-barrel Holley carburetor, Crane performance camshaft.' I guess I'm not the man I'd like to be, but you should have done Miss Ulman on the grass. That's what grass is for." Chirp Bennet hung up his phone and stood to leave.

"Yeah, well, later," Simon said.

Before Simon hung up, the voice of the guard who screened all conversations cut in on the line and said, "You know the brother is right. And I'm not saying that because I'm an African American, so please don't play the race card. Oh, by the way, they said to tell you your dinner is ready, Apple. Get it while it's hot."

90

Simon had always rejected wearing a lobster bib the few times he'd gone to devour one of those atavistic delicacies. Accepting a bib seemed regressive and demeaning both to himself and to the broiled or boiled creature laying split apart on his plate.

The bib was a plastic carpet that flew Simon back to his days in a highchair, when his lack of size, strength and coordination forced him to accept trading the ultimate joy of a pillow breast and fountain nipple for a spoonful of mush shoved toward his sucking mouth. Every cell in his infantile brain urged him to spit that food back at the tit-miser who fed him, but his body was too hungry to allow for a political statement. So he swallowed stewed pears, mashed carrots and bananas without relish. After that shameful capitulation, he drank his milk from a glass bottle with a rubber nipple and fell asleep.

It was no bib for Simon Apple, thank you very much.

The succulent crustacean waiting to offer up its tender meat and tasty roe had lived the life of a cannibal and a pirate. After surviving by murder, procreating by intimidation, enduring mayhem and assault on the bed of the brutal northern sea, one stupid mistake had landed it inside a lobster trap. The captive was plucked into an unsuspected kingdom of air, tossed onto a mountain of ice, thrown into a tank with banded pincers and, undefended, left to crawl through a slimy clot of other doomed, damned *homarus americanus*, transported to a slaughter house where thick fingers smelling of garlic circled its squirming middle and wriggling legs, then dropped it into the steaming hell of a lobster pot (better than being turned upside down, sliced down the middle then sacrificed to cremating flames) where it sensed, in its last sentient moment, its color change to a sunset mix of red and orange—a Cinderella gift of beauty granted on the verge of extinction. Ironically, the very death blush would make its transformed cadaver so much more appetizing to some salivating gourmet. To wear a bib, always decorated with a sugary drawing of the victim, a crustacean whose history—beginning, middle to violent end—was worthy of a Russian novel, seemed a superficial act, a sad denial of the primitive connection between the eater and that delicious predator whose ancestors dated back to the Big Bang, the celestial fart that created the universe ("and nothing more," Einstein was rumored to say in private). A bib is armament, like a carapace. A tool for species distancing.

Definitely no bib, thanks for asking.

Just as Simon was about to dig out a chunk of tender white tail meat, he heard a harsh, judgmental voice from just outside his cell. "He's refusing to use a bib!" The voice was obviously annoyed that the prisoner took the bibless route.

Simon saw a video camera pointed at him. Alongside the camera, a man stood holding a microphone. It was someone Simon recognized but he couldn't place the who, how, where, when or why of any past encounter. "He's going after the tail first. Me, I prefer to save the tail and pincers for last. I start by breaking off the legs and kind of inhaling what's inside them. It's like the overture to a concert. Not that there's a right way or a wrong way. But that's the Speed Sage way."

"What's this about?" Simon said. "I'm trying to get through my last meal."

"That's what this is about," Speed Sage said. "We're shooting a documentary for *Fox News*. On last meals, especially yours."

"For some kind of Grand Guignol reality show?"

"In a way. The gimmick is to show the audience, A, that compassionate conservatism works, that even the worst offenders are treated with dignity and, B, that the animal rights folks are treading on thin ice when they accuse the system of cruel and unusual punishment if a recipe happens to call for meat or, in your case, shellfish. Our crew followed that lobster from its home waters right to your cell and, believe me, no prince was ever treated better. And C, certain parties want a record of your last hours. They want to make sure you're neatly folded and put away."

"I didn't think those certain parties wanted to make a fuss over my folding," Simon said.

"They decided a certain amount of closure was called for," Speed Sage said. "Can we get on with it now? Try the potatoes or the slaw. Have a sip of cranberry juice. Look like you're enjoying yourself. Take the nutcracker and crack that shell." Speed Sage cuddled his microphone and whispered, "*Mmmmm*, ladies and gents, let nobody accuse Simon Apple of anorexia, and by anorexia Speed ain't referring to Czar Nicholas's missing daughter as played by Ingrid Bergman. OK, on with the show. We're live here in the J. Edgar Hoover Correctional Facility watching convicted monk-murderer Simon Apple feast on a dinner fit for Bonnie and Clyde. The main course will be topped off by an entire key lime pie smothered in whipped cream and surrounded by a drizzle of raspberry sauce, as requested by the ruthless perp. And you're picking up the tab, fellow taxpayers. You and me both."

"The football game." Simon said. "At the Munchkin Academy. You were the sportscaster."

"That's it. And you were the seedling with the antlers. We're old friends, ladies and gents, we go back a few years. This kid was some kind of running back. And look at him now. I knew he'd make good when I saw him break apart the *de*fense of one of toughest teams in the diaper league. So how did it come to pass that a boy like you is sitting in there while a bum like Speed Sage is out here still doing the play-by-play?"

"Side effects," Simon said.

"Meaning what?" Speed Sage said.

"If you want the real story . . ."

Warden Donal gave the signal to pull the plug; the camera stopped rolling, the microphone quit. Speed Sage was ushered off Death Row, defending the people's right to freedom of the press.

Two trusties came and cleared away the remains of Simon's last meal. When Simon said he wasn't finished yet and asked about his key lime pie with whipped cream and a raspberry drizzle, they shrugged. When he requested permission to keep the unused bib as a souvenir for his stepmother, that sincere and serious request was interpreted as both snide and frivolous, then summarily denied.

91

"How was the dinner?" Robert J. said. "Still smells good in here."

"They snatched it out from under me. I never got my pie."

"Probably for the best. I hear it's better not to have a full stomach. They'll give you rubber underwear just before . . ." Simon watched his father fight off tears. "We never could have a real conversation," Robert J. said.

"Nobody's fault," Simon said. "Do words between father and son matter that much except for the unspoken ones?"

"I always cared for you. I admit you weren't the easiest child to offer unconditional love, what with your susceptibility to side effects that didn't seem to bother normal kids. It's hard to explain but you made your mother and me feel guilty, as if we'd created some kind of pharmacological monster. Those drugs you reacted to have been a boon to mankind, generally speaking. Oh, I know you're going to tell me prescriptions account for a few casualties each year but most of those are in underdeveloped countries."

"Who told you that? Legal drugs probably kill more people than the illegal ones and they happen to be equal opportunity killers. Not to mention overpriced."

"Look who's talking about killers," Robert J. said. "You're the one getting the lethal injection in a few hours. Not a pharmacist."

"A few hours? Is that all that's left?" Simon said. "I thought they just served an early dinner."

"I shouldn't have put it that way, son. You mean the world to Rowena and me. Even your biological mother is deeply affected by all this unpleasantness. I heard her interviewed on the radio by either Larry King or Speed Sage and she shed tears for you."

"My biological mom came to see me."

"She said she might drop in. Francine is a good person at heart. I don't think she'd have left me if it weren't for you. You were a bit of a burden, Simon."

"I didn't know you felt that way."

"It makes sense when you think about it."

"I guess it does," Simon said. "Sorry."

"Water under the bridge. You are aware that I knew you were getting off on my album," Robert J. said. "That was very wrong of you, invading an artist's privacy."

"I agree," Simon said, "and I apologize. But discovering that my dad was the town voyeur was a little upsetting. You always said that running Quikpix was a sacred trust that made you feel as important as Dr. Fikel, that you performed a public service. Then I found that album. Civic porn. And to set the record straight, I never got off on your album. I got off on Marlene Dietrich, Fay Wray, Vera Zorina,

Claudette Colbert, Rita Hayworth, Lauren Bacall, Natalie Wood, Sophia Loren, Leslie Caron, Goldie Hawn, Linda Evans, Marilyn Monroe, Sally Field etcetera and so forth. The first team."

"Sally Field? The Flying Nun? That's disgusting."

"I don't want to argue with you," Simon said. "At this point, I'd settle for a tight hug and a kiss goodbye."

"A hug and a kiss?"

"A handshake, then."

"What made you do it, Simon?"

"Do what?"

"What you did."

"I never did what I did," Simon said. "I wrote you about . . ."

"Rabbi Bakla and Father Mahoney said you refuse to ask for contrition. You could be risking supreme discomfort for the rest of eternity."

"Pop, do you have any conception of how a side effect or black box on a warning label affects the economic well-being of every man, woman and child in the nation? It was all explained when they took me down to the White House. Blindfolded for obvious reasons. When I realized where—"

"They took you to the White House. Of course they did. I'm sorry you feel they snatched your lobster away too soon. Truly sorry. Bless you, Simon. Remember that you were loved within limits. Your mother and I were not unconditional people."

"I was going to leave my lobster bib to Rowena," Simon said. "As a keepsake. I'd like her to know that. I always felt close to her."

"I'll tell her. She'll be touched," Robert J. said. "And let's keep that album business to ourselves."

"Not a word," Simon said.

92

"There's a woman who claims to be your aunt," the guard said. "Victoria Wyzowik. You want to see her?"

"Did you say Victoria?" Memories of love and betrayal clashed behind Simon's eyes like the colors in a Jackson Pollock. His ears filled with a saintly hum while basilisks gnawed at his full stomach. He felt himself being tucked into bed and tossed into boiling water like his late lobster.

If tears would turn to diamonds, how rich this boy would
    be!
He'd buy the earth and sun and moon and give some
    stars to me

"Well? Yes or no?" the guard said.

"Yes," Simon said. "Absolutely."

"My sweet Simon," Victoria said. More than forty years had thickened and shrunken the woman he remembered and streaked her hair, but she was absolutely Victoria. That face was remarkably unchanged, especially her eyes. Simon crawled inside those eyes; they held him the way a mirror holds its reflections forever, made clearer and deeper than any photograph. Victoria was in his eyes too, bending over his wrecked father, sucking the devil out of him as if his sex was a straw. Slurp, slurp.

"You must have passed Robert J. in the corridor," Simon said. "He just left here."

"He didn't recognize me," Victoria said. "Do you?"

"Oh, I do," Simon said.

"Are your memories of Victoria fond or hateful?"

"A broth of both. You'll never know how much I loved you back then. And what I went through when I caught you . . . why go into that? I suppose I understand what went on that night, at least to a degree. Maybe I should even thank you for saving my father's life or at least his spirit. Did you expect to get kicked out of our house for what must have seemed an act of charity to you, or were your sights set on becoming the next Mrs. Apple?"

"I didn't want to leave you, child. Nursing you was the greatest pleasure I ever felt."

"Nursing me? I don't remember any nursing going on."

"What sharp teeth you have, what urgent hunger."

"That sounds right," Simon said. "But I have no recollection of . . ."

"You were very small. I like to think of myself as your first love."

"I'd say that was an accurate assessment. What I felt for my mother was reflexive. What I felt for you was more like opening a gift. That doubled the pain when you left. Why didn't you say good-bye? Why didn't you send a postcard? Don't answer. Those were stupid questions. But the nursing business . . ."

"It's true. I still have your teethmarks on my nipples. My husband gives me a hard time about those tiny tattoos. Voltan makes jokes about my suckling a tiger cub."

"Voltan? Not Voltan Zerminsky?"

"You know his work?"

"Aphrodite, in the garden of The Museum of Modern Art? That's you? I had an eerie feeling . . ."

"It's Aphrodite, not Victoria. I was merely her conduit."

"Incredible. Mrs. Zerminsky! Belated congratulations. You know, after you left, Robert J. got me a stepmother—Rowena Trask, half his age. Nice girl. No complaints. All's well that ends well, to coin a phrase."

"Ah, dear Simon. I'm sure that monk deserved what he got."

"Between us, the monk never got. He was in to see me the other day."

"Of course he was. I believe in angels." Simon watched Victoria unbutton her blouse. Her breasts fell free.

"Are you thirsty, little Simon? Go ahead, drink. But don't bite."

"Victoria, I'm bowled over by the gesture but I was weaned a while ago. And considering what went on between you and my dad, I wouldn't feel right. But if I could just lay my cheek against those breasts, which, if I may say so, are magnificent for a mature woman, I wouldn't refuse that comfort. And look, those must be the marks you talked about, there, around the aureole. I must have been marking you like a tree, a trick I learned from the woodsman in that story you told me about two thousand times."

"The woodsman who found his way home."

"Through the forest. Chased by a werewolf," Simon said.

"A vampire," Victoria said. "You were too young to hear about werewolves."

Simon rested his face against Victoria Wyzowik's bosom with his eyes closed, listening to her strong heart and feeling her chest's easy rise and fall.

"None of this would have come to pass if they gave me a suspended sentence," Simon said. Victoria patted his hair and sang:

> *If tears would turn to diamonds, how rich this boy would*
> *be!*
> *He'd buy the earth and sun and moon and give some*
> *stars to me.*

"I have some news you'll be pleased to hear," Victoria said. "Voltan has been commissioned to create a monument to Regis Van Clay. I understand from certain of Mr. Van Clay's comments that your paths have crossed."

"Our paths have crossed once or twice," Simon said.

"You've had a profound effect on the man."

"You have a therapeutic bosom," Simon said, snuggling closer, kissing the pale scars left by his feeding frenzies.

"It will be Voltan's most ambitious project, a massive memorial. What a shame you won't be here to bear witness," Victoria said.

"Incidental," Simon said, "to the bigger picture."

"Sweet boy," Victoria said. "How often did I tell Fritzel you were special?"

93

In the middle of a lava enema, one of Belladonna's specialties, Regis made a quick call to Brian Beem. He was all smiles when Belladonna punched a blunt knitting needle through his upper left eyelid.

"Oh, that felt good, Belladonna. Today, everything feels good. They've already got Simon Apple in a hospital gown. That's euphemistic for shroud. In a matter of hours he'll be strapped onto a gurney, wheeled into the Death Chamber, hooked up to an IV. First he'll be given our latest formula for *Bridgecataphan* aka *Hyberpoid* and lapse into a merciful coma-like fog so that when another Regis Pharmaceuticals breakthrough, *Ebolapril Irreversus* aka *Cemavoma* is introduced into his aorta, then his organs begin to rupture and literally melt into a chemically rich slush ideal for fertilizing genetically engineered legumes. Except for a few contortions that might bother the witnesses more than they will the subject, who'd be brain dead. Or so we think based on animal studies or whatever they use for testing in the countries we outsource to for that sort of work. A final infusion of *Neuroniflash* aka *Deckorpa* should pull the plug on any surviving cells with the efficiency of a butcher knife and none of the mess. Plus the fact that every one of those drugs is strictly kosher, conforming to the toughest dietary laws on the planet. Bye bye Simon Apple."

"Wouldn't it be more sensible to use some of the body parts for transplant?" Belladonna said.

"Yes," Regis said, "but where the death penalty is called for there's a need to communicate what I call the certainty of finality for real closure. In some societies, the condemned are shredded then burned. It's something like being drawn and quartered which I've always felt was one of the more effective deterrents to crime. Would you want to be given a pancreas whose previous owner was a monk murderer?"

"I'm not sure," Belladonna said, using her remote to tighten the band circling Regis's foreskin.

"Besides, the chemicals make organ transplants contraindicated. You're doing all the things I like best tonight," Regis said. "You're treating me as if it was my birthday."

"I have the impression you're in the mood for celebration," Belladonna said, sending a jolt of current through Regis's sinus cavity.

"It's nearly game time," Regis said.

94

"So much affection," Simon said. "My greatest delight comes from holding you, Polly Moon."

"We had so little time together. It was my fault. Can you forgive me, Simon, because I can't forgive me. I was such a self-centered bitch."

"You were you. The joy is that we found each other and none too soon."

"I don't understand, Simon. Your lawyer called fifteen minutes ago and said he might have discovered another justification for an appeal. You refused to let him—"

"Polly, total strangers have filed appeals I never wanted appealed for two decades. I didn't contest the verdict or the sentence. Not when I understood what's at stake for the nation. I want to get past all this."

"When you get past this there may be no place left to pass. I want more time with you."

"I can only say so much. I explained that. I'm on a mission like Nathan Hale. I only regret that I have but one life to give for my country. And not enough life to give to you."

"I don't know if I should tell you this, but I think I'm pregnant. You're a daddy, Simon Apple."

"Polly, that's impossible. We haven't been together for twenty years."

"Oh, I know it's a miracle. You could call it a virgin birth. But I could swear you came to me during the Equinox and—"

"It's the thought that counts, darling. I'm so worried about you, Polly. I've got a few bucks squirreled away. I've left instructions with Marvin Klipstein naming you my sole heir. Actually, soul heir. He might be able to negotiate rights to a movie or one of those biographies."

"I belong to AFTRA, SAG, ASCAP and Equity." Polly said. "I get royalties from *The Windchime Concerto*. I'll be fine."

"About *The Windchime*, you might be interested in knowing—"

"Simon. Remember you once told me that these days side effects have replaced what used to be called fate? Well, if that's true, a psychic could read a person's future better with a list of their prescriptions than with numerology, astrology, I Ching, Kabala or Tarot. I might go into the psychic business. POLLY'S PARLOR. ASK YOUR DOCTOR. What do you think?"

"It could work," Simon said. "You might be on to something big."

"Imagine. In a world where the affluent enlightened reject bad habits like aging and dying, science will offer more and more prescriptions leading to fresh, imaginative side effects far surpassing the reliables like diarrhea, constipation, acid reflux, upper respiratory distress, cardiac arrhythmia, visual disturbance, memory loss, impotence, kidney failure, liver enlargement, rectal itch, polyp proliferation, weakness, dizziness, cough, headache, hallucinations, sore throat, ear ache, mouth pain, bluish complexion, vomiting, insomnia, muscle ache, yellowing eyes, skin numbness, tingling, bruising, bleeding, swelling, seizures, cramps, hostility, mood changes, suicidal urges, so on and so forth. It's very exciting. Half the new drugs that come to market will be for ailments that didn't exist last week. Those drugs will cause a whole new batch of afflictions requiring cures—all leading to incredibly creative side effects. Take the fuss over silicone implants. There's still disagreement about those artificial breasts being a boon or a health hazard. Before they were recalled those breasts accounted for tens of thousands of marriages and maybe hundreds of thousands of children, every one a consumer. So you see, side effects aren't all bad,"

"My little optimist," Simon said.

"How are you, Simon?" Rabbi Bakla said. He and Father Mahoney pushed past the guard and entered Simon's cell. "That's quite an outfit they've got you in. Nice, simple lines. Almost Grecian." Simon felt an inner moan; he didn't want this last moment with Polly interrupted.

"And who might the lovely young lady be?" Father Mahoney said.

"Polly Moon," Simon said. "Meet Rabbi Bakla and Father Mahoney, darling. They're battling for custody of my invisible essence. Life eternal."

"That's a bit extreme," Rabbi Bakla said. "But since you mentioned life eternal, you might want to know you've been granted special dispensation concerning that lobster you ordered. The news came to me directly from the Knesset in Israel. How did you get the State Department involved?"

"I'm not sure," Simon said, crediting former Agent Brian Beem with an act of kindness. "Now I'm asking another favor. We want you to marry us. Here and now."

"You have no license. The state requires—"

"I'm giving my life to the state," Simon said. "We want you to sanctify this union for ethical, legal and romantic reasons. I could call Oprah Winfrey and let her run with the story."

"I'm with child," Polly said.

"In a symbolic sense," Simon said. "She's under a lot of stress."

"A Death House wedding?" Father Mahoney said. "It's the kind of story that might play very well in the media. We could split the publicity between religions."

"According to my watch you'd only have half an hour together as man and wife," Rabbi Bakla said. "Not much of a honeymoon."

"Your watch might be wrong," Polly said.

"Stand side by side," Rabbi Bakla said.

Simon Apple took Polly Moon's hand. He noticed Father Mahoney and Rabbi Bakla looking at the skull and crossbones tattooed on her right wrist. "From another incarnation," Simon said.

"We frown on body piercing," Rabbi Bakla said. "Or adornments of the flesh."

"Their rules are rigid," Father Mahoney said. "But, Rabbi, the girl isn't converting, she's only marrying an unrepentant barbarian."

"Do you, Simon Apple, take this woman . . . ?"

"I do," Simon said. "I did."

"Do you, Polly Moon, take this man . . . ?"

"Do cannibals eat mermaids? Do mermaids eat sardines?"

"Is that a yes?"

"It is."

"In accordance with the laws of . . ."

"We now pronounce you man and wife."

Simon and Polly locked in a tight embrace. They heard the squeaky wheels of a gurney sing to them from down the corridor.

95

Regis raised his arms so that Trilby could buckle the harness holding a pair of angel wings to his naked back. She already had her own set of wings anchored firmly in place.

Those chest and shoulder riggings were linked to a disk on her bedroom ceiling by almost invisibly thin strands of titanium wiring. The disk was painted with a benevolent moon face—the sly, winking friar's face that once stared down from billboards for Admiration

Cigars. "Go!" Trilby said. The moon began to revolve as the two angels were lifted off Trilby's fleecy carpet and spun faster and faster. "You can flap your wings by moving your arms like so," Trilby said, demonstrating. Hidden lights blanketed the couple in rainbow colors as the werewolf wail of a Theramin played in the background.

"Are you enjoying the flight? I hope you do since you paid for it all, dearest."

"I'm not sure," Regis said. "I feel like a UFO. How do you get it to stop?"

"You just say, 'Stop.' "

"Wonderful," Regis said. "I heard that you and Belladonna went to visit Simon Apple. I was not pleased."

"There's no keeping anything from you, Regis."

"You asked him to sign over his body. That was a lovely thing for you to do in tandem, considering that you despise one another."

"We had planned to pool our resources," Trilby said. "And we don't despise one another. It's a simple case of jealousy. We both adore you and we know how much that terrible man upsets you. We thought that having some tangible proof that Apple was no longer a threat to your fabulous empire would keep you as healthy and vigorous as you deserve to be."

"Continue," Regis said. "Any ego replenishment is more than welcome. It's peculiar that I feel so unsure of my place in the scheme of things. I've been waiting twenty years for tonight to happen. It's the damn legal system. Even with some very powerful people in my pocket, bleeding heart judges kept delaying what is basically an act of patriotic necessity. When I tally what Simon Apple cost my company, my stockholders, my reputation, my nation with his damnable side effects—all that wicked labeling—my small and large intestines curdle. And it was only getting worse. The last Regis Pharmaceuticals product used on Apple, something called *Compassarate Dioxide*, gave the sonofabitch some kind of deadly skin condition, horrendous hives, prune cheeks . . . ah, let's forget that one. It was never meant for medicinal use. In fact, it was never meant for marketing except to the military. Even if it has been banned by every branch of the service since somebody is worried about possible lawsuits filed by contaminated pilots, soldiers, sailors, marines and a few factory workers, there's bad news and good news. Lucky for us, that gook does wonders for stereo sound systems and most of those are made in China and India so there's still a healthy buck to be made. By the way, you want to know what cured Apple?"

"Yes, I do," Trilby said. "In case I ever get hives and prune cheeks."

"Oatmeal baths. Oatmeal. What would have happened if Apple came up with a side effect from oatmeal? Do you think the government would have gone against Quaker Oats? Put a warning on that idiot pilgrim face they use on their boxes? Not in a million years. But if they could have hung another side effect around my neck, you can bet your G-spot they would have. Sugarbush, do you know what it took to make sure Apple was kept off Regis Pharmaceuticals drugs in the Death House—the cost of having full-time monitors kept on the prison staff, paid for by guess who? Imagine the dollars wasted over twenty years and that fucker never had so much as a cold. He never needed an aspirin. Not a suppository. Nothing. He's healthy as a horse. And there's more. I had to diffuse protests claiming death by lethal injection is cruel and unusual. Can you imagine? I spent another fortune developing a whole new line of drugs for quicker, more effective, comfortable, economical—and strictly kosher— lethal injections. Money that could have gone to deserving doctors out there in the front lines, the ones who write the RXs that keep us going. It makes me wince. It's a wonder your Regis didn't burst a blood vessel."

"Perish the thought," Trilby said. "I love my Regis."

"The irony is I know the death penalty will come back into vogue despite dry-pussy judges and spineless politicos. And we'll end up with substantial profits from those bye-bye chemicals. But it will take years and years the way things work these days. You can't even execute a convicted monk murderer without due process. What a laugh. They should call it undue process. In the old west, if a rustler was caught in the morning he was dangling by lunchtime."

"Are you hungry, honey?" Trilby said. "I have some smoked oysters waiting."

"This spinning around has me dizzy," Regis said. "Stop!"

The moon quit turning, the wings detached, Regis and Trilby

tumbled onto her delicious bed. "What I've done for humanity does make a difference, doesn't it? " Regis said. "It hasn't all been a selfish quest for glory, has it? My father would be proud, wouldn't he?"

"Yes, no and yes, "Trilby said. "Have some champagne." She poured the sparkling wine into a glass shaped like a slipper. "Regis, you're one of the most important men of this or any other generation. Century. Millennium. That ever was or ever will be."

"Thank you, Trilby. What time have you got?"

"You're my only guest this evening, Regis."

"No, I mean literally. Clock time."

"A quarter to midnight."

"They're wheeling him in now."

"You know," Trilby said, "the only thing that bothers me and I'm sure I'm being too much of an alarmist, but it was you who taught me—"

"Make your point. I want to fuck."

"You mentioned a whole new line of drugs for successful lethal injecting . . ."

"*Bridgecataphan* aka *Hyberpoid, Ebolapril Irreversus* aka *Cemavoma,* and *Neuroniflash* aka *Deckorpa,*" Regis said. "In little bottles that click into place so easily any idiot could—"

"How do you come up with those marvelous names? Well, I was saying to myself, Trilby, you shouldn't mention anything to upset Regis, not on a night like this, but what if Simon Apple ends up getting some terrible side effect *from* his lethal injections? That could force my Sweetiepie to paste new warning labels on those little bottles. It could impact the company's bottom line. Those drugs could end up on the scrap heap of good intentions. And my little stock portfolio—"

Regis bolted upright, gasping for breath. He grabbed for Trilby's French telephone, dialing frantically. "Give me Warden Donal's office—I know it's after hours—I know you have an execution scheduled—I know he's not at his desk—Whoever you are, listen carefully. This is Regis Van Clay—Yes, that one. I must speak with the warden or Brian Beem—Of course he's one of the witnesses. Probably in the front row—I realize it will be difficult but this is a matter of life and death—No, I was not trying to be funny. Get Donal or Beem on the line immediately—It's two minutes to twelve, asshole. You can't mean that every phone in the chamber is being used by the press. I know phone reception is jammed during—There's always a line kept open in case of the governor granting—I told you, this is Van Clay. Regis Van Clay. Do not, I repeat, do not proceed with— This execution has got to be stopped. Don't dare tell me you're not empowered to—Hello? Hello?" Regis heard the sound of empty air.

Trilby leaned over to kiss one of the puncture wounds inflicted, then expertly sutured, by Belladonna. "Did I say something bad, Uncle Regis?"

"Do you begin to comprehend what Apple has cost me by forcing us to slap warning labels on *Cripthalizine* aka *Cribangel*, *Nonacripthae* aka *Hercumite*, *Viloxidril* aka *Symmavane*, *Aquathaline* aka *Zepharia*, *Expeloton* aka *Sepronalol*, *Xanelul* aka *Harpacinimon*, *Solacitrex* aka *Silentush*, *Thumicsk* aka *Retdema*, and the amalgam of *Thumicsk* and *Solacitrex*—"

"Aka *Stalagamide*," Trilby said. "You see, I do listen and learn."

"Let's not forget *Compassarate Dioxide*, which never did get an aka. I've got to remember to have my Regis Muse Horizons team come up with a zippy—"

"Regis, you're turning the color of an persimmon. Please calm yourself. I wasn't serious. It was just silly Trilly making a joke. I shouldn't have mentioned—"

"Are you aware that we're into trillions in lost revenue?"

"I'm trying to grasp . . . you know I'm a simple girl, Regis. Trillions elude me," Trilby said in a frightened voice. She noticed the pupils in Regis's eyes rolling counterclockwise.

"On the bright side," Regis said, "I can envision a very active demand for *Bridgecataphan* aka *Hyberpoid*, *Ebolapril Irreversus* aka *Cemavoma* and *Neuroniflash* aka *Deckorpa*. Even if we do lose the death penalty market in the U.S.A., I'd wager those items—cleverly marketed, packaged and presented—would have powerful Third World appeal, an attractive growth area. Instead of 'Ask your *doctor*' our tag line would be 'Ask your *dictator*.' " Regis, perspiring a flood, rested his chin on his fist. "If Simon Apple does survive in any kind of working order, or even as a vegetable, I can always get my boys to find a cure for survival."

"You always see your glass as half full," Trilby said. "It's what I love most about you. Now lay back, take deep breaths, and let's pretend we're both marshmallows."

"Maybe I should think about creating a pill specifically designed to cause side effects," Regis said, slamming his fists on the mattress.

"Hush," Trilby cooed. That's no way for a marshmallow to behave. Let me coddle your blood pressure, dear one."

96

Being wheeled on his back into the Death Chamber, escorted by a cortege of luminaries along with his guards, Simon felt like a potentate borne on a litter to his coronation. He was neatly wrapped in a ceremonial robe, securely strapped in place, attached to an IV by transparent plastic tubes plugged into the tops of both wrists by thick needles. Finding receptive veins and inserting those needles had been a painful process but that memory was quickly retreating.

Simon saw that both tubes carried pinkish fluid flowing into his body. He remembered a nurse remarking on the wasteful use of a backup system when one tube was quite sufficient, but her comment brought only a sharp reprimand from the doctor in charge of his pending assassination. Simon was feeling better and better. The streams of pinkish wine, mingling with his blood, had definitely affected his thinking. What he needed was a cup of strong coffee. He tried hard to tell somebody that he took his coffee black with no sugar but the words congealed in his mouth.

His eyes began seeing the world through a kaleidoscope of soft pastels. He heard quiet whispers replace the sound of the squealing gurney wheels when the parade suddenly stopped. He thought the whispering came from Rabbi Bakla and Father Mahoney but he couldn't be certain. Simon managed to turn his head toward a large stained glass window illustrated by portraits of faces he recognized and the faces of strangers. He saw Brian Beem, Warden Donal, Speed Sage speaking into a portable microphone, Dr. Fikel from Glenda sitting next to—could it be Tabitha Ulman or was it Victoria or possibly Polly Moon—beautiful Placebo—come to cheer him on? And Marvin Klipstein, Esq., taking notes, always thinking ahead. Those faces, familiar and unknown, were so frozen, so fearful, so molded by suspense, it made Simon want to laugh but his own face had gone rigid too.

Then he saw the purple liquid in his IV tubes turn milky brown and felt a twinge of anxiety as the new juice came closer to his skin. He felt his body spasm, drenched in pain that stormed over him like the storm that drowned Manhattan the day he pushed a refrigerator with its own ice-making machine past the herd of Steinway pianos in the building where the great Wallace Waldo sat in his conference room watching Benny Valaris, William Shakespeare's casting director, bugger a chorus line of hopeful Lady Macbeths. Then up Fifth Avenue toward Polly Moon's penthouse. The trip took some doing but her tip eclipsed the effort. Placebo. His wife!

Things began to go black when the pain ebbed leaving Simon in such a void he missed the cramps and spasms. A third color was inching down the plastic tubes, a heavy greenish gray moving slower than the others but surely on course, on target, on schedule.

Simon heard a scurry of bodies surrounding his pallet and felt himself slapped and prodded, felt the tubes ripped from his wrists, fell deeper into the velvet darkness that took him into its quicksand heart.

97

"No vital signs. This man is dead."

"Use the paddles again," Brian Beem said. "Inject a bolus of adrenalin directly into—"

"Look at the cardiac monitor. Flatlined. No brain waves. Simon Apple is dead."

"The prisoner expired at one minute past twelve o'clock midnight," Warden Donal said, "in accordance with—"

"Fuck us all," Beem said. "When Regis Van Clay gets here we've got to present a united front. Our story is that we did what we could to stop the execution, but his call came too late. There is such a thing as too late. Too late is too late."

"Get the corpse out of here," Warden Donal said to an aide. "Bury the body in Potters Field. Cover the corpse with lime."

"You'd better hold back on the lime," Brian Beem said. "Until we hear what Mr. Van Clay has to say about disposal plans. Grisly as it sounds, I think he wants the remains as a trophy or just to make absolutely sure Simon Apple is no longer on the scene."

"Fine. We'll wait for him in my office. I think we could all use a drink."

"Excellent thought," Brian Beem said. "We're going to need all the courage we can swallow. Regis sounded pissing hysterical. Furious. Frenzied. And he's a very vindictive man."

"How could he expect me to ask the governor to commute Apple's sentence after the fact?" the warden said.

"Don't try to be rational at a time like this," Brian Beem said.

When Regis Van Clay arrived, his limousine was followed by something that looked like a cross between a hearse and an armored car. He seemed surprisingly calm and in control. "I realize I've acted badly tonight," Regis said. "You people performed to the best of your ability. Simon Apple is dead, you all agree to that. I was wrong to have asked that his life be spared."

"I want to say how impressed we were with the way that cocktail of yours dispatched the perpetrator. One, two, three, *fini.* Congratulations, Mr. Van Clay, and please extend my thanks and admiration to all the folks in your company who contributed to the formula. Compared with the stuff we used last month, I won't go into specifics, this execution was, if I can use the word in such dire circumstances, perfect."

"Thank you, Warden Donal. Thank you all. Now, I would like the body placed in the maximum-security transport parked downstairs. I have all the necessary papers allowing me to take possession of the deceased."

"Would it be improper for me to ask why you . . . ?" Warden Donal said.

"Please get on with it," Regis said, forcing a smile.

Warden Donal made a call to the Death Chamber. He shook his head from side to side then hung up the phone. "I'm afraid I have some negative news for you, Mr. Van Clay. There appears to be some screwup with the Apple body. It was already claimed by a lady. It seems she and Simon Apple were married by a rabbi and a priest earlier this evening. As Mr. Apple's spouse, and since there was no prior objection, when the coroner finished certifying Apple's demise, the woman had every right—"

"Find the two of them," Regis said to Brian Beem in a voice that slithered like a wet snake. "Or I will hold you personally responsible for allowing Apple to evade custody yet again. The fiscal fate of the United States of America hangs in the balance here. Do you understand what I'm saying?"

"There is no 'two of them' to find," Beem said."Apple is legally dead. No heartbeat. No brain waves. No reason for agitation."

"Easy for you to say," Regis said. "Don't jump to conclusions. You don't know that subversive shit. Simon Apple is a corkscrew turning in my heart. Until I know he's a well-baked Apple locked in an urn I will not rest easily. Who would marry that menace? Can we plead insanity? Is it too late to get an annulment?"

"The woman seemed genuinely distraught. She claims she's pregnant." Warden Donal said. "I wouldn't be too concerned if there is reason for concern."

"Excuse me?" Regis said. "Pregnant? Is it possible that Simon Apple's chromosomes are still swimming in the gene pool?

"Postmortem pregnancy is a common fantasy of a bereaved lover. There's absolutely no chance that Simon Apple left any progeny. Zero chance," Warden Donal said. "Well, maybe a ghost of a chance. There's always the possibility that the marriage was consummated. But considering the time frame, I'd say the only way they could have conjugated is by mail. It's inconceivable that the lady conceived."

"This is no time for humor," Regis said. "Do you see me laughing?"

"I'm sorry," Warden Donal said. "I just want to put your mind at ease. By the way, Mr. Van Clay, I've been meaning to ask you, is it true the major drug companies spend more on gifts and perks to seduce doctors into pushing your merchandise than you people spend on research?"

"By the way, Warden Donal, I've been meaning to ask you,

how'd you like to be put in charge of a nice little prison in Kazakhstan? Jesus, Mary and Joseph, the wife *is* pregnant. I feel it in my bones."

98

Polly Moon followed her hunches. She also nursed a remnant of necrophilia dating back to her Goth days at Glenda High. She and her friends had spent many happy hours smoking pot and chanting arcane phrases culled from *The Book of the Dead for Dummies*, a volume of forgotten lore that somehow found its way onto a shelf of the school library.

Their object was to stir the dust of a few Egyptians who dated back to the days when gods and goddesses leaned close to earth and, bored or just listless, cohabited with mere mortals. The Goths were anxious to interview someone seduced or violated by creatures with human bodies and hawk heads, cat heads, hippo heads or some reasonable facsimile of those deities. Despite all the chanting, no citizens of the Nile Delta abandoned their sarcophagi, unwrapped themselves and came to Glenda to set things straight. Polly Moon never paid the library's late charges due on the book; every year or so she got a threatening letter.

Before he took his final ride on the squeaky gurney, Simon had whispered a request that Polly claim his corpse. He told her his motives were partly sentimental but mostly self-indulgent. He didn't want to be dropped into a tank of piranha by Regis Van Clay's junior executives or mauled and minced by Regis Pharmaceuticals forensic scientists, looking for clues to his biochemical makeup.

Simon apologized for burdening his new wife with such a morbid assignment but there was no one else he could turn to; his wish was have his ashes scattered without ceremony in some peaceful place like Serene Harbor where he could watch the seasons change while he waited for Polly Moon to lie beside him.

Polly had other ideas, going back to her earlier fascination with things mystical. She seriously considered finding someone at the American Museum of Natural History who might know a thing or two about mummification or at least a renegade taxidermist interested in making a few non-taxable dollars. She wanted to preserve her husband for the time being, maybe forever, possibly until the highly unlikely hour when she fell in love with someone else.

She already had a loft large enough to accommodate him in a room of his own with ample space to allow for her to live and work comfortably. It was Simon's lawyer, Marvin Klipstein, Esq., who untangled the legal knots involving past litigation with her larcenous producer, Albert Essman, and discovered that Polly Moon's settlement gave her ownership of the building in Manhattan's Soho district that once housed Essman's spacious recording studio. That building converted into six rental units that brought in enormous monthly income. The building also had a back staircase wide enough for six burly pallbearers from Montibello to carry Simon's casket up seven flights after it was lifted off Shen Wa's newest truck.

"Pleasure to be of service," Shen Wa said. "Though I must say, I did not disagree with your husband's execution even if innocent man die. Nice boy, Simon, but too many side effects. You watch TV drug commercials? Half are for cure diseases nobody ever heard of last week but now scare the hell out of people. Next week, here come a whole new batch of sicknesses and more drugs to cure those, then recalls and more drugs and so on and so forth. Everybody busy taking pulse, swallowing tons of crap. Makes for a nice economy. Same with fashion. One year, big tits in, get implants, feel good. Next season, big tits out, implants dangerous, small tits in. Hooray! Whole new wardrobe. Long skirts, short skirts, loose pants, tight pants. Old image, new image. Very creative system."

The day after Simon Apple's arrival in New York, Polly went out to buy as many bags of ice as she needed to fill the tub where Simon rested pending further developments. When she returned to the loft she found Simon's casket open. Her husband had managed to escape that confinement and find his way to a Lay-Z-Boy chair in the living room where he sat with his legs propped up as if he was ready to watch a ball game and down a few bottles of Bud.

The realization that Simon Apple was alive, albeit slightly comatose, came slowly but when it hit home, Polly Moon let out a scream. She also became aware that he was spinning a web. Silken strands originating from every orifice were slowly wrapping around him like tendrils of wisteria. Simon was packaging himself inside a cocoon. Her husband had warned Polly that he might suffer some unexpected complications from *Bridgecataphan* aka *Hyberpoid*, *Ebolapril Irreversus* aka *Cemavoma* and *Neuroniflash* aka *Deckorpa*, singly or in combination, considering his past history.

Know thyself had been one of Simon's favorite expressions; he certainly knew himself well enough to accept that, after the life he'd lived, a simple death was too much to expect.

99

With Simon snug in his silky cave, Polly Moon went into business for herself.

Curiously, it was Lucille Van Clay who told her husband about the amazing woman downtown, an absolute rage, who could see beyond the most remote horizon and predict everything coming down the pike by a technique she called Medication Meditation. "She reads prescriptions as if they were Tarot Cards. I hear she's wonderful. It's virtually impossible to get an appointment to see her for months and months. Could you use your influence?"

Regis shrugged.

From inside his casing, Simon Apple began to sing, mimicking what he heard as the music of the spheres. He looked out at an endless expanse of heavenly bodies, bursting stars, whirling planets, flashing meteors, a universe of nothingness slashed by silver blades of ruthless comets.

He looked for signs of intelligent life or at least some cluster of aliens not unlike the folks back in Glenda. Sure enough, he found them. Simon watched the crowds go by—an unruly bunch of mobile appetites, some fretful, some doubtful, some oddly hopeful.

They played together, ate together, clung together, laughed together, wept together, photographed one another, carried anointed slips of paper to the local pharmacy.

Prescriptions promising to ease their pain.

✌

The author would like to thank all sincere, dedicated researchers and medical professionals making their stand firmly on the side of life, with a special nod to the doctors and nurses affiliated with Mt. Sinai Hospital in New York City. Many very gifted and patient people helped enormously with this project. A bow to author and editor, Linda Stewart, for her huge contribution of time and talent. Kudos to iconic artist/cartoonist/writer, Gahan Wilson, who conjured our cover. Many thanks to Chet and Sue Gottfried for their many skills and encouragement. To Susan Lamb and Carole Potter for their assurance and support. And to the enduring memory of Nancy Connable for her insight, wisdom and sweetness of spirit over many years. A wall of Platinum Platters to the swinging rock band, Simon Apple (*River to the Sea*), Jeff Miller, Buzz Saylor, Dan Merill and every artist on the team, who generously agreed to share our hero's name. And to so many others—you know who you are!

LaVergne, TN USA
20 August 2009
155414LV00006B/11/P